KEY MATHS

▶ **David Baker**
The Anthony Gell School, Wirksworth

▶ **Paul Hogan**
St. Wilfrid's Church of England High School, Blackburn

▶ **Chris Humble**
Gillotts School, Henley-on-Thames

▶ **Barbara Job**
Christleton County High School, Chester

▶ **Peter Sherran**
Weston Road High School, Stafford

Series Editor: **Paul Hogan**

First published in 1998 by
Stanley Thornes (Publishers) Ltd
Second edition published in 2001 by
Nelson Thornes Ltd
Delta Place
27 Bath Road
CHELTENHAM
GL53 7TH
United Kingdom

02 03 04 05 / 10 9 8 7 6 5 4 3

A catalogue record for this book is available from the British Library.

ISBN 0-7487-6205-1

Illustrations by Maltings Partnership, Peters and Zabransky, Oxford Illustrators, Clinton Banbury
Page make-up by Tech Set Ltd

Printed and bound in China by Midas

Acknowledgements
The publishers thank the following for permission to reproduce copyright material:
Alton Towers: 417, 426; Art Directory: 117 (bottom); Bruce Coleman: 242 (Mark Carwardine); Eye Ubiquitous: 163 (T Futter), 181 (T Futter); Getty Images: 240 (Tony Stone Images/S Lowry/ Univ. of Ulster), 85 (top – Tony Stone Images/ Kristian Hilsen), 86; Image Bank: 235 (Leo Mason); John Walmsley Photography: 133, 139, 155, 211, 217; Leslie Garland Picture Library: 115 (top), 116, 117 (top, top middle), 395 (Vincent Lowe), 409 (Vincent Lowe); Martyn Chillmaid: 47 (top), 48, 50, 85 (bottom), 104, 275, 276, 277, 278, 291, 359, 369, 386; Rex Features: 216 (Vic Thomasson); Skyscan Balloon Photography: 99; Still Pictures: 211 (top – David Hoffman), 212 (David Hoffman); Topham Picturepoint; 47 (bottom – Press Association), 53, 78; TRIP: 117 (bottom middle – J Stanley), 118 (Dinardia)
All other photographs Nelson Thornes Archive.

The publishers have made every effort to contact copyright holders but apologise if any have been overlooked.

Contents

19 The power of graphs ICT   *1*
1 Lines and curves   *2*
2 More curved graphs!   *12*

20 Simultaneous equations ICT   *27*
1 Using graphs   *28*
2 Using algebra   *32*
3 Changing the subject   *38*

21 Probability ICT   *47*
1 Sample space diagrams   *48*
2 Finding probabilities   *53*

22 Standard form ICT   *65*
1 Big numbers   *66*
2 Small numbers   *73*

23 Area   *85*
1 Counting and estimating   *86*
2 All the formulas   *91*
3 Nets and surface areas   *104*

24 Pattern power ICT   *115*
1 Time for a change   *116*
2 Sequences   *119*

25 Statistics ICT   *133*
1 Comparing sets of data   *134*
2 Cumulative frequency   *139*
3 Box and whisker diagrams   *150*

26 Angles and bearings ICT   *163*
1 Angles   *164*
2 Get your bearings   *181*

27 Mainly quadratics ICT   *191*
1 Brackets and factorising   *192*
2 Factorising and solving quadratics   *199*

28 Working with errors ICT   *211*
1 Reading scales   *212*
2 Rounding and estimating   *217*
3 Error bounds   *225*

29 **Percentages and decimals** *237*
1 Using multipliers *238*
2 Finance *247*

30 **Solid shapes** *259*
1 Drawing shapes *260*
2 Units of mass and capacity *267*
3 Volume *274*
4 Density *289*
5 Dimensions *292*

31 **More probability** *299*
1 Tree diagrams *300*
2 Changing probabilities *308*

32 **Inner space** *321*
1 Identical shapes *322*
2 About turn *328*
3 Similar triangles *338*

33 **Constructions and loci** *347*
1 Constructions *348*
2 Loci *357*

34 **Solving equations** *373*
1 Using graphs *374*
2 Trial and improvement *384*

35 **Using trigonometry** *395*
1 Angles and lengths *396*
2 Bearing up *403*
3 Finding the hypotenuse *409*

36 **<Inequalities>** *417*
1 Solving inequalities using algebra *418*
2 Solving inequalities using graphs *426*

Answers Test Yourself *444*

19 The power of graphs

1 Lines and curves
Drawing straight line graphs
Drawing quadratic graphs

CORE

2 More curved graphs!
Drawing cubic graphs
Looking at the symmetry of cubic graphs
Drawing graphs involving $\dfrac{1}{x}$

QUESTIONS

EXTENSION

TEST YOURSELF

CORE

1 Lines and curves

Each of the searchlights has a special mirror inside it. It is in the shape of a parabola. It focuses the light in to a beam.

A parabola is the shape of the graph produced by a quadratic equation.

In this section you will learn how to draw this type of graph.

The equation of a straight line is $y = mx + c$.
m is the gradient of the line.
c is called the intercept.
It is the point where the graph crosses the y axis.

The equation of this straight line is $y = 3x - 4$.
The gradient of the line is 3.
The graph crosses the y axis at -4.

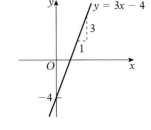

To draw the graph of a straight line you can fill in a table.

Example   Draw the graph of $y = 3x - 4$. Use x values from -4 to $+4$.

(1) Draw a table. Put the x values along the top.

(2) Use a separate row for each part of the equation.
In this case there is one row for the $3x$ and one row for the -4
Fill in these two rows.

(3) Add the two rows together to get the y values.

x	-4	-3	-2	-1	0	1	2	3	4
$3x$	-12	-9	-6	-3	0	3	6	9	12
-4	-4	-4	-4	-4	-4	-4	-4	-4	-4
y	-16	-13	-10	-7	-4	-1	2	5	8

(4) Use the x and y values as co-ordinates to plot your graph.

(5) Make sure that you label your graph.

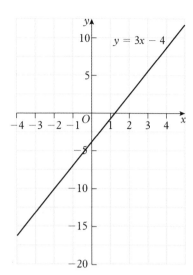

$y = 3x - 4$

Exercise 19:1

1 **a** Copy this table for $y = 2x + 3$.

x	-4	-3	-2	-1	0	1	2	3	4
$2x$	-8	-6	-4	-2	0	2	4	6	8
$+3$	3	3	3	3	3	3	3	3	3
y	-5	-3	-1	1	3	5	7	9	11

  b Fill in the missing values.
  c Draw axes with x from -4 to 4 and y from -6 to 12.
  d Draw the graph of $y = 2x + 3$.
     Don't forget to label it.

2 **a** Copy this table for $y = 3x - 1$.

x	-4	-3	-2	-1	0	1	2	3	4
$3x$		-9			0		6		
-1		-1			-1		-1		
y		-10			-1		5		

  b Fill in the missing values.
  c Draw axes with x from -4 to 4 and y from -15 to 15.
  d Draw the graph of $y = 3x - 1$.
     Don't forget to label it.

3 For each of these equations:

(1) Draw a table.

(2) Fill in the values.

(3) Draw a set of axes. They need to fit the values in your table.

(4) Draw the graph of the equation.

a $y = 2x - 6$

b $y = 4x - 2$

c $y = \frac{1}{2}x + 3$

d $y = 0.2x - 2$

If the number in front of the x term of the equation is negative, the line slopes downwards.

You have to be a little more careful when you fill in the table.

Example Draw the graph of $y = 5 - 2x$. Use x values from -4 to $+4$.

The table looks like this:

x	-4	-3	-2	-1	0	1	2	3	4
5	5	5	5	5	5	5	5	5	5
$-2x$	8	6	4	2	0	-2	-4	-6	-8
y	13	11	9	7	5	3	1	-1	-3

Notice that when $x = -4$, $-2x = 8$.
This is because $-2 \times -4 = 8$.

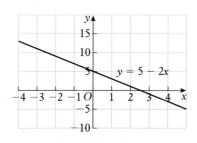

This is the graph of $y = 5 - 2x$.

---

4 For each of these equations:

(1) Draw a table.

(2) Fill in the values.

(3) Draw a set of axes that fits the values in your table.

(4) Draw the graph of the equation.

a $y = 3 - 2x$

b $y = 6 - x$

c $y = 0.5 - 4x$

d $y = 3 - \frac{1}{2}x$

Quadratic graphs

| Quadratic | A **quadratic** equation or formula is one which has an x^2 in it.

It must not have any other powers of x such as x^3 or $\dfrac{1}{x}$.
It can have xs and numbers in it.

These are all quadratic equations:
$y = x^2 + 3$
$y = 3x^2 + 5x - 3$
$y = 8x - x^2$

Graphs of quadratic equations are curves not straight lines.

Go thro. Nº1 & do Nos.

Exercise 19:2

1 a Copy this table. Fill it in.
Remember x^2 means $x \times x$.

Go thro.

x	-5	-4	-3	-2	-1	0	1	2	3	4	5
$y = x^2$	25	16	9			0	1				

b Draw an x axis from -5 to $+5$
and a y axis from 0 to 25.
c Plot the points from your table.
d Join the points with a **smooth** curve.
Label your curve $y = x^2$.
This type of curve is called a **parabola**.
All quadratic graphs are parabolas.

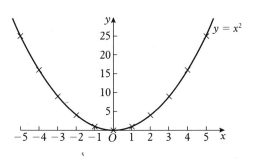

2 a Copy this table for $y = x^2 + 5$.

x	-4	-3	-2	-1	0	1	2	3	4
x^2	16	9	4	1	0	1	4	9	16
$+5$	5	5	5	5	5	5	5	5	5
y	21	14	9	6	5	6	9	14	21

b Fill in the missing values.

c Draw axes with x from -4 to $+4$ and y from 0 to 25.
d Draw the graph of $y = x^2 + 5$
Make the curve as smooth as you can.

3 **a** Copy this table for $y = x^2 - 3$.

discuss but leave out

x	-4	-3	-2	-1	0	1	2	3	4
x^2	16	9			0			9	
-3	-3	-3			-3			-3	
y	13	6			-3			6	

b Fill in the missing values.
c Draw axes with x from -4 to $+4$ and y from -5 to 15.
d Draw the graph of $y = x^2 - 3$

4 Look at the graphs you have drawn for questions **1** to **3**.
a All the graphs are symmetrical.
Write down the equation of the line of symmetry.

Go thro

b Look at graph **2**.
What effect has the $+5$ in the equation had on the graph?
c Look at graph **3**.
What effect has the -3 in the equation had on the graph?
d What would the graph of $y = x^2 + 10$ look like?
Sketch the graph.

Quadratic formulas can have multiples of x^2 in them.
It is important to remember that $3x^2$ means find x^2 *then* multiply by 3.

5 **a** Copy this table for $y = 3x^2 + 4$

x	-4	-3	-2	-1	0	1	2	3	4
$3x^2$	48	27				3	12		
$+4$	4	4				4	4		
y	52	31				7	16		

b Fill in the missing values.
c Draw axes with x from -4 to $+4$ and y from 0 to 60.
d Draw the graph of $y = 3x^2 + 4$

Quadratic formulas can have three terms in them.

They can have an x^2 term, an x term and a number term.

The number term is sometimes called the constant term.

To draw a graph of these formulas, you will need three rows of working in your table.

Example

Draw the curve of $y = x^2 + 3x + 1$
Use x values from -5 to $+3$

(1) Complete a table showing each part of the formula $y = x^2 + 3x + 1$ separately.

x	-5	-4	-3	-2	-1	0	1	2	3
x^2	25	16	9	4	1	0	1	4	9
$+3x$	-15	-12	-9	-6	-3	0	3	6	9
$+1$	1	1	1	1	1	1	1	1	1
y	11	5	1	-1	-1	1	5	11	19

(2) Draw an x axis from -5 to $+3$ and a y axis from -2 to 20.

(3) Plot the points from your table.

(4) Join the points with a **smooth** curve.
Your finished curve should look like this:

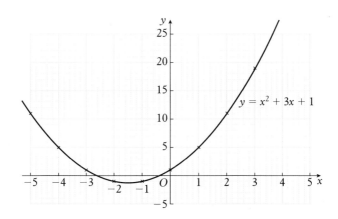

$y = x^2 + 3x + 1$

Exercise 19:3

1 a Copy and complete this table for $y = x^2 + 2x + 3$

x	-5	-4	-3	-2	-1	0	1	2	3
x^2	25	16				0			9
$+2x$	-10	-8				0			6
$+3$	3	3				3			3
y	18	11				3			18

  b Draw an x axis from -5 to $+3$ and a y axis from 0 to 20.
  c Plot the points from your table.
  d Join the points with a **smooth** curve.

2 a Copy and complete this table for $y = x^2 + 3x - 5$

x	-5	-4	-3	-2	-1	0	1	2	3
x^2	25	16				0			
$+3x$	-15	-12				0			
-5	-5	-5				-5			
y	5	-1				-5			

  b Draw an x axis from -5 to $+3$ and a y axis from -10 to 15.
  c Plot the graph of $y = x^2 + 3x - 5$ from your table.
  d Draw the line of symmetry on your graph.
  e Write down the equation of the line of symmetry.

3 a Complete this table for $y = x^2 - x - 3$
    Notice how both the minus signs in the formula are included in the table.
    Remember that if $x = -5$ then $-x = 5$

x	-5	-4	-3	-2	-1	0	1	2	3
x^2	25	16							
$-x$	5	4					-1	-2	
-3	-3	-3							
y	27	17							

  b Draw an x axis from -5 to $+3$ and a y axis from -5 to 30.
  c Plot the points from your table.
  d Join the points with a **smooth** curve.

4 For each part of this question:
  (1) Draw a table using the x values given.
  (2) Draw axes to fit the values in the table.
  (3) Draw a graph from your table.

a $y = 2x^2 + 2x - 5$ x from -4 to $+4$
b $y = x^2 - x - 3$ x from -4 to $+4$
c $y = 3x^2 + x$ x from -4 to $+4$
d $y = x^2 - 3x$ x from -4 to $+4$

If the x^2 term in a quadratic formula is negative, the graph is turned upside down.

It is important to remember that $-x^2$ means find x^2 and *then* make the answer minus. Because x^2 is always a positive number, $-x^2$ will always be negative.

Example   Work out $-3x^2$ when   **a** $x = 4$ **b** $x = -5$

    a $x = 4$ **b** $x = -5$

$$-3x^2 = -3 \times 4^2 \qquad\qquad -3x^2 = -3 \times (-5)^2$$
$$= -3 \times 16 \qquad\qquad\qquad\quad = -3 \times 25$$
$$= -48 \qquad\qquad\qquad\qquad\quad = -75$$

Exercise 19:4

1 **a** Copy and complete this table for $y = -x^2 + 2x$.

x	-5	-4	-3	-2	-1	0	1	2	3
$-x^2$	-25	-16				0		-4	-9
$+2x$	-10	-8				0			6
y	-35	-24				0			-3

b Draw an axis from -5 to $+3$ and a y axis from -35 to 5.
c Plot the points from your table.
d Join the points with a **smooth** curve. The curve should look like this.

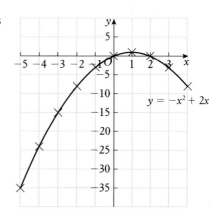

$y = -x^2 + 2x$

2 **a** Copy and complete this table for $y = -x^2 - 2x + 10$

x	-4	-3	-2	-1	0	1	2	3	4
$-x^2$	-16			-1	0	-10		-9	
$-2x$	8		4		0	-20			-8
$+10$	10	10			10	10 10			
y	2				10	-10			

b Draw an axis with x from -4 to $+4$ and a y axis from -15 to 15.
c Draw the graph of $y = -x^2 - 2x + 10$
d Write down the equation of the line of symmetry of the curve.

3 Look carefully at this table for the graph of $y = (x + 1)^2$

GO THRO.

x	-4	-3	-2	-1	0	1	2	3	4
$x + 1$	-3	-2	-1	0	1				
y	9	4	1	0	1				

a Copy and complete the table.
b Draw a graph of $y = (x + 1)^2$

4 For each part of this question:
    (1) Draw a table using the x values given.
    (2) Draw axes to fit the values in the table.
    (3) Draw a graph from your table.

    a $y = -2x^2 + 2x + 12$ x from -4 to $+4$
discuss   **b** $y = (x - 3)^2$ x from -4 to $+4$
 →**c** $y = -(x + 4)^2$ x from -4 to $+4$ $-(x^2 + 8x + 16)$
    d $y = -\frac{1}{2}x^2 + 2x - 3$ x from -4 to $+4$ $\Rightarrow -x^2 - 8x - 16$

Exercise 19:5

1 A ball is thrown in the air at a speed of 20 m/s.
The height of the ball during its journey is
calculated using the formula
$h = 20t - 5t^2$. t is the number of seconds
the ball has been in the air.

a Copy this table. Fill in the missing values.

t	0	0.5	1	1.5	2	2.5	3	3.5	4
$20t$	0			30					80
$-5t^2$	0			-11.25					-80
h	0			18.75					0

b Draw axes with t on the horizontal scale and h on the vertical scale.
c Draw the path of the ball as it travels through the air.
d What is the maximum height that the ball reaches?

2 The formula that the police use to calculate car stopping distances is
$$d = \frac{s^2 + 20s}{60}$$

d is the stopping distance in metres and s is the speed of the car in miles per hour.

a Copy this table and fill it in. It shows stopping distances for speeds from 10 mph to 70 mph.

s	10	20	30	40	50	60	70
s^2							
$20s$							
$d = \dfrac{s^2 + 20s}{60}$							

b Draw a graph to show the stopping distances of cars.
c Use your graph to estimate the stopping distance of a car travelling at 55 mph.

SCREECH!!!

2 More curved graphs!

There are lots of ways to choose an equation that will make a curve.

Cubic

A **cubic** equation or formula is one which has an x^3 in it.

It must not have any higher powers of x or terms like $\dfrac{1}{x}$, $\dfrac{1}{x^2}$, etc.

It can have x^2 and x terms and numbers.

$y = 5x^3 - 2x$ and $y = \dfrac{x^3}{2} + x^2 - 5$ are cubic equations.

$y = 5x^3 - \dfrac{2}{x}$ and $y = 2x^4 + x^3 + 1$ are not cubic equations.

The graph of a cubic equation is a curve. It is different from a quadratic curve.

Exercise 19:6

1 Write down the letters of the cubic equations.

A $y = x^2 - 3x + 2$ D $y = 2x^3$ G $y = x - 0.5x^3$

B $y = x^3$ E $y = x^3 + x^4$ H $y = x^3 - 2x^2 - 3$

C $y = x^3 + 2x - 1$ F $y = x^3 - \dfrac{1}{x}$ I $y = \dfrac{1}{x^3}$

Sometimes a cubic is written in factorised form.

2 Write down the letters of the cubic equations.

A $y = x^2(x + 2)$ C $y = x(x + 1)^2$ E $y = x(x + 1)(x - 2)$

B $y = x^3(x - 5)$ D $y = (x - 2)^3$ F $y = x^3(x^3 + 2)$

3 **a** Copy these axes on to graph paper.

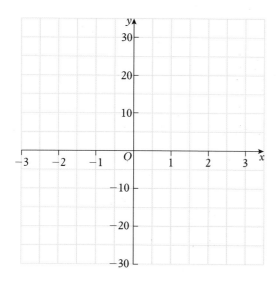

b Copy the table. Fill in the missing values.
You can work out x^3 as $x \times x \times x$ or you can use the x^y key on your calculator.

x		-3	-2	-1	0	1	2	3
$y = x^3$		-27					8	

c Plot the points from your table.
Join them with a smooth curve.
Label your graph $y = x^3$.
d The curve has rotational symmetry.
(1) Write down the order.
(2) Give the co-ordinates of the centre of rotation.

4 **a** Copy the table for $y = x^3 + 3$. Fill in the missing values.

x		-3	-2	-1	0	1	2	3
x^3		-27					8	
$+3$		3					3	
y		-24				11		

b Plot the points from your table on the same diagram as question **3**.
Join them with a smooth curve.
Label the curve $y = x^3 + 3$.
c Describe the symmetry of the curve.

5 **a** Copy the table for $y = x^3 - 3$. Fill in the missing values.

x	-3	-2	-1	0	1	2	3
x^3	-27					8	
-3	-3					-3	
y	-30					5	

b Plot the points from your table on the same diagram as question **3**.
Join them with a smooth curve.
Label the curve $y = x^3 - 3$

c Describe the symmetry of the curve.

6 **a** Draw the graph of $y = x^3 + 2$ on the same diagram.
Don't use a table of values.

b Explain how you were able to draw the graph in **a**.

c Draw the graph of $y = x^3 - 2$ on the same diagram.

All of the cubic graphs drawn so far have flattened in the middle and then turned upwards again. Some cubic graphs dip in the middle before turning upwards.

Example Draw the graph of $y = x^3 - 8x + 5$
Use x values from -4 to 4.

(1) Complete a table showing each part of the equation separately.

x	-4	-3	-2	-1	0	1	2	3	4
x^3	-64	-27	-8	-1	0	1	8	27	64
$-8x$	32	24	16	8	0	-8	-16	-24	-32
$+5$	5	5	5	5	5	5	5	5	5
y	-27	2	13	12	5	-2	-3	8	37

(2) Draw an x axis from -4 to 4 and a y axis from -30 to 40.
Remember that you can use a different scale for the y axis.

(3) Plot the points from your table.

(4) Join the points with a smooth curve.

Your finished curve should look like this.

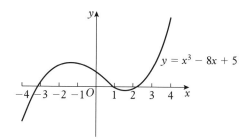

$y = x^3 - 8x + 5$

Exercise 19:7

1 **a** Copy this table for $y = x^3 - 5x + 10$

x	-4	-3	-2	-1	0	1	2	3	4
x^3	-64			-1				27	
$-5x$	20			5				-15	
$+10$	10			10				10	
y	-34			14				22	

  b Fill in the missing values.
  c Draw axes with x from -4 to 4 and y from -35 to 55.
  d Draw the graph of $y = x^3 - 5x + 10$

2 **a** Copy this table for $y = x^3 - 6x - 5$

x	-4	-3	-2	-1	0	1	2	3	4
x^3	-64			-1				27	
$-6x$	24			6				-18	
-5	-5			-5				-5	
y	-45			0				4	

  b Fill in the missing values.
  c Draw axes with x from -4 to 4 and y from -45 to 35.
  d Draw the graph of $y = x^3 - 6x - 5$

3 **a** Copy this table for $y = x^3 + 6x - 5$

x	-3	-2	-1	0	1	2	3
x^3			-1				27
$+6x$			-6				18
-5			-5				-5
y			-12				40

b Fill in the missing values.
c Draw axes with x from -3 to 3 and y from -50 to 40.
d Draw the graph of $y = x^3 + 6x - 5$
e Describe how this curve is different to the ones that you have drawn before.

So far, you have found three types of graph for cubic equations.

One thing that these graphs have in common is that, apart from the bit in the middle, they all slope upwards from left to right. But, if the x^3 term is negative then the opposite happens.

Exercise 19:8

1 **a** Copy this table for $y = -x^3 - 4x + 10$

x	-3	-2	-1	0	1	2	3
$-x^3$			1				-27
$-4x$			4				-12
$+10$			10				10
y			15				-29

   b Fill in the missing values.
   c Draw axes with x from -3 to 3 and y from -30 to 50.
   d Draw the graph of $y = -x^3 - 4x + 10$
   e Describe the shape of the curve.

2 **a** Copy this table for $y = -x^3 + 10x$

x	-4	-3	-2	-1	0	1	2	3	4
$-x^3$	64			1				-27	
$+10x$	-40			-10				30	
y	24			-9				3	

   b Fill in the missing values.
   c Draw axes with x from -4 to 4 and y from -25 to 25.
   d Draw the graph of $y = -x^3 + 10x$
   e Describe the shape of the curve.

3 **a** Copy this table for $y = -x^3 + 3x^2 - 3x$

x	-2	-1	0	1	2	3	4
$-x^3$	8				-8		
$+3x^2$	12				12		
$-3x$	6				-6		
y	26				-2		

   b Fill in the missing values.
   c Draw axes with x from -2 to 4 and y from -30 to 30.
   d Draw the graph of $y = -x^3 + 3x^2 - 3x$
   e Describe the shape of the curve.

Twist and turn

You will need tracing paper for this investigation.
It will be helpful if you have a graph plotter that will print the graphs.

1   You have already drawn the graphs of some cubic equations.
Trace each of these curves and then rotate the tracing paper through 180°.
Does the traced curve always match the original when it is upside down?

2   Draw the graphs of some new cubic equations. Use a graph plotter if you have one.
Do all of these curves have rotational symmetry?

3   The centre of rotational symmetry for many of the curves that you have drawn
lies on the y axis. Try to find a rule for when this happens.

4   Find the x co-ordinate of the centre of rotational symmetry for each of these.

a $y = x^3 + 3x^2$ **e** $y = x^3 + 9x^2$

b $y = x^3 - 3x^2$ **f** $y = x^3 - 9x^2$

c $y = x^3 + 6x^2$ **g** $y = 2x^3 + 12x^2$

d $y = x^3 - 6x^2$ **h** $y = 5x^3 - 15x^2$

5   Look at your answers to question **4**.
Try to find a rule when the equation takes the form

a $y = x^3 + bx$ **b** $y = ax^3 + bx$

6   Find the x co-ordinate of the centre of rotational symmetry for each of these.
Compare your results with question **4**.

a $y = x^3 + 3x^2 + 4$ **e** $y = x^3 + 9x^2 + 3x$

b $y = x^3 - 3x^2 - 3$ **f** $y = x^3 - 9x^2 - 2$

c $y = x^3 + 6x^2 + x$ **g** $y = 2x^3 + 12x^2 + x - 5$

d $y = x^3 - 6x^2 - 2x$ **h** $y = 5x^3 - 15x^2 - 2x + 6$

7   Use your results from question **6** to find a rule when the equation takes the
form $y = ax^3 + bx^2 + cx + d$.

Another type of equation that has a curved graph is one where the x appears on the bottom line of a fraction.

Example   Draw the graph of $y = \dfrac{5}{x}$. Use values of x from 1 to 5.

(1) Complete a table of values. Remember that $\dfrac{5}{x}$ means $5 \div x$.

x	1	2	3	4	5
y	5	2.5	1.7	1.25	1

(2) Draw x and y axes from 1 to 5.
(3) Plot the points from your table.
(4) Join the points with a smooth curve.

Your finished curve should look like this.

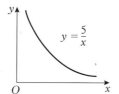

Exercise 19:9

1 **a** Draw x and y axes from -5 to 5.
   b Copy the table. Fill it in.
      Give the y values to 2 dp when you need to round.

x	0.2	0.3	0.4	0.5	1	2	3	4	5
$y = \dfrac{1}{x}$									

   c Plot the points from the table. Join them with a smooth curve.

2 **a** Copy the table. Fill it in.
Round the y values to 2 dp when necessary.

TABLE

x	-5	-4	-3	-2	-1	-0.5	-0.4	-0.3	-0.2
$y = \dfrac{1}{x}$									

b Plot the points on the same diagram as question **1**.
Join the points with a smooth curve.

Your diagram should now look like this.

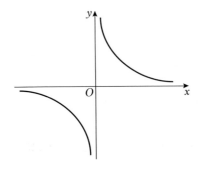

The graph of $y = \dfrac{1}{x}$ is in two halves. The two halves don't meet because

it is impossible to find a value for y when $x = 0$.

3 **a** How many lines of symmetry does the graph of $y = \dfrac{1}{x}$ have?

b Draw the lines of symmetry on your diagram.
c Label each line of symmetry with its equation.
d Describe the rotational symmetry of the graph.

4 **a** Draw the graph of $y = \dfrac{1}{x}$ again on a new set of axes from -5 to 5.

b Draw the graph of $y = \dfrac{1}{x} + 1$ on the same diagram. Label your graph.

c Draw the graph of $y = \dfrac{1}{x} - 1$ on the same diagram. Label your graph.

5 **a** Draw x and y axes from -6 to 6.

b Copy the table. Complete it for $y = x + \dfrac{1}{x}$

Give the y values to 2 dp when you need to round.

x	0.2	0.3	0.4	0.5	1	2	3	4	5
$\dfrac{1}{x}$	5					0.5			
y	5.2					2.5			

c Plot the points from the table. Join them with a smooth curve.

6 **a** Copy the table. Complete it for $y = x + \dfrac{1}{x}$

Give the y values to 2 dp when you need to round.

x	-5	-4	-3	-2	-1	-0.5	-0.4	-0.3	-0.2
$\dfrac{1}{x}$	-0.2					-2			
y	-5.2					-2.5			

b Plot the points from your table on the same diagram as question **5**.
c Join the points with a smooth curve.
d Describe the symmetry of the complete graph of $y = x + \dfrac{1}{x}$

7 **a** Copy the table. Fill it in.
Give the y values to 2 dp when you need to round.

x	-3	-2	-1	-0.5	0.5	1	2	3
$y = \dfrac{1}{x^2}$		0.25						0.11

b Draw an x axis from -3 to 3 and a y axis from 0 to 5.
c Plot the points from your table.
d Join the points using two smooth curves.

Your diagram should look like this.

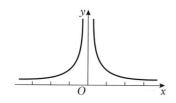

1 **a** Copy this table for $y = 2x - 7$

x	-4	-3	-2	-1	0	1	2	3	4
$2x$		-6			0		4		
-7		-7			-7		-7		
y		-13			-7		-3		

b Fill in the missing values.
c Draw axes with x from -4 to 4 and y from -15 to $+5$.
d Draw the graph of $y = 2x - 7$
Don't forget to label it.

2 For each of these equations:
(1) Draw a table.
(2) Fill in the values.
(3) Draw a set of axes. They need to fit the values in your table.
(4) Draw the graph of the equation.

a $y = 4x - 3$ **b** $y = 6 - 2x$ **c** $y = \frac{1}{2}x - 2$ **d** $y = 0.8x + 3$

3 **a** Copy this table for $y = 2x^2 + 8$

x	-4	-3	-2	-1	0	1	2	3	4
$2x^2$	32		8			2			
$+8$	8		8			8			
y	40		16			10			

b Fill in the missing values.
c Draw axes with x from -4 to $+4$ and y from 0 to 50.
d Draw the graph of $y = 2x^2 + 8$
Make the curve as smooth as you can.

4 **a** Copy and complete this table for $y = -2x^2 + x - 2$

x	-5	-4	-3	-2	-1	0	1	2	3
$-2x^2$			-18				-2		
$+x$			-3				1		
-2			-2				-2		
y			-23				-3		

b Draw an x axis from -5 to $+3$ and a y axis from -60 to 30.
c Plot the points from your table.
d Draw the line of symmetry on your graph.
e Write down the equation of the line of symmetry.

5 A stone is dropped from the top of a cliff.
The distance the stone has travelled is worked out using the formula
$d = 4.9t^2$
d is the distance in metres and t is the time in seconds.

a Copy this table. Fill in the values of d.

t	1	2	3	4	5	6	7	8
d								

b Draw a graph to show the distance that the stone has fallen.
Put t on the horizontal axis and d on the vertical axis.
c Another cliff is 280 m high.
Use your graph to estimate the time it would take for a stone to fall
from this height.

6 a Copy the table. Complete it for $y = \dfrac{1}{x^2} + 1$

Give the y values to 2 dp when you need to round.

x	-3	-2	-1	-0.5	0.5	1	2	3
$\dfrac{1}{x^2}$		0.25						0.11
$+1$		1						1
y		1.25						1.11

b Draw an x axis from -3 to 3 and a y axis from 0 to 5.
c Plot the points from your table.
d Join the points using two smooth curves.

7 a Copy the table. Complete it for $y = x^2 + \dfrac{1}{x}$

Round the y values to 2 dp where necessary.

x	-3	-2	-1	-0.5	-0.2	0.2	0.5	1	2	3
x^2		4								9
$+\dfrac{1}{x}$		-0.5								0.33
y		3.5								9.33

b Draw an x axis from -3 to 3 and a y axis from -5 to 10.
c Plot the points from your table.
d Join the points using two smooth curves.

1 These are the sketches of the graphs
$y = x^2$ and $y = -x^2$.
Use these to help you sketch each
of these graphs.

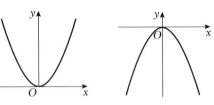

a $y = x^2 + 3$　　**e** $y = -x^2$
b $y = x^2 + 7$　　**f** $y = -x^2 + 2$
c $y = x^2 - 2$　　**g** $y = -x^2 - 5$
d $y = x^2 - 5$　　**h** $y = -x^2 + 3.2$

2 **a** Draw an x axis from -5 to $+5$ and a y axis from 0 to 30.
　　b Draw the graph of $y = x^2$ on your axes.
　　c Copy and complete this table for $y = (x - 3)^2$

x	-2	-1	0	1	2	3	4	5
y	25	16	9					

　　d Plot the graph of $y = (x - 3)^2$ from your table.
　　e Copy and complete this table for $y = (x + 2)^2$

x	-4	-3	-2	-1	0	1	2	3
y	4	1					16	

　　f Plot the graph of $y = (x + 2)^2$ from your table.

Compare your three graphs.
　　g Describe how $y = x^2$ has moved to get the graph of $y = (x - 3)^2$
　　h Describe how $y = x^2$ has moved to get the graph of $y = (x + 2)^2$

3 Match each of these equations with its graph.
　　a $y = 5x + 3$　　　　**c** $y = x^2 - 3x + 2$　　　**e** $y = x^3 - 2x$

　　b $y = 4 - x^2$　　　　**d** $y = \dfrac{1}{x} + 3$　　　**f** $y = 4x - x^3$

Write down pairs of letters and numbers.

(1)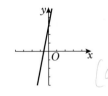

(3)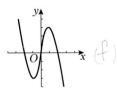

(5)

(2)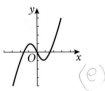

(4)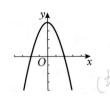

(6)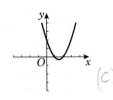

1 **a** Draw and fill in a table of values for $y = 2x - 3$
    b Copy these axes.
    c Draw the graph of $y = 2x - 3$
    d Draw and fill in a table of values for $y = 6 - x$
    e Draw the graph of $y = 6 - x$ on the same set of axes.
    f Write down the co-ordinates of the point where the two lines cross.

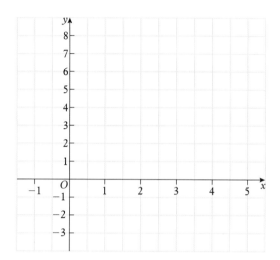

2 Look at these equations.
    A $y = 7 - x^2$ QUADRATIC **B** $y = 3 - 2x$ LINEAR **C** $y = 5x^2 + x^3 - 1$ CUBIC
    Write down the special name for each equation.
    Choose from linear, quadratic and cubic.

3 Copy this table for $y = x^2 - 4x + 3$

x	-2	-1	0	1	2	3	4	5	6
x^2	4						16		
$-4x$	8						-16		
$+3$	$+3$						$+3$		
y	15						3		

    a Fill in the missing values in the table.
    b Draw axes with x from -3 to 7 and y from -2 to 16.
    c Draw the graph of $y = x^2 - 4x + 3$
    d Draw the line of symmetry on your graph.
    e Write down the equation of the line of symmetry.
    f What is the value of y when $x = 2.5$?
    g What are the values of x when $y = 10$?
    h What value of x gives $x^2 - 4x + 3$ its lowest value?

4 Copy this table for $y = x^3 - x^2 - 6x$

x	-3	-2	-1	0	1	2	3	4
x^3	-27							64
$-x^2$	-9							-16
$-6x$	$+18$							-24
y	-18							24

a Fill in the missing values in the table.
b Draw axes with x from -3 to 4 and y from -20 to 25.
c Draw the graph of $y = x^3 - x^2 - 6x$
d What is the value of y when $x = -1.5$?
e What are the values of x when $y = 1$?
f On the same set of axes draw the line AB where A is the point $(-3, -10)$ and B is the point $(4, 10)$.
g Find the gradient of the line AB to 1 dp.
h Write down the co-ordinates of the points where the line AB cuts the curve.

5 Match each of these equations with its graph.

A $y = 7 - 2x$　　　**C** $y = \dfrac{1}{x} - 2$　　　**E** $y = 10x - x^3$

B $y = x^2 + 1$　　　**D** $y = -x^3$　　　**F** $y = 1 - x^2$

(1)
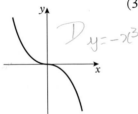

(3)
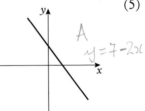

(5)
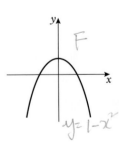

(2)
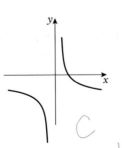

(4)
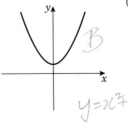

(6)
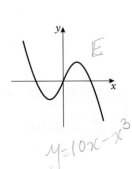

20 Simultaneous equations

1 Using graphs
Playing a game – Match Point
Using graphs to solve simultaneous equations

2 Using algebra
Solving simultaneous equations using algebra
- subtracting the two equations
- adding the two equations
- multiplying one equation before adding or subtracting
- multiplying both equations before adding or subtracting

Setting up simultaneous equations before solving them

CORE

3 Changing the subject
Rearranging formulas involving $+$, $-$, $\times$ and $\div$
Rearranging formulas involving squares and square roots
Solving simultaneous equations by substitution

QUESTIONS

EXTENSION

TEST YOURSELF

1 Using graphs

Points of intersection are sometimes of interest.

Game: Match Point

This is a game for two players.
One player needs Worksheet 20:1(A).
The other needs Worksheet 20:1(B).

Game (1)
Look at the equation for Game (1) on your worksheet. Keep it to yourself.
The equation for Player A is different from the one for Player B.
Decide who will start the game.

On your turn …
Find a pair of values x and y, that make your equation work. They will
always be between 0 and 20.
Write your values as co-ordinates on your game sheet.
Tell your partner the values that you have found.

On your partner's turn …
Write your partner's values as co-ordinates on your game sheet.
Check to see if this pair of values makes your equation work.
If they work then your partner wins the game. Underline the winning values.
If not it is your turn again.

Play the other games on the sheet in the same way.
When you have played all six games you will need Worksheet 20:2.

(1) Plot all of the points found for each game on the matching grid.
(2) What pattern should your points make on each grid?
(3) What pattern should your partner's points make on each grid?
(4) What is special about the position of the winning point on each grid?
(5) What is special about the x and y values at each winning point?

| **Simultaneous equations** | When you solve two equations at the same time you are solving **simultaneous equations**. |

Example

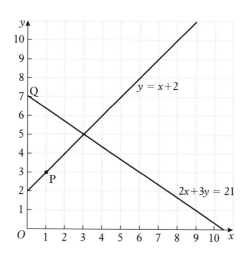

a Check that the (x, y) co-ordinates at P work in the equation $y = x + 2$.

b Check that the (x, y) co-ordinates at Q work in the equation $2x + 3y = 21$.

c Use the diagram to solve the simultaneous equations:

  (1) $y = x + 2$
  (2) $2x + 3y = 21$

d Check that the solution works in both equations.

a P has co-ordinates $(1, 3)$.
   So at P: $x = 1$ and $y = 3$.
     $3 = 1 + 2$ so $y = x + 2$ ✓

b Q has co-ordinates $(0, 7)$.
   So at Q: $x = 0$ and $y = 7$.
     $2x + 3y = 2 \times 0 + 3 \times 7 = 21$ ✓

c The lines intersect at $(3, 5)$ so the solution is $x = 3$ and $y = 5$.

d $5 = 3 + 2$ so $y = x + 2$ ✓
   $2x + 3y = 2 \times 3 + 3 \times 5 = 21$ ✓

Exercise 20:1

1 a Check that the (x, y) co-ordinates at P work in the equation $y = x - 1$.
 b Check that the (x, y) co-ordinates at Q work in the equation $x + 3y = 9$.
 c Use the diagram to solve the simultaneous equations:
   (1) $y = x - 1$
   (2) $x + 3y = 9$
 d Check that the solution works in both equations.

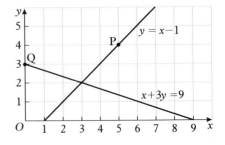

2 a Check that the (x, y) co-ordinates at P work in the equation $y = x + 5$.
 b Check that the (x, y) co-ordinates at Q work in the equation $x + 2y = 4$.
 c Use the diagram to solve the simultaneous equations:
   (1) $y = x + 5$
   (2) $x + 2y = 4$
 d Check that the solution works in both equations.

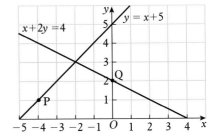

3

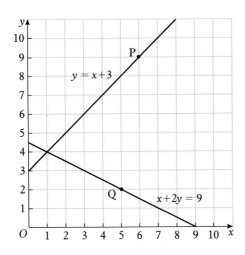

 a Check that the (x, y) co-ordinates at P work in the equation $y = x + 3$.
 b Check that the (x, y) co-ordinates at Q work in the equation $x + 2y = 9$.
 c Use the diagram to solve the simultaneous equations:
   (1) $y = x + 3$
   (2) $x + 2y = 9$
 d Check that the solution works in both equations.

Answer questions **4–6** using this diagram.

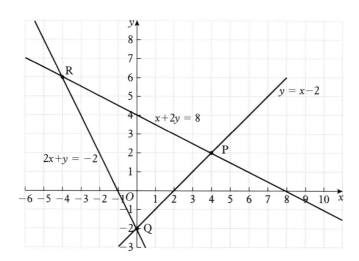

4 **a** Write down a pair of simultaneous equations that work at P.
   b Solve the equations.
   c Check that the solution works in both equations.

5 **a** Write down a pair of simultaneous equations that work at Q.
   b Solve the equations.
   c Check that the solution works in both equations.

6 **a** Write down a pair of simultaneous equations that work at R.
   b Solve the equations.
   c Check that the solution works in both equations.

7 **a** Draw a set of axes on squared paper.
      Use values of x from 0 to 7 and values of y from -5 to 5.
   b Plot some points for the equation $2x + 3y = 12$.
   c Draw the graph of $2x + 3y = 12$.
   d Plot some points for the equation $y = 2x - 4$.
   e Draw the graph of $y = 2x - 4$.
   f Solve the simultaneous equations $2x + 3y = 12$ and $y = 2x - 4$.
   g Check that your solution works in both equations.

GO
THRO.

Copy out
for hmw.

2 Using algebra

Sometimes you have to get rid of things to make progress.

You can solve simultaneous equations using algebra.

Example Solve this pair of simultaneous equations

$$5x + y = 20$$
$$2x + y = 11$$

Number the equations

(1) $5x + y = 20$
(2) $2x + y = 11$

Subtract to get rid of y
This finds x

Subtracting $3x = 9$
$x = 3$

Use equation (1) to find y

Put $x = 3$ in equation (1)
$5 \times 3 + y = 20$
$15 + y = 20$
$y = 5$
The answer is $x = 3, y = 5$

Use equation (2) to check your answer $2x + y = 6 + 5 = 11$ ✓

Exercise 20:2

Solve these pairs of simultaneous equations.
Start by subtracting the equations each time.

1 $3x + y = 17$ (1) subs $x = 4$ into (1)
$x + y = 9$ (2) $3 \times 4 + y = 17$
Subtract $2x = 8, x = 4$ $12 + y = 17$
$y = 5$

2 $3x + 2y = 16$
$x + 2y = 12$
then do
check in (2)

3 $5x + y = 28$
$2x + y = 13$

4 $3x + 2y = 23$
$2x + 2y = 20$

5 $5x + 3y = 26$
       $2x + 3y = 14$

6 $4x + y = 26$
       $x + y = 11$

7 $6x + y = -18$
       $2x + y = 10$

8 $9x + y = -37$ (1)
       $3x + y = -13$ (2)

(handwritten) subst. $x = -4$ into (1)
$-36 + y = -37$
$y = -1$
$6x = -24$ ∴ $x = -4$, $y = -1$
Use (2) to check
$3x + y = -13$
$-12 - 1 = -13$ ✓

9 $2x + 3y = 18$
       $2x + y = 10$

10 $5x + 4y = 40$
       $5x + y = 25$

(handwritten) hmw.

Example   Solve this pair of simultaneous equations $3x + y = 19$
                                                        $x - y = 1$

Number the equations   (1) $3x + y = 19$
                        (2) $x - y = 1$

Add to get rid of y Adding $4x = 20$
This finds x $x = 5$

Use equation (1) to find y Put $x = 5$ in equation (1)
                                $3 \times 5 + y = 19$
                                $15 + y = 19$
                                $y = 4$
                            The answer is $x = 5, y = 4$

Use equation (2) to check your answer $x - y = 5 - 4 = 1$ ✓

Exercise 20:3

Solve these pairs of simultaneous equations.
Start by adding the equations each time.

1 $2x + y = 14$ (1)
       $3x - y = 11$ (2)

(handwritten) subs. $x = 5$ into (1)
$10 + y = 14$
$y = 4$
$5x = 25$
$x = 5$
Use (2) to check
$3x - y = 11$
$15 - 4 = 11$ ✓

2 $5x + y = 26$
       $2x - y = 2$

3 $4x + 2y = 30$
       $2x - 2y = 6$

4 $x + 5y = 15$
       $3x - 5y = 25$

5 $4x + y = 16$
       $3x - y = -2$

6 $7x + 5y = -85$
       $3x - 5y = -15$

If the terms have the same number in front of them and the signs are the same, you get rid of them by subtracting the equations.

If the terms have the same number in front of them but the signs are different, you get rid of them by adding the equations.

Example   Use each pair of equations to make a new equation just in terms of x.

a $7x + 3y = 25$ **b** $11x - 19y = 36$
$3x - 3y = 15$ $8x - 19y = 21$

a   The y terms both have a 3 in front of them but the signs are different.
Adding the equations gives $10x = 40$.
You can check that the solution is $x = 4, y = -1$.

b   The y terms are identical.
Subtracting the equations gives $3x = 15$.
You can check that the solution is $x = 5, y = 1$.

Exercise 20:4

Solve these pairs of simultaneous equations.
You need to decide whether to add or subtract the equations.

1 $x + y = 15$
$5x - y = 9$

2 $4x + 2y = 28$
$x - 2y = 2$

3 $5x + 3y = 19$
$2x + 3y = 13$

4 $3x - y = 11$
$2x - y = 5$

5 $3x + 2y = 16$ (1)
$x + 2y = 12$ (2)

$2x = 4$ subs into (1)
$x = 2$ $3x + 2y = 16$
$6 + 2y = 16$
$x=2, y=5$ $2y = 10$ ∴ $y=5$

6   (1) $4x - 5y = 15$ subs into (1)
(2) $3x - 5y = -5$ $80 - 5y = 15$
$x = 20$ $80 - 15 = 5y$
$65 = 5y$
$13 = y$

7 $4x + 2y = 38$
$+ 3x - 2y = 11$
$7x = 49$
$x = 7$ $4x + 2y = 38$
$28 + 2y = 38$
$2y = 10$, $y=5$

8 $5x + 3y = 27$
$+ 4x - 3y = 0$
$9x = 27$
$x = 3$ $5x + 3y = 27$
$15 + 3y = 27$
$3y = 12$, $y = 4$

9 $3x + 4y = 7$
$- 3x + 3y = -3$
$y = 10$ $3x + 4y = 7$
$3x + 40 = 7$
$3x = -33$, $x = -11$

10   (1) $5x - 9y = -23$
(2) $2x - 9y = 7$
$3x = -30$
$x = -10$ subs into (1)
$5x - 9y = -23$
$-50 - 9y = -23$
$-50 + 23 = 9y$
$-27 = 9y$
$-3 = y$
∴ $y=-5$ $x=-10, y=-3$

34

You sometimes have to multiply one of the equations by a number
before adding or subtracting.

Example　　Solve this pair of simultaneous equations

$$2x + 3y = 13$$
$$4x - y = 5$$

Number the equations

(1) $2x + 3y = 13$
(2) $4x - y = 5$

To get rid of the ys
you need to multiply (2) by **3**
so that you have $3y$ in
each equation.

(1) $\quad 2x + 3y = 13$
(2) $\times$ **3** $\quad 12x - 3y = 15$

Add to get rid of y
This finds x

Adding $14x = 28$
$x = 2$

Use equation (1) to find y

Put $x = 2$ in equation (1)
$$2 \times 2 + 3y = 13$$
$$4 + 3y = 13$$
$$3y = 9$$
$$y = 3$$
The answer is $x = 2, y = 3$

Use equation (2) to check your answer

$4x - y = 8 - 3 = 5$ ✓

Exercise 20:5

Solve these pairs of simultaneous equations.
You need to multiply one equation by a number.

1　　$2x + 3y = 19$
　　　　$x + y = 8$

4　　$5p - 2q = 7$
　　　　$3p + q = 13$

2　　$5x - 3y = 16$
　　　　$x + y = 16$

● **5**　　$7c - 3d = 26$
　　　　$c - d = 10$

3　　$3a + 2b = 8$
　　　　$2a - b = 3$

(handwritten) (1) $3a + 2b = 8$
$\times 2$ (2) $+ 4a - 2b = 6$
$7a = 14$
$a = 2$
Subs $a = 2$ into 1)
$6 + 2b = 8$
$2b = 2$
$b = 1$

● **6**　　$j + 3k = 17$
　　　　$2j - 5k = 23$

(handwritten) (1) $\times 2 \to 2j + 6k = 34$
(2) $- \quad 2j - 5k = 23$
$11k = 11$
$k = 1$
subs $k = 1$ into (1)
$j + 3 = 17$
$j = 14$

35

You sometimes have to multiply both equations by a number before adding or subtracting.

Example   Solve this pair of simultaneous equations

$$3x + 5y = 30$$
$$2x + 3y = 19$$

Number the equations

(1) $3x + 5y = 30$
(2) $2x + 3y = 19$

Multiply (1) by 2
Multiply (2) by 3

(1) $\times$ 2 $6x + 10y = 60$
(2) $\times$ 3 $6x + 9y = 57$

Now subtract to get rid of x $y = 3$

Use equation (1) to find y

Put $y = 3$ in equation (1)
$$3x + 15 = 30$$
$$3x = 15$$
$$x = 5$$
The answer is $x = 5, y = 3$

Use equation (2) to check your answer

$$2x + 3y = 2 \times 5 + 3 \times 3 = 10 + 9 = 19 \checkmark$$

Exercise 20:6

Solve these pairs of simultaneous equations.
You will need to multiply one or both of the equations by a number.

1 $3x + 2y = 18$
      $x + y = 7$

● **4** $4p - 2q = 7$
      $3p + q = 11\frac{1}{2}$

2 $7x - 3y = 48$
      $2x + y = 10$

● **5** $5m + 3n = 17$
      $2m + 5n = 12\frac{1}{2}$

3 $3a + 4b = 41$ (1)×4 $12a + 16b = 164$
      $4a - 5b = 3$ (2)×3 $17a - 15b = 9$

31b = 155
b = 5

36 subs b=5 into (1)
3a + 20 = 41
3a = 21
a = 7

6 $g + 4h = -9$ (1)×5 $5g + 20h = -45$
      $5g - 2h = -1$ (2) $5g - 2h = -1$

22h = -44
h = -2

subs h=2 into (1)
g - 8 = -9
g = -1

You can use simultaneous equations to solve problems.

Example   In a sale, all compact discs are one price.
All tapes are also one price.
Jenny buys two compact discs and one tape for £10.
Peter buys one compact disc and two tapes for £8.
Find the cost of a compact disc and the cost of a tape.

You need to use letters to stand for the unknown amounts.
You can then write equations to represent the information in the question.

Using £c for the cost of a compact disc and £t for the cost of a tape:

Jenny's equation is $\qquad\qquad 2c + t = 10$
Peter's equation is $\qquad\qquad c + 2t = 8$

You solve these in the usual way to find that $c = 4$, $t = 2$.

This means that the cost of a compact disc is £4 and the cost of a tape is £2.

Exercise 20:7

1 Paul and Petra took part in a school quiz.
They had to choose a standard or a hard question on each turn.
Paul answered 3 standard and 2 hard questions correctly and scored 7 points.
Petra answered 1 standard and 4 hard questions correctly and scored 9 points.
Find the points awarded for a standard question and for a hard question.

(handwritten working:)
$3s + 2h = 7$ (1)
$s + 4h = 9$ (2)
(1) × 2
$6s + 4h = 14$
$s + 4h = 9$
$5s = 5$
$s = 1$
subs into (2)
$1 + 4h = 9$
$4h = 9 - 1$
$4h = 8$
$h = 2$
$s = 1, h = 2$

2 A school sells two types of calculator.
One is a basic model and the other is a scientific.
The cost of one basic and one scientific is £10.
The cost of 3 basic and 2 scientific is £24.
Find the cost of a basic model and the cost of a scientific model.

3 Hannah buys 4 choc ices and 3 cornets for £11.25
Terri buys 3 choc ices and 2 cornets for £8
Find the cost of 1 choc ice and the cost of 1 cornet.

3 Changing the subject

Liz's Mum is asking what she's doing today.
Liz doesn't want to talk about it.
She is trying to change the subject.

You need to be able to change the subject in Maths too.
This doesn't mean getting your teacher to talk about something else!

The subject of a formula is the letter that appears on its own on the left-hand side.
v is the subject in the formula $v = u + at$.
Changing the subject of a formula uses the same skills as solving an equation.
But instead of getting a number as an answer, you are now trying to get a different letter on its own.

Examples **1** Make u the subject of the formula $v = u + at$

You need to remove the at term from the right-hand side.
This will leave the u by itself.
The at is *added* to the RHS (Right Hand Side) at the moment.
So *subtract at* from each side.
$$v - at = u + at - at$$
$$v - at = u$$
Write the new formula the other way round with the subject on the LHS (Left Hand Side).
$$u = v - at$$

2 Make g the subject of the formula $v = 6g$
Write the formula the other way round. This gets the $6g$ on the LHS.
$$6g = v$$
The g is *multiplied by 6* at the moment.
So *divide by 6* on each side.
$$\frac{6g}{6} = \frac{v}{6}$$
$$g = \frac{v}{6}$$
g is now the subject of the formula.

3 Make y the subject of the formula $x = 4y - 2z$
First, you need to remove the $2z$ term from the RHS
This will leave the $4y$ by itself.
The $2z$ is *subtracted* at the moment.
So *add* $2z$ to each side.
$$x + 2z = 4y - 2z + 2z$$
$$x + 2z = 4y$$
Now write the formula the other way round
$$4y = x + 2z$$
The y is *multiplied by* 4 at the moment.
So *divide by* 4 on each side to leave the y on its own.
$$y = \frac{x + 2z}{4}$$
y is now the subject of the formula.

Exercise 20:8

Make the red letter the subject in each of these formulas.

1 $y = b + n$

2 $u = f - 7$

3 $e = s - 4u$

4 $p = 6a$

5 $h = 5g$

6 $v = 3t + u$

7 $k = 5r - 3z$

8 $r = wx + yt$ $r - yt = wx \rightarrow x = \frac{r - yt}{w}$

9 $5v = u + at$ $5v - u = at$ $t = \frac{5v - u}{a}$

10 $k = 5t - 3z$ $3z = 5t - k$ $z = \frac{5t - k}{3}$

Example   Make u the subject of the formula $v = \dfrac{u}{5}$

Write the formula the other way round. This gets the u term on the LHS.
$$\frac{u}{5} = v$$
The u is *divided by* 5 at the moment.
So *multiply by* 5 on each side.
$$5 \times \frac{u}{5} = 5 \times v$$
$$u = 5v$$
u is now the subject of the formula.

Exercise 20:9

Make the red letter the subject in each of these formulas.

1 $y = \dfrac{e}{5}$

2 $u = \dfrac{p}{15}$

3 $e = \dfrac{m}{3}$

4 $p = \dfrac{w}{4}$

5 $h = \dfrac{x}{7}$

6 $v = \dfrac{a}{5} - 5$

7 $k = \dfrac{y}{5} + 4$

8 $3r = \dfrac{5w}{8}$

[handwritten: $24r = 5w$; $\dfrac{24r}{5} = w$: $w = \dfrac{24r}{5}$]

9 $v = \dfrac{5x}{7} - 1$

[handwritten: $v + 1 = \dfrac{5x}{7}$; $7(v+1) = 5x$; $\dfrac{7(v+1)}{5} = x$]

10 $4k = 5t - \dfrac{k}{6}$

[handwritten: $\dfrac{k}{6} = 5t - 4k$; $k = 6(5t - 4k)$; $(\times 6)$ $k + 24k = 30t$; $25k = 30t \rightarrow k = \dfrac{30t}{25} = \dfrac{6t}{5}$]

Some equations have lots of terms.
You need to remember **BODMAS** to help you to change the subject of these equations.

Example   Make *t* the subject of the formula $c = \dfrac{zt + yb}{2}$

Look at the letter *t* on the RHS of the formula.
Using **BODMAS** the *t* has

been	multiplied by *z*
then had	*yb* added to it
and then been	divided by 2

Undo these operations in the reverse order by using their inverses.

First	multiply by 2	$2c = zt + yb$
then	subtract *yb*	$2c - yb = zt$
and then	divide by *z*	$\dfrac{2c - yb}{z} = t$

So $t = \dfrac{2c - yb}{z}$

t is now the subject of the formula.

Exercise 20:10

Make the red letter the subject in each of these formulas.

1 $t = \dfrac{z + g}{7}$

2 $r = \dfrac{4h + 6j}{6}$

3 $3t = \dfrac{4f + 7r}{2}$

6 $\dfrac{r}{4} = \dfrac{h + 8e}{3}$

(handwritten)
$\dfrac{3r}{4} = h + 8e$
$\dfrac{3r}{4} - 8e = h$ or $h = \dfrac{3r}{4} - 8e$

4 $at = \dfrac{pz + 5t}{y}$

7 $3d = \dfrac{4h + 6j}{5}$

5 $yk = \dfrac{ur + gj}{8}$

8 $5u = \dfrac{4h - 3d}{t}$

(handwritten)
$5ut = 4h - 3d.$
$3d = 4h - 5ut$
$d = \dfrac{4h - 5ut}{3}$

Some formulas have squares and square roots in them.
These two operations are the inverses of each other.
To remove a square, square root each side.
To remove a square root, square each side.

Examples   **1**   Make t the subject of the formula $s = \sqrt{t + r}$

To remove the square root, square each side
$$s^2 = t + r$$
Now subtract r
$$s^2 - r = t$$
So $t = s^2 - r$

2   Make g the subject of the formula $r = 3g^2$

First divide by the 3
$$\frac{r}{3} = g^2$$

To remove the square, square root both sides:
$$g = \sqrt{\frac{r}{3}}$$

Exercise 20:11

Make the **bold** letter the subject in each of these formulas.

1 $w = \sqrt{2t - s}$

4 $A = \pi r^2$

2 $d = \sqrt{5t + 6p}$
(handwritten) $d^2 = 5t + 6p$
$d^2 - 5t = 6p.$
$\dfrac{d^2 - 5t}{6} = p$
or $p = \dfrac{d^2 - 5t}{6}$

5 $e^2 = t^2 - 6f$

3 $y = \sqrt{\dfrac{6x}{5}}$

6 $k - 5 = gh - 2p^2$
(handwritten) $2p^2 + k - 5 = gh$
$2p^2 = gh - k + 5$
$p^2 = \dfrac{gh - k + 5}{2}$
$P = \sqrt{\dfrac{gh - k + 5}{2}}$

41

You can use substitution to solve simultaneous equations.

Example 1 Solve this pair of simultaneous equations

(1) $2x + y = 8$
(2) $y = 3x - 7$

Use equation (2) to substitute
for y in equation (1) $2x + (3x - 7) = 8$
Simplify the equation $5x - 7 = 8$
Add 7 to both sides $5x = 15$
Divide both sides by 5 $x = 3$

Put this in equation (2) to find y $y = 3 \times 3 - 7$
                                         $y = 2$

The solution is $x = 3, y = 2$ Check in (1) $2 \times 3 + 2 = 8$ ✓

Example 2 Solve this pair of simultaneous equations

(1) $3x - 2y = 9$
(2) $y + 2x = 13$

Make y the subject of equation (2)
Take $2x$ from both sides $y = 13 - 2x$
Substitute for y in equation (1)
Remember to use brackets. $3x - 2(13 - 2x) = 9$
Simplify the equation $3x - 26 + 4x = 9$
                                       $7x - 26 = 9$
Add 26 to both sides $7x = 35$
Divide both sides by 7 $x = 5$

Put this in equation (2) to find y $y + 2 \times 5 = 13$
                                         $y = 3$

The solution is $x = 5, y = 3$ Check in (1) $3 \times 5 - 2 \times 3 = 9$ ✓

Exercise 20:12

Solve these pairs of simultaneous equations using substitution.

1 $2x + y = 16$
$y = x + 7$

$2x + (x + 7) = 16$
$3x + 7 = 16$
$3x = 9$
$x = 3$

Subs. into (2)
$y = 3 + 7$
$= 10$
$x = 3, y = 10$

2 $3x + y = 17$
$y = 2x - 8$

3 $2x + 3y = 26$
$y = x + 2$

4 $3x - 2y = 14$
$y = x - 3$

5 $2x + 5y = 69$
$y - x = 4 \rightarrow y = x + 4$

$2x + 5(x + 4) = 69$
$2x + 5x + 20 = 69$
$7x = 49$
$x = 7$

Subs. into (2) $y = 7 + 4$
$x = 7, y = 11.$ $= 11$

6 $4x + 3y = -18$
$y - 2x = 4$

1 Sue and Kim are trying to solve the simultaneous equations $y = 2x - 1$ and $2x + y = 11$. Sue thinks that the solution is $x = 5, y = 9$. Kim thinks that the solution is $x = 3, y = 5$. Who is right? Explain your answer.

2 **a** Draw a set of axes on squared paper. Use values of x from -3 and $+3$ and values of y from -4 to $+7$.

    b Plot some points for the equation $y = 4x - 3$

    c Draw the graph of $y = 4x - 3$

    d Plot some points for the equation $2x - 3y = -6$

    e Draw the graph of $2x - 3y = -6$

    f Solve the simultaneous equations $y = 4x - 3$ and $2x - 3y = -6$

    g Check that your solution works in both equations.

3 **a** Draw a set of x and y axes on graph paper from $x = -4$ to $x = 4$ and from $y = -4$ to $y = 4$. Use 2 cm per unit for both axes.

    b Draw the graph of $y = \dfrac{4}{x}$

    c On the same set of axes draw the graph of $y = x$.

    d Solve the simultaneous equations $y = \dfrac{4}{x}$ and $y = x$.

4 Solve these pairs of simultaneous equations. Start by subtracting the equations each time.

    a $5x + 3y = 28$
       $4x + 3y = 23$

    c $5x - 4y = 14$
       $4x - 4y = 8$

    b $11x + 2y = 43$
       $6x + 2y = 28$

    d $3p - 4q = -11$
       $p - 4q = -17$

5 Solve these pairs of simultaneous equations. Start by adding the equations each time.

    a $3x + 2y = 26$
       $2x - 2y = 4$

    c $3m + 5n = 31$
       $10m - 5n = -5$

    b $3x - 8y = 11$
       $2x + 8y = 18$

    d $7i - 3j = 19$
       $6i + 3j = 33$

6 Solve these pairs of simultaneous equations.
You need to decide whether to add or subtract the equations.

a $2x + y = 13$
$3x - y = 12$

c $3x + 2y = 12$
$x + 2y = 2$

b $4x + 2y = 6$
$x - 2y = 9$

d $6x + 3y = 21$
$2x + 3y = 11$

7 Make the red letter the subject in each of these formulas.

a $p - 5 = q$

d $u(v + w) = x$

b $3m + 4 = n$

e $u(v + w) = x$

c $pq - r = s$

f $g = k - fh$

8 Make the red letter the subject in each of these formulas.

a $r = \dfrac{p}{q}$

d $w = \dfrac{x}{y}$

b $h = \dfrac{j + m}{n}$

e $y = \sqrt{x - 3w}$

c $t = \dfrac{u}{r} + v$

f $g = \sqrt{ax + b}$

9 Larry is using this formula $h = \dfrac{4a - 3b^2}{2}$

a Use the formula to find the value of h when $a = 12$ and $b = 2$.
b Rearrange the formula to make a the subject.
c Find the value of a when $h = 14$ and $b = 6$.

10 Solve these pairs of simultaneous equations using substitution.

a $y = 2x - 3$
$3y + 4x = 31$

c $x = 12 - y$
$2y = 31 - 3x$

b $x = 2y - 7$
$3y = 3 - x$

d $y = 7 - 5x$
$21 = 3y + 4x$

1 Solve the simultaneous equations shown by the lines in these diagrams.

a

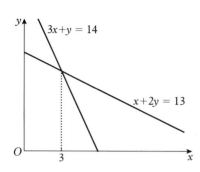

c

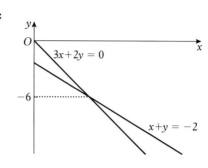

b

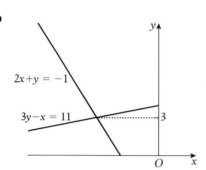

d

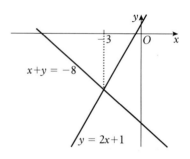

2 Solve these pairs of simultaneous equations.

a $3x + 5y = 36$
  $x + y = 10$

d $4m - 5n = 1$
  $3m - 2n = -8$

b $4x - 9y = 8$
  $x + y = 15$

e $3x + 2y = 7$
  $y = 2x + 14$

c $2p - 3q = -23$
  $3p - 2q = -22$

f $5x + 4y = -29$
  $2y = 10 + x$

3 Three bags of chips cost £2 more than one portion of fish.
Three portions of fish and one bag of chips cost £7.
  a How much is a bag of chips?
  b How much is a portion of fish?

1 **a** Draw a set of axes on squared paper.
Use values of x from -1 to 4 and values of y from -4 to 8.

   b Plot some points for the equation $y = 3x - 1$

   c Draw the graph of $y = 3x - 1$

   d Plot some points for the equation $2x + y = 4$

   e Draw the graph of $2x + y = 4$

   f Solve the simultaneous equations $y = 3x - 1$ and $2x + y = 4$

   g Check that your solution works in both equations.

2 Solve these pairs of simultaneous equations.

   a $3x - 2y = 7$
   $x + 2y = 5$

   c $3x - y = 13$
   $2x + 3y = 5$

   b $5x - 2y = 10$
   $3x - 2y = 2$

   d $7x + 2y = 28$
   $2x + 3y = 25$

3 Make the red letter the subject in each of these formulas.

   a $g = 4h - 7$

   c $y = \dfrac{3x}{4} - 6$

   b $w = \dfrac{t}{5} + 2$

   d $s = 10 + 3t^2$

4 Sally is using this formula: $A = \dfrac{\sqrt{w^2 + 3xy}}{10}$

   a Use the formula to find the value of A when $w = -1$, $x = 8$ and $y = 2$.

   b Rearrange the formula to make w the subject.

   c Find the value of w when $A = 1$, $x = 4$ and $y = 7$.

5 Solve these pairs of simultaneous equations using substitution.

   a $y = 5 - 2x$
   $3y + x = 10$

   b $x = 4y - 6$
   $14 = 8y - 3x$

21 Probability

1 Sample space diagrams
Drawing sample space diagrams
Finding probabilities with sample space
   diagrams
Finding the expected number

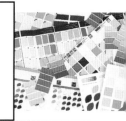

CORE

2 Finding probabilities
Looking at independent events
Using the formula $P(A \text{ and } B) = P(A) \times P(B)$
Finding the probability of an event happening
   more than once
Looking at mutually exclusive events
Using the formula $P(A \text{ or } B) = P(A) + P(B)$

QUESTIONS

EXTENSION

TEST YOURSELF

1 Sample space diagrams

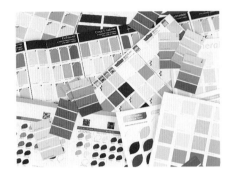

Nicola and her father are buying paint. They are trying to find the best colour to use for redecorating her bedroom.
They have to decide which paint colours to mix. They are using a paint chart to help them. It shows all the possible colours.

You can use diagrams to help in probability.

| **Sample space** | A **sample space** is a list of all the things that can happen in a probability experiment. |

| **Outcome** | Each thing that can happen in an experiment is called an **outcome**. |

| **Sample space diagram** | A table which shows all of the possible outcomes is called a **sample space diagram**. |

Example

Toby rolls a dice and spins a coin.

a Draw a sample space diagram to show all the possible outcomes.
b Write down the total number of possible outcomes.
c Write down the probability that Toby gets a Head and a 5.

a Draw a table. Put all the numbers for the dice along the top. Put Head and Tail down the side for the coin.
Fill in each possible outcome.

		Dice					
		1	2	3	4	5	6
Coin	Head	H, 1	H, 2	H, 3	H, 4	H, 5	H, 6
	Tail	T, 1	T, 2	T, 3	T, 4	T, 5	T, 6

b There are 12 possible outcomes. They are equally likely.
c A Head and a 5 appears once.
The probability of getting a **Head** and a 5 is $\frac{1}{12}$

Exercise 21:1

1 Jamie uses this spinner and throws a coin.

 EASY to start with

a Copy this sample space diagram.
Fill it in.

		Spinner		
		1	2	3
Coin	H	H, 1	H, 2	H, 3
	T	T 1	T 2	T 3

b Write down the total number of possible outcomes. 6

Write down the probability of getting:
c a 2 and a head   1/6
d an even number and a tail.   1/6

2 Luke is playing in a football match and Roz is playing in a netball match.
Both Luke and Roz are equally likely to win, lose or draw their game.
a Copy this sample space diagram showing all the possible outcomes.
Fill it in.

		Luke		
		Win	Lose	Draw
Roz	Win	W, W	W L	W D
	Lose	L W	L L	L, D
	Draw	D W	L D	D D

Write down the probability that:
b they will both win   1/9
c neither will win   4/9
d only one of them will win.   4/9

3 Ben rolls an 8-sided dice and an ordinary dice.
a Draw a sample space diagram to show all the
possible outcomes of rolling the two dice.

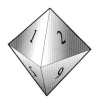

Write down the probability of getting:
b a 7 on the 8-sided dice and a 4 on the ordinary dice
c double 6
d a number less than 3 on both dice.

4 Mrs Jones has decided to change the flowers in one of her garden tubs.
She has two bags of tulips. Each bag contains one bulb of each of the
colours red, yellow, black, pink and white.
She takes one bulb at random from each bag.
a Draw a sample space diagram to show all the possible outcomes.

Write down the probability that the tulips will be:
b the same colour
c different colours.

5 John has made two dice.
He writes the numbers 1, 1, 2, 3, 7, 8 on the first dice
and the numbers 4, 4, 5, 5, 6, 6 on the second dice.
John rolls the two dice.
a Draw a sample space diagram to show all the possible outcomes.

Write down the probability that the numbers on the two dice:
b add up to 8 $\frac{4}{36} = \frac{1}{9}$
c are the same   ○
d are both even numbers. $\frac{8}{36} = \frac{2}{9}$

6 A red dice and a black dice are thrown together.
a Draw a sample space diagram to
show all the possible outcomes.

Write down the probability
b of getting two odd numbers
c of getting an even number and an odd number
d that the sum of the two numbers is less than 5
e that the difference between the two numbers is 2
f that $r < b$ where r is the number on the red dice
and b is the number on the black dice.

You can work out how many times an event is likely to happen when you
repeat an experiment.

A bag contains two red balls and three blue balls.
A ball is chosen at random from the bag and then replaced.
This is done 40 times.

The total number of possible outcomes is 5. There are 2 red balls.

The probability of getting a red ball is $\frac{2}{5}$.

This means that, on average, you expect 2 red balls in every 5 chosen.

To find the expected number of red balls when you choose a ball 40 times:
First you divide 40 by 5 to find how many groups of 5 there are in 40.
You then multiply by 2 since you expect to get 2 red balls in every 5.

So the expected number of red balls $= 40 \div 5 \times 2$
$$= 16$$

This is the same as $40 \times \dfrac{2}{5}$ where $\frac{2}{5}$ is the probability of getting a red ball

So: Work out the probability that the event happens once.
     Then multiply by the number of times the experiment is repeated.

The **expected number = number of trials × probability**

Exercise 21:2

1 A bag contains four red balls and six blue balls. *10 balls altogether*
  a A ball is chosen at random.
      Write down the probability that it is blue. *$\frac{6}{10} = 3/5$*
  b A ball is chosen at random from the bag and then replaced.
      This is done 100 times. *100 × 3/5*
      How many blue balls would you expect? *60 times*

2 The probability that a shopper, selected at random, in a supermarket
     buys cat food is 0.45.
     How many shoppers out of 800 would you expect to buy cat food?

3 **a** The probability that Martin is late for
         school on a particular day is 0.05.
         There are 75 days in the Autumn Term.
         How many days would you expect
         Martin to be late? *75 × 0.05 → 3.75 days*
     b The Spring Term is 11 weeks long. *54 days*
         Martin is late on 3 days.
         Is he more or less punctual?
         Explain your answer.

11 wks → 55 days

55 × 0.05 → 2.75 days late.

∴ less punctual.

4 Jenny has made these two spinners to use in a game to raise money at the school fair.

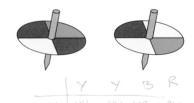

To play the game you spin both spinners. You win a prize if they both land on the same colour.

a Draw a sample space diagram for this game.

b Write down the probability that a player will win.

c Jenny charges 20p to play the game.
How much will she collect from 50 players?

d How many winners would you expect out of every 50 players?

e How much money should Jenny give out as a prize? Explain your answer.

	Y	Y	B	R
Y	YY	YY	YB	RY
R	RY	RY	RB	RR
R	RY	RY	RB	RR
B	BY	BY	BB	BR

$\frac{5}{16}$

50 × 20p
£10

$\frac{5 \times 50}{16}$ = 15·625
= $\frac{5}{16}$

16 × ? < £10   prob. 50p → £8 (still makes profit)

5 Mia has a bag of coloured counters.
She chooses a counter at random, notes the colour and then replaces it.
Mia does this 60 times.

a Mia expects to get 12 black counters.
Find the probability that a black counter will be chosen. $\frac{1}{5}$

b Mia has 10 counters in the bag.
How many of these are black? 2

6 Tom tosses two coins.

a Draw a sample space diagram showing all the possible outcomes.

Write down the probability of getting

b two heads

c a head and a tail.

Tom tosses the two coins 80 times.

d How many times would you expect him to get a head and a tail?

7 Sam rolls a dice a number of times.   PROBABILITY $\frac{1}{6}$
He expects to get ten 6s.   10 times is $\frac{1}{6}$ of 60
How many times did he roll the dice? 60

8 Louise is a driving examiner.
60% of the drivers that Louise tests pass the exam.
In one month Louise failed 64 drivers.   40% = 64
About how many drivers did she examine? 100% = 160

2 Finding probabilities

All the balls in the machine have an equal chance of being the first ball out.
What has happened in previous draws has no effect on the next draw.

Independent events	Two events are **independent** if the outcome of one has no effect on the outcome of the other.

If you roll a fair dice and toss a coin you can get 1, 2, 3, 4, 5 or 6 on the dice and either a head or a tail with the coin.

Whatever you get on the dice has no effect on what you get with the coin.

Exercise 21:3

Look at the events in questions **1–5**.
Write down whether each pair of events is independent.

1 Peter throws a dart and scores double 20.
He removes his dart from the board. *IND.*
Rebecca throws a dart and scores 18.

2 Alison chooses a red Smartie at random from a tube and eats it.
Richard then chooses a red Smartie at random from the same tube. *NOT IND*

3 Jenny draws a red playing card from a pack of 52 cards. She keeps the *NOT IND*
card and shuffles the rest of the pack. Jenny then draws a black card.

4 Tim wins his next tennis match and Louise passes her music exam. *IND.*

5 Anna spins this spinner and it lands on 6.
She spins it again and it lands on 2. *IND*

Pritesh uses this spinner and throws a dice.

This sample space diagram shows all the possible outcomes.

		Dice					
		1	2	3	4	5	6
	red	R, 1	R, 2	R, 3	R, 4	R, 5	R, 6
Spinner	blue	B, 1	B, 2	B, 3	B, 4	B, 5	B, 6
	green	G, 1	G, 2	G, 3	G, 4	G, 5	G, 6

P(blue and an even number) $= \frac{3}{18} = \frac{1}{6}$

You can work out this probability using independent events.

Probability of independent events

If two **events** A and B are **independent** then the **probability** of them both happening is called P(A *and* B)

also P(A **and** B) $= P$(A) $\times P$(B)

So for Pritesh:
P(blue *and* an even number) $= P$(blue) $\times P$(even number)
$$= \tfrac{1}{3} \times \tfrac{1}{2} = \tfrac{1}{6}$$

This is the same answer as you get using the sample space diagram. This method is much quicker to use.

Example

Mary throws a dice and tosses a coin.
Find the probability that she gets a head and a 4.

Let H be the event 'getting a head' and F be the event 'getting a 4'.
Then P(H) $= \tfrac{1}{2}$ and P(F) $= \tfrac{1}{6}$
H and F are independent
So P(H *and* F) $= \tfrac{1}{2} \times \tfrac{1}{6} = \tfrac{1}{12}$

Exercise 21:4

1 The probability that Sara will pass her medical exam is $\frac{4}{5}$.
The probability that Jamie will pass his medical exam is $\frac{2}{3}$.
Find the probability that Sara and Jamie both pass their exam.

2 The probability that Alan will miss his bus on any day is $\frac{1}{4}$.
Find the probability that he will miss the bus today and miss the bus tomorrow.

$P\left(A \text{ and } B\right) = \frac{1}{4} \times \frac{1}{4} = \frac{1}{16}$

3 R and S are independent events.
$P(R) = 0.23$ and $P(S) = 0.65$
Find $P(R \text{ and } S)$.

4 The probability that it will rain on a particular day
in April is 0.6
Write down the probability that:
a it won't rain on a particular day
b it will rain on one day and on the next day
c it will rain on one day but not on the next day.

5 Jenny has a 20% chance of making a spelling mistake
on one page of writing.
a Write this probability as a fraction. $\frac{1}{5}$

Jenny writes two pages.
b Find the probability that she makes a spelling mistake on the first
page and on the second page. $\frac{1}{5} \times \frac{1}{5} = \frac{1}{25}$

6 A and B are independent events.
$P(B) = \frac{3}{5}$ and $P(A \text{ and } B) = \frac{12}{45}$.
Find the value of $P(A)$.

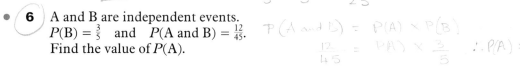
$P(A \text{ and } B) = P(A) \times P(B)$
$\frac{12}{45} = P(A) \times \frac{3}{5}$ $\therefore P(A) = \frac{4}{9}$

7 Anna and Richard are auditioning for different parts in a play.
The probability that Anna will get her part is $\frac{3}{5}$ and the probability that
Richard will get his part is $\frac{5}{8}$.
What is the probability that:
a both Anna and Richard will get a part
b neither will get a part
c only Richard gets a part.

8 Carmen is responsible for checking the components of the braking
system for new cars. A component has a 2% chance of being faulty.
a Write this probability as a decimal.

Two components are selected at random. Find the probability that:
b both components are faulty
c neither component is faulty.

You can use independent events to find the probability of an event happening more
than once.
You multiply the probability of it happening once by itself.

Example   A dice is rolled three times. Find the probability of getting three 6s.

The probability of a 6 on one roll is $\frac{1}{6}$
Each roll is independent so multiply the probabilities.

$P(\text{three 6s}) = P(\text{6 on 1}^{\text{st}} \text{ roll}) \times P(\text{6 on 2}^{\text{nd}} \text{ roll}) \times P(\text{6 on 3}^{\text{rd}} \text{ roll})$
$= \frac{1}{6} \times \frac{1}{6} \times \frac{1}{6} = \frac{1}{216}$

Exercise 21:5

1 a Write down the probability of getting a
red with this spinner. ¹/₄

The spinner is used twice.
b Find the probability of getting two reds. $\frac{1}{4} \times \frac{1}{4} = \frac{1}{16}$

2 A dice is rolled twice.
Find the probability of getting two 4s.

3 The spinner in question **1** is used three times.
Find the probability of getting three blues.

4 The probability of Bill being late for work on any morning is 0.15
Find the probability that he is late:
a on two consecutive mornings
b on three consecutive mornings.

5 Jamie tosses a coin ten times.
Find the probability that Jamie gets:
a a head with the first toss ¹/₂
b all heads with the first three tosses $\frac{1}{2} \times \frac{1}{2} \times \frac{1}{2} = \left(\frac{1}{8}\right)$ (or $\frac{1}{2^0}$)
c all heads on all ten tosses.
$\frac{1}{2} \times \frac{1}{2} \times \frac{1}{2} \times \frac{1}{2} \times \frac{1}{2} \times \frac{1}{2} \times \frac{1}{2} \times \frac{1}{2} \times \frac{1}{2} \times \frac{1}{2} = \frac{1}{1024}$

6 The probability that a letter sent by First Class
post will arrive the next day is ¾. Five letters are
sent by First Class post on the same day.
Find the probability that, on the next day:
a all five letters will arrive $(3/4)^5$ $\frac{3}{4} \times \frac{3}{4} \times \frac{3}{4} \times \frac{3}{4} \times \frac{3}{4} = \frac{243}{1024}$
b no letters will arrive. $(1/4)^5$ $\frac{1}{4} \times \frac{1}{4} \times \frac{1}{4} \times \frac{1}{4} \times \frac{1}{4} = \frac{1}{1024}$

A firm sends out 260 letters by First Class post.
c How many would you expect to arrive the
next day? 195 letters $\left(\frac{3}{4} \times 260\right)$

7 A factory produces boxes of chocolates.
Each box of chocolates is tested twice.
The first test is a check on the contents,
the second test is a check on the packaging.
The probability of a box passing the first
test is 0.94 and the probability of it passing
the second is 0.90.
The two tests are independent.

Find the probability that a box of chocolates:
a fails the first test
b passes both tests
c passes the first test but fails the second
d fails the first test but passes the second
e fails at least one test.

If a box of chocolates fails only one test it is sold as substandard.
If both tests are failed the box of chocolates is destroyed.
Out of a production of 1000 boxes of chocolates how many would you expect to be:
f sold as substandard
g destroyed?

Mutually exclusive	Events are **mutually exclusive** if they cannot happen at the same time.

When a coin is tossed it can land showing either a head or a tail.
It cannot show *both* a head and a tail at the same time.
One outcome automatically excludes the other.
The events 'head' and 'tail' are mutually exclusive.

Probability of mutually exclusive events	For two **mutually exclusive events** A and B, the **probability** that *either* event A *or* event B will occur can be found by *adding* their probabilities together.

$$P(A \text{ or } B) = P(A) + P(B)$$

When a dice is thrown E is the event 'getting an even number' and T is the event 'getting a three'.
The events E and T are mutually exclusive.
$P(E) = \frac{1}{3}$ and $P(T) = \frac{1}{6}$
So $P(E \text{ or } T) = \frac{1}{3} + \frac{1}{6} = \frac{1}{2}$

Exercise 21:6

1 State whether each pair of events is mutually exclusive.
a When throwing a dice:
'getting a 2' and 'getting an even number'.
b When picking a card at random from a pack of cards:
'getting a red card' and 'getting an ace'.
c When choosing a person at random from a group of people:
'getting a man with brown hair' and 'getting a woman with grey hair'.

2 Rachel has a spinner with ten equal sections.
4 are red, 3 are blue, 1 is black and the rest are yellow.
Rachel uses the spinner once.
Find the probability that the colour she gets is:
  a black $\frac{1}{10}$
  b red $\frac{4}{10}$ OR $\frac{2}{5}$
  c yellow $\frac{2}{10}$ OR $\frac{1}{5}$
  d red or blue
  e black or yellow
  f not red.

$\frac{4}{10} + \frac{3}{10} = \frac{7}{10}$ (d)

$\frac{1}{10} + \frac{2}{10} = 3/10$ —(e)

$1 - \frac{4}{10} = 6/10$ OR $3/5$.

3 In a school raffle Michelle buys
5 tickets and Jonathan buys 10 tickets.
300 tickets are sold altogether.
What is the probability that:
  a Michelle wins first prize
  b Michelle or Jonathan wins first prize?

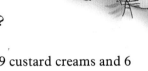

4 A tin of biscuits contains 3 shortbreads, 9 custard creams and 6
bourbons. Jemima chooses a biscuit at random.
Find the probability that Jemima chooses:
  a a shortbread
  b a bourbon
  c a shortbread or a bourbon
  d a custard cream or a bourbon.

5 The events G and H are mutually exclusive
$P(G) = \frac{1}{3}$ $P(H) = \frac{3}{5}$
Find $P(G$ or $H)$.

$\frac{1}{3} + \frac{3}{5} \rightarrow \frac{5}{15} + \frac{9}{15} = \frac{14}{15}$

6 The events M and S are mutually exclusive
$P(M) = \frac{2}{5}$ $P(M$ or $S) = \frac{3}{4}$
Find $P(S)$.

Exercise 21:7

In this exercise think about whether the events are independent or
mutually exclusive before you work out each probability.

1 The probabilities that Damon and Michael will pass their driving tests
are $\frac{2}{3}$ and $\frac{1}{5}$ respectively. Find the probability that:
  a Damon *and* Michael pass $\frac{2}{3} \times \frac{1}{5} = \frac{2}{15}$
  b they both fail
  c only Damon passes. $\frac{1}{3} \times \frac{4}{5} = \frac{4}{15}$

$\frac{2}{3} \times \frac{4}{5} = \frac{8}{15}$

2 John rolls a dice.
Find the probability that he gets:
  a a 6
  b a 1 or a 6
  c an even number
  d a 3 or an even number
  e a number less than 3
  f a prime number.

3 Harry is taking his end of year exams. These are the probabilities of Harry passing each exam.
P(passing Maths) = 0.65
P(passing English) = 0.8
P(passing French) = 0.45

Assuming that the events are independent find the probability that Harry will:
  a pass all three exams 0·65 × 0·8 × 0·45 = 0·234
  b fail all three exams 0·35 × 0·2 × 0·55 = 0·0385
  c pass English but fail Maths 0·8 × 0·35 = 0·28
  d pass Maths but fail French. 0·65 × 0·55 = 0·3575

4 Katy checks the oil and screenwash container in her car every two weeks to see if they need topping up.
The probability that she needs to top up the oil is 0.25 and the probability that she needs to top up the screenwash is 0.3

Find the probability that the next time Katy checks her car:
  a both need topping up 0·25 × 0·3 = 0·075
  b only the oil needs topping up 0·25 × 0·7 = 0·175
  c neither needs topping up. 0·75 × 0·7 = 0·525

5 Sian prints pictures on to sweat shirts. She has four designs and three colours.

The four designs are: animal, bird, insect, fish.
The three colours are: red, blue, black.

Sian chooses the design and colour at random.
Find the probability that she chooses:
  a an animal design
  b a bird design in red
  c a fish or insect design
  d an animal or bird design in black
  e a design in blue
  f a bird or fish design in blue or red.

1 Ruth chooses two numbers at random from the numbers 1, 2, 3, 4 and 5.
She cannot choose a number more than once.
   a Show all the possible selections of numbers in a sample space diagram.

Write down the probability that she chooses:
   b the numbers 1 and 4
   c two even numbers
   d either both even numbers or both odd numbers.

2 Ian spins a 5-sided spinner numbered 1 to 5 at the same time as rolling a
fair dice numbered 1 to 6. He writes down the two numbers he gets.
   a Draw a sample space diagram to show all the possible outcomes.

Find the probability that:
   b the total score is 7
   c the score is the same on the dice and the spinner
   d the total is less than 5
   e the score on the dice and the spinner is the same and the total score
   is less than 5.

3 Matt rolls these two 4-sided dice.
He writes down the two numbers that they land on.
   a Draw a sample space diagram to show all the
   possible outcomes.

Write down the probability that the two numbers are:
   b both the same
   c both even
   d both prime.

4 The school canteen has estimated the probability that a pupil chooses
coke, milk or orange drink to drink at lunchtime. The estimated
probabilities are 0.57, 0.29 and 0.14 respectively.
About 700 pupils eat in the canteen each day.
How many of each type of drink should the canteen order for the next
five school days?

5 A and B are independent events.
$P(A) = \frac{3}{5}$ and $P(B) = \frac{1}{4}$
Find $P(A \text{ and } B)$.

6 The probability of Sara having carrots for Sunday dinner is $\frac{3}{4}$.
The probability of her having apple pie for pudding is $\frac{1}{10}$.
Find the probability that Sara has
   a carrots but not apple pie
   b apple pie but not carrots
   c both carrots and apple pie
   d neither carrots nor apple pie.

7   R and S are independent events.
  $P(R) = 0.2$ and $P(S) = 0.7$
  Find $P(R \text{ and } S)$.

8   The probability that Mark has homework on a Monday is 0.8
  The probability that Mark goes out on a Monday is 0.35
  Find the probability that he has homework and goes out next Monday.

9   Birth statistics show that the probability of a baby being male is 0.51
  The Fletcher and Edmundson families are each expecting a baby.
  What is the probability that both babies are girls?

10   The probability of Diane walking to school on any day is 0.2

  Find the probability that Diane
  a   does not walk to school on Monday
  b   walks to school on Monday and Tuesday
  c   walks to school on Monday, Tuesday and Wednesday.

11   The events R and S are mutually exclusive.
  $P(R) = \frac{1}{4}$ and $P(S) = \frac{2}{3}$.
  Find $P(R \text{ or } S)$.

12   Derek uses this spinner.
  Let A be the event 'getting a red'.
  Let B be the event 'getting an even number'.
  Are A and B mutually exclusive?
  Explain your answer.

13   Ken has done a survey. The table gives his results

	Male	Female
Adult	21	14
Child	8	12

  a   How many people were involved in the survey?

  Ken chooses a person at random from his survey. Let R be the event
  'choosing a female' and S be the event 'choosing an adult'.
  b   Find $P(R)$
  c   Find $P(S)$
  d   Does $P(R \text{ and } S) = P(R) + P(S)$?
     Explain your answer.

1   A bag contains 5 white disks, 3 black disks and 2 green disks. Robert takes a disk from the bag at random. Let the events getting a white, getting a black or getting a green disc be W, B or G respectively. Write down:

a $P(W)$ **c** $P(G')$

b $P(B')$ **d** $P(W$ or $B)$.

Robert takes a disk from the bag at random and then replaces it. He does this three times. Find the probability that:

e all three discs are black

f none of the three discs are black

g only the first disc is black

h only one of the three discs is black.

2   This spinner is used many times. Find the probability of getting blue:

a on the first spin

b on the first 2 spins

c on the first 3 spins

d on the first 4 spins

e on the first n spins.

3   William has a biased coin. The probability of getting a head when it is tossed is 0.6 He tosses the coin three times. Find the probability that he gets:

a 3 tails

b 3 heads

c only one tail.

4   A bag contains 20 balls. 7 are red, 5 are blue and the rest are green. Rob picks out a ball at random and then replaces it. He then picks out a second ball at random. Find the probability that:

a both balls are blue

b the first ball is blue and the second is green

c one ball is blue and one is green

d only one ball is blue

e at least one ball is blue.

1 Kim has two dice.
One dice has the numbers 1 to 6 on its faces.
The other dice has six different coloured faces.
The colours are red, blue, green, yellow, brown and purple.

  a Copy this sample space diagram.
   Fill it in.

	red	blue	green	yellow	brown	purple
1	1R	1B	1G	1Y	1B	1P
2	2R	2B	2G	2Y	2B	2P
3	3R	3B	3G	3Y	3B	3P
4	4R	4B	4G	4Y	4B	4P
5	5R	5B	5G	5Y	5B	5P
6	6R	6B	6G	6Y	6B	6P

  b Kim spins the two dice.
   Write down the probability that she gets

   (1) green and 3 $\frac{1}{36}$

   (2) blue and an even number $\frac{3}{36} = \frac{1}{12}$

   (3) a number less than 4 $\frac{18}{36} = \frac{1}{2}$

   (4) purple and a prime number $\frac{3}{36} = \frac{1}{12}$

2 Police stopped 50 cars at random to check their tyres, lights and
seatbelts. 7 cars had faulty tyres, 3 had faulty lights and 1 had faulty
seatbelts. No car had more than 1 fault.
The police stop another 200 cars.

  a What is the probability that the first car will have faulty lights? $\frac{3}{50}$
  b How many of the 200 cars would you expect to have faulty tyres?

   $\frac{3}{50} \times 200 = 12$

3 Danny uses this spinner 3 times.
Write down the probability that he
gets 3 even numbers.

   $\frac{2}{5} \times \frac{2}{5} \times \frac{2}{5} = \frac{8}{125}$

4 The probability that Paul will win his squash match is 0.7
The probability that his sister will win her tennis match is 0.9
Find the probability that they both

  a win $0.7 \times 0.9 = 0.63$
  b lose. $0.3 \times 0.1 = 0.03$

5 **a** Two events Q and R are independent.
P(Q) = $\frac{1}{4}$ and P(R) = $\frac{3}{8}$
Find P(Q and R). $\frac{1}{4} \times \frac{3}{8} = \frac{3}{32}$

b Two events S and T are mutually exclusive.
P(S) = $\frac{1}{2}$ and P(T) = $\frac{1}{6}$ $\frac{1}{2} + \frac{1}{6} = \frac{4}{6} = \frac{2}{3}$
Find P(S or T).

c P(A) = 0.4, P(B) = 0.2 and P(A and B) = 0.075
Explain how you can tell from these values that the events are not
independent. *if they were P(A and B) would be*
0.4 × 0.2 = 0.08

d P(C) = 0.85 and P(D) = 0.3
Are C and D mutually exclusive?
Explain how you can tell. *No, because if they are,*
then P(C) + P(D) would be 1
& they are not

6 James has a biased dice.
The table shows the probability of getting the different scores.

Score	1	2	3	4	5	6
Probability	0.15	...	0.25	0.05	0.3	0.05

a Find the probability of scoring a 2. $1-(0.15 + 0.25 + 0.05 + 0.3 + 0.05)$
b James throws the dice.
   (1) Which number is the most likely score? *No. above largest decimal*
   (2) What is the probability that he gets an odd number? *ADD ODD PROBS*
c James throws the dice twice.
   He adds the two scores.
   What is the probability that he gets a total score of 12?
   $0.05 \times 0.05 = 0.0025$

7 A factory makes resistors.
The probability that a resistor will be faulty is 0.0045
The factory makes 35 600 resistors in one week.
How many of these would you expect to be faulty?
$0.0045 \times 35600 = 160.2$
≈ 160 resistors

22 Standard form

1 **Big** numbers
Revising powers including squares and cubes
Using your calculator to do powers
Writing big numbers in standard form
Writing big standard form numbers as
  ordinary numbers
Using your calculator for standard form

CORE

2 Small **numbers**
Revising negative powers
Writing small numbers in standard form
Writing small standard form numbers as
  ordinary numbers
Using your calculator for standard form
Rounding answers in standard form
Non-calculator questions
Comparing the size of numbers in standard form

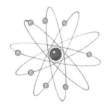

QUESTIONS

EXTENSION

TEST YOURSELF

1 **Big** numbers

Pluto is the furthest planet from the Sun in our solar system.

The distance from the Sun to Pluto is 5 907 000 000 miles correct to the nearest million miles!

This is the most digits that many calculators can fit in their display. You may find that your calculator cannot fit all the digits into its display.

There is a way of putting numbers like this and bigger ones into your calculator. Before you see it you need to remember about powers.

Power

The number 5^3 is 5 to the **power** of 3.
This means $5 \times 5 \times 5$.
The **power** tells you how many 5s to multiply together.
$5^3 = 5 \times 5 \times 5 = 125$

Exercise 22:1

1 Copy these. Fill them in.

a $2^3 = \ldots \times \ldots \times \ldots$
   $= $

b $4^2 = \ldots \times \ldots$
   $= $

c $7^3 = \ldots \times \ldots \times \ldots$
   $= $

d $4^3 = \ldots \times \ldots \times \ldots$
   $= $

e $10^4 = \ldots \times \ldots \times \ldots \times \ldots$
   $= $

f $10^5 = $
   $= $

2 Work these out.

a 3^2 **e** 4^4 **i** 2^5 **m** 10^3
b 5^2 **f** 5^4 **j** 3^5 **n** 10^6
c 3^3 **g** 6^2 **k** 4^5 **o** 10^7
d 5^3 **h** 7^3 **l** 8^3 **p** 10^8

3 Write each of these using a power.

a 3×3 **c** $5 \times 5 \times 5$ **e** $2 \times 2 \times 2 \times 2$
b $4 \times 4 \times 4$ **d** $8 \times 8 \times 8 \times 8$ **f** $7 \times 7 \times 7 \times 7 \times 7$

4 Copy these. Fill them in.

    a $2 \times 2 \times 2 \times 3 \times 3 = 2^{\cdots} \times 3^{\cdots}$ **c** $3 \times 3 \times 3 \times 4 \times 4 \times 4 = 3^{\cdots} \times 4^{\cdots}$

    b $2 \times 3 \times 3 \times 3 \times 3 = 2^{\cdots} \times 3^{\cdots}$ **d** $5 \times 5 \times 4 \times 4 \times 4 \times 4 = 4^{\cdots} \times 5^{\cdots}$

Square

Square is a special name for a power of 2.
4^2 is 4 to the power of 2.
You can also say this as 'the square of 4' or '4 squared'.

Cube

Cube is a special name for a power of 3.
5^3 is 5 to the power of 3.
You can also say this as 'the cube of 5' or '5 cubed'.

---

5 Work out the value of each of these.

    a   the square of 3   **d**   5 squared   **g**   4 cubed

    b   the cube of 6   **e**   10 cubed   **h**   8 squared

    c   the square of 10   **f**   12 squared   **i**   the cube of 5

Square root

To find the **square root** you have to do the opposite of squaring.
You know that $4^2 = 4 \times 4 = 16$.
The square root of 16 is 4. The square root has a symbol of its own.
$\sqrt{}$ means the square root of.
So $\sqrt{16} = 4$.

---

6 Work out the value of each of these.

    a $\sqrt{4}$ **d** $\sqrt{36}$ **g** $\sqrt{144}$

    b $\sqrt{9}$ **e** $\sqrt{100}$ **h** $\sqrt{10\,000}$

    c $\sqrt{25}$ **f** $\sqrt{81}$ **i** $\sqrt{1\,000\,000}$

7 Find the square root key, , on your calculator.

Use the key to check your answers to question **6**.

For part **a** key in:

As well as a key you have other keys on your calculator that you can use for doing powers.

x^2 key

The **x^2 key** is for squaring.

Key in: **3** **x^2** **=**

to work out that $3^2 = 9$.

x^y or y^x key

The **x^y or y^x key** is for working out any power.

Key in:  **5** **y^x** **3** **=** **5** **x^y** **3** **=**

to work out that $5^3 = 125$.

8 Use your calculator to check your answers to question **2**.

9 Use your calculator to work these out.

a 7.1^2	**e** 2.8^4	**i** 2.2^5	**m** 9.2^3
b 8.5^2	**f** 5.1^4	**j** 8.3^5	**n** 23.1^4
c 4.1^3	**g** 7.6^2	**k** 4.3^5	**o** 1.01^5
d 9.3^3	**h** 7.1^3	**l** 1.62^3	**p** 12.92^6

10 a Use your calculator to work these out.
 (1) 10^2 (3) 10^4 (5) 10^6
 (2) 10^3 (4) 10^5 (6) 10^7

b Look at your answers to **a**.
Write down the answers to these questions.
 (1) 10^8 (3) 10^{10} (5) 10^{12}
 (2) 10^9 (4) 10^{11} (6) 10^{13}

c Now do part **b** using **x^y** or **y^x** on your calculator.
Write down exactly what you get on your calculator next to your answers to **b**.

d Your answers to **c** should give you a clue about how your calculator shows really big numbers.
Write a sentence or a short paragraph to explain what it is doing.

| Standard form |

Very large numbers are written down using **standard form**. Standard form is like a code that you need to use when numbers get so big that they won't fit on a calculator. You can use standard form for smaller numbers too if you want to! A number is in standard form if it has two parts: **a number between 1 and 10** multiplied by 10 to a power.

So to write a number in standard form you split it into two parts that are multiplied together.
The first part must be a number between 1 and 10.
1 is allowed but 10 isn't.
The second part is a power of 10.
2×10^{12} is a number in standard form.
0.5×10^{12} is not in standard form because 0.5 is not between 1 and 10.
10×10^5 is not in standard form because 10 is not allowed as the first number.
10×10^5 is the same as 1×10^6. This is now in standard form.

To write an ordinary number in standard form you need to get a number between 1 and 10 using the same digits. Then you need to multiply it by 10 enough times to get back to the correct number. The number of times you need to multiply is the power of 10.

Look at the number $36\,000$. The number between 1 and 10 for this number is 3.6

3.6×10	$= 3.6 \times 10^1$	$= 36$
$3.6 \times 10 \times 10$	$= 3.6 \times 10^2$	$= 360$
$3.6 \times 10 \times 10 \times 10$	$= 3.6 \times 10^3$	$= 3600$
$3.6 \times 10 \times 10 \times 10 \times 10$	$= 3.6 \times 10^4$	$= 36\,000$

So the number $36\,000$ is 3.6×10^4 in standard form.

You can imagine putting the decimal point into the number and then moving it back to where it should be like this.

$$36\,000 = 3.6 \times 10\,000$$
$$= 3.6 \times 10^4$$

3.6 0 0 0
1 2 3 4

Example Write these numbers in standard form.
a $2\,000\,000$ **b** $125\,000\,000$

a $2\,000\,000 = 2 \times 1\,000\,000$
$= 2 \times 10^6$

2.0 0 0 0 0 0
1 2 3 4 5 6

b $120\,000\,000 = 1.2 \times 100\,000\,000$
$= 1.2 \times 10^8$

1.2 0 0 0 0 0 0 0
1 2 3 4 5 6 7 8

Exercise 22:2

1. Write down if each of these numbers is written in standard form.
   If a number is not in standard form, explain why.
   a 2×10^4 ✓   c 1×10^3 ✓   e 0.6×10^8 ✗   g 11×10^3 ✗
   b 2.5×10^7 ✓   d 9×10^3 ✓   f 4.26×10^5 ✓   h 14×10 ✗

2. Write each of these numbers in standard form.
   a 30 000
   b 4 000 000
   c 2000
   d 300 000
   e 14 000 000
   f 780 000
   g 14 400
   h 7 810 000
   i 23 470 000 2.347×10^7
   j 133 600 1.336×10^5
   k 10 000 000 000 1×10^{10}
   l 10 000 000 000 000 1×10^{13}

Writing a standard form number as an ordinary number

To write a standard form number as an ordinary number is easy!
Just keep multiplying by 10.

Go thro.

$$2.8 \times 10^5 = 2.8 \times 10 \times 10 \times 10 \times 10 \times 10$$
$$= 280 000$$

You can think of moving the decimal point again.

$$5.1 \times 10^6 = 5.1 \times 10 \times 10 \times 10 \times 10 \times 10 \times 10$$
$$= 5 100 000$$

$$5.1\ 0\ 0\ 0\ 0\ 0$$
$$1\ \ 2\ \ 3\ \ 4\ \ 5\ \ 6$$

3. These numbers are written in standard form.
   Write them as ordinary numbers.   — 92640
   a 3.0×10^3 c 9.264×10^4 e 2×10^6 2 000 000
   b 8.3×10^7 d 6.07×10^5 f 1×10^9

4. Avogadro's number is a constant used in Physics.
   It is $6.022\ 57 \times 10^{23}$.
   Write this as an ordinary number.

When your calculator gets a big answer it will give you the answer in standard form.
New calculators are really helpful.

Go thro.

2×10^{12} will appear as $2.\ \times 10^{12}$

You must write your answer as 2×10^{12} and not use the strange sizes that the calculator does.

If you have an older calculator your display will look like this $2.^{12}$ or 2^{12}

If you have a calculator like this you must **not** write down the calculator display as your answer. You must still write your answer as 2×10^{12} and you have to remember to put the $\times 10$ part in.

To see what sort of calculator you have, key in $2\,000\,000 \times 1\,000\,000 =$

Exercise 22:3

1. Write these calculator displays as numbers in standard form.

   a $3.^{\times 10^{11}}$

   b $4.^{\times 10^{16}}$

   c $2.4^{\times 10^{12}}$

   d $7.1^{\times 10^{06}}$ 7.1×10^{6}

   e $4.^{13}$

   f $5.^{08}$

   g 7.1^{06}

   h 2.51^{16}

   i 6.04^{15}

2. Work these out. Give your answers in standard form.
   a $1\,000\,000 \times 3\,000\,000$
   b $4\,000\,000 \times 3\,000\,000$
   c $6\,000\,000 \times 4\,000\,000$ → 24 000000
       24×10^{12}
       2.4×10^{13}
   d $12\,000\,000 \times 3\,000\,000$
   e $200\,000 \times 300\,000$
   f $180\,000 \times 450\,000$
       000000

You can enter numbers that are written in standard form into your calculator. You need to use the **Exp** or **EXP** or **EE** key.

Exp EXP EE keys

The **Exp** or **EXP** or **EE** key means 'times 10 to the power of'. You use it to enter numbers that are in standard form into your calculator. Find the key that your calculator has and use it from now on wherever you see **Exp**. To enter the number 2×10^9

Key in: **2** **Exp** **9**
And you will get the right display for 2×10^9.

exponential.

Example

Work out $(3 \times 10^7) \times (2.5 \times 10^8)$
Key in:

3 **Exp** **7** **×** **2** **.** **5** **Exp** **8** **=**

The answer is 7.5×10^{15}.

3 Work these out. Give your answers in standard form.
   a $(7.1 \times 10^5) \times (2.8 \times 10^8)$ 1.988×10^{14}
   b $(8.5 \times 10^{12}) \times (5.1 \times 10^{14})$
   c $(4.1 \times 10^3) \times (7.6 \times 10^{12})$
   d $(9.3 \times 10^3) \times (7.1 \times 10^{13})$
   e $(2.2 \times 10^{25}) \div (2 \times 10^3)$
   f $(8.4 \times 10^{15}) \div (2.1 \times 10^4)$
   g $(4.8 \times 10^{25}) \div (1.2 \times 10^5)$
   h $(1.62 \times 10^{23}) \div (8.1 \times 10^6)$

4 The capacity of a computer is measured in bytes.
   One kilobyte is 1.024×10^3 bytes.
   One gigabyte is 1 000 000 kilobytes.
   How many bytes are in a gigabyte?
   Give your answer in standard form.

   $(1.024 \times 10^3) \times 10^6$

   1.024×10^9

5 The table gives the masses of four planets.

Earth	5.98×10^{24} kg
Jupiter	1.25×10^{27} kg
Saturn	5.69×10^{26} kg
Venus	4.87×10^{24} kg

   a Which planet has the largest mass?
   b How much heavier is the Earth than Venus?
   You need to work out $(5.98 \times 10^{24}) - (4.87 \times 10^{24})$.
   c How much heavier is Jupiter than Venus?
   You need to work out $(1.25 \times 10^{27}) - (4.87 \times 10^{24})$.
   d How many *times* heavier than the Earth is Saturn?
   You need to work out $(5.69 \times 10^{26}) \div (5.98 \times 10^{24})$.
   Give your answer to the nearest whole number.
   e How many times heavier than Venus is Jupiter?
   You need to work out $(1.25 \times 10^{27}) \div (4.87 \times 10^{24})$.
   Give your answer to the nearest whole number.

6 You have 4.7×10^{12} blood cells in every litre of your blood.
   Your body contains about 4.9 litres of blood.
   About how many blood cells do you have in your body?

2 Small **numbers**

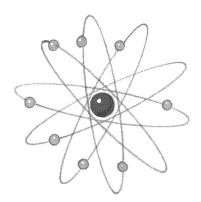

Very small numbers are seen in atomic physics. You use negative powers of 10 for very small numbers.

The diameter of an oxygen atom is about 3.5×10^{-8} cm.

You need to be able to deal with negative powers.

To simplify $5^2 \div 5^5$ you work out $\dfrac{\cancel{5} \times \cancel{5}}{\cancel{5} \times \cancel{5} \times 5 \times 5 \times 5} = \dfrac{1}{5 \times 5 \times 5} = \dfrac{1}{5^3}$

So when you divide, you can subtract the powers

So $5^2 \div 5^5 = 5^{2-5} = 5^{-3}$ so $5^{-3} = \dfrac{1}{5^3}$

Similarly $6^{-2} = \dfrac{1}{6^2}$ and $8^{-4} = \dfrac{1}{8^4}$

You can write this as a rule using letters $x^{-m} = \dfrac{1}{x^m}$

Exercise 22:4

1 Write each of these as a fraction.

a 4^{-5} $\frac{1}{4^5}$ **b** 7^{-3} $\frac{1}{7^3}$ **c** 10^{-4} $\frac{1}{10^4}$ **d** 10^{-2}

2 Write each of these using a negative power.

a $\dfrac{1}{3^2}$ 3^{-2} **b** $\dfrac{1}{9^4}$ 9^{-4} **c** $\dfrac{1}{10^3}$ 10^{-3} **d** $\dfrac{1}{10^7}$

3 Simplify

a $10^3 \times 10^{-4}$ 10^{-1}
b $10^5 \div 10^2$ 10^3
c $10^{-3} \times 10^{-5}$ 10^{-8}
d $10^2 \div 10^{-7}$ 10^9
e $10^{-5} \div 10^{-7}$ 10^2
f 10×10^8 10^9.

When very small numbers are changed into standard form the power of the 10 is negative.

Look at the number 0.000 076.
The number between 1 and 10 for this number is **7.6**

$7.6 \div 10$ $= 7.6 \times \frac{1}{10}$ $= 7.6 \times 10^{-1}$ $= 0.76$

$7.6 \div 100$ $= 7.6 \times \frac{1}{10^2}$ $= 7.6 \times 10^{-2}$ $= 0.076$

$7.6 \div 1000$ $= 7.6 \times \frac{1}{10^3}$ $= 7.6 \times 10^{-3}$ $= 0.0076$

$7.6 \div 10\ 000$ $= 7.6 \times \frac{1}{10^4}$ $= 7.6 \times 10^{-4}$ $= 0.000\ 76$

$7.6 \div 100\ 000$ $= 7.6 \times \frac{1}{10^5}$ $= 7.6 \times 10^{-5}$ $= 0.000\ 076$

So the number 0.000 076 is 7.6×10^{-5} in standard form.

You can imagine putting the decimal point into the number and then moving it back to where it should be like this.
Here it needs to move **5** places to the left.

$$0.000\ 076 = 7.6 \times 10^{-5}$$

The minus sign in the power tells you that the movement is to the left.

Example   Write these numbers in standard form.
   a 0.000 000 8   **b** 0.000 000 056

a $0.000\ 000\ 8 = 8 \times 10^{-7}$

b $0.000\ 000\ 056 = 5.6 \times 10^{-8}$

---

4 Write these numbers in standard form

a 0.000 09
b 0.000 000 007 8
c 0.000 045
d 0.003
e 0.000 000 000 9
f 0.06
g 0.5 5×10^{-1}
h 0.005 007 5.007×10^{-3}
i 0.024 501 2.4501×10^{-2}

To write a small standard form number as an ordinary number you keep dividing by 10.

$$3.8 \times 10^{-4} = 3.8 \div 10 \div 10 \div 10 \div 10$$
$$= 0.000\,38$$

You can think of moving the decimal point again.

Example Write these as ordinary numbers.
  a 7×10^{-5} **b** 2.91×10^{-3}

a Start by writing down the 7.
The negative power tells you 7
that the number is very small.
Write some zeros on the left of the 7 0 0 0 0 0 0 0 7
  5 4 3 2 1

The point needs to move 5 places
to the left.
The number is 0.000 07

b Write down the 2.91 2.9 1
Put some zeros on the left.
Move the point 3 places to the left. 0 0 0 0 0 0 2.9 1
  3 2 1
The number is 0.002 91

5 These numbers are written in standard form.
Write them as ordinary numbers.
  a 4×10^{-5} **d** 1.7×10^{-6} **g** 8.034×10^{-4} 0.0008034
  b 5.0×10^{-4} **e** 3.9×10^{-1} **h** 1.056×10^{-7} 0.000 000 1056
  c 7.3×10^{-2} **f** 7.2×10^{-3} **i** 1×10^{-12} 0.00000000.00 0001

6 Write these numbers in standard form
  a 40 000 **d** 0.005 7 5.7×10^{-3} **g** 0.000 000 008 9
  b 257 000 **e** 7 802 000 7.802×10^{6} **h** 240 000 000 000
  c 0.000 3 **f** 0.067 6.7×10^{-2} **i** 0.000 000 01

7 These numbers are written in standard form.
Write them as ordinary numbers.
  a 4×10^{3} **d** 5.1×10^{-4} 0.00051 **g** 4.97×10^{5}
  b 6.7×10^{-2} **e** 8×10^{-1} 0.8 **h** 3.006×10^{-3}
  c 2.4×10^{6} **f** 7.2×10^{3} 7200. **i** 6.0701×10^{7}

8 The diameter of an atom is about 0.000 000 000 1 m.
Write this in standard form.

You can still use a calculator to help you with very small numbers in standard form.

You use the **+/-** or **(−)** key to enter negative powers.

To enter 7×10^{-4} you key in: **7** **Exp** **+/-** **4**

  7 **Exp** **(−)** **4**

Example   Find the value of $4.8 \times 10^{-3} \div 6 \times 10^{-2}$

Key in   **4** **.** **8** **Exp** **+/-** **3** **÷** **6** **Exp** **+/-** **2** **=**

Key in   **4** **.** **8** **Exp** **(−)** **3** **÷** **6** **Exp** **(−)** **2** **=**

Answer   0.08

Exercise 22:5

1 Enter these numbers into your calculator using the **Exp** key.
Write down the calculator display for each one.
  a 6×10^4 **c** 4.056×10^{12} 4.056^{12} **e** 2.7×10^{-23}
  b 7.2×10^9 **d** 7×10^{-7} $7.-07$ **f** 6.003×10^{-13}

2 Use your calculator to work these out.
  a $(9 \times 10^5) \times (2 \times 10^7)$ $1\cdot8\times10^{13}$ **d** $(4.15 \times 10^5) \div (8.3 \times 10^{-6})$
  b $(7.8 \times 10^3) \div (2.6 \times 10^{-7})$ 3×10^{10} **e** $(9.25 \times 10^5) \div (3.7 \times 10^{-6})$
  c $(8.2 \times 10^3) \times (7 \times 10^{-6})$ **f** $(4.5 \times 10^{-4}) \times (5.0 \times 10^{-6})$
  $2\cdot25\times10^{-9}$

3 The thickness of the paper a firm produces is 6.0×10^{-2} mm.
  a A book contains 400 pages. $6\cdot0\times10^{-2}\times400\to(6\cdot0\times10^{-2})\times(4\times10^2)$
  What is the thickness of these pages altogether? $=24\times10^0$
  Give your answer in standard form. $2\cdot4\times10^1$
  b The thickness of the pages of another book is 4.2 cm. $4\cdot2cm\to42mm$ $(4\cdot2\times10^1)\div(6\cdot0\times10^{-3})$
  How many pages are there? $6\cdot7\times10^3$
  c A new paper is made which is twice as thick as the old paper. $7\times10^2=700$
  Calculate the thickness of the new paper.
  Give your answer in standard form.
  $2\times6\cdot0\times10^{-2}\to12\times10^{-2}=1\cdot2\times10^{-1}$

4 The diagram shows the rectangular end of a crystal.

    a Find the area of the rectangle.
    b Find the perimeter of the rectangle.

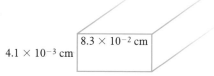

4.1×10^{-3} cm 8.3×10^{-2} cm

5 The diagram shows a crystal in the shape of a triangular prism.

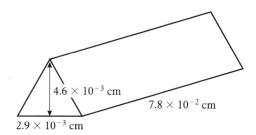

4.6×10^{-3} cm

7.8×10^{-2} cm

2.9×10^{-3} cm

    a Find the area of the triangular face of the crystal.
    b Find the volume of the crystal.

You sometimes have to round your answers.

Example   Find the value of $(5.6 \times 10^7) \div (7.1 \times 10^{-6})$.
    Give your answer in standard form correct to 3 significant figures.

    Use your calculator to find the answer.

    This calculator display shows what you will get. **7.8873239** ^{12}

    You need to round the number **7.887 323 9** to 3 sf.
    This is **7.89**

    The answer to the question is 7.89×10^{12} to 3 sf.

---

6 Use your calculator to work these out.
    Give your answers to 3 sf.
    a $(4.13 \times 10^5) \times (9.821 \times 10^9)$ 4.06×10^{15}
    b $(7.32 \times 10^4) \div (7.56 \times 10^{-6})$ 9.68×10^9
    c $(3.67 \times 10^{-8}) \times (4.82 \times 10^{-6})$ 1.77×10^{-13}
    d $(7.7 \times 10^4) \div (2.6 \times 10^{-9})$
    e $(1.34 \times 10^{-2}) \div (6.7 \times 10^{-11})$
    f $(1.84 \times 10^{-4}) \times (7.69 \times 10^{-6})$

7 Use your calculator to work these out.
Give your answers to 3 sf.

a $\dfrac{(2.6 \times 10^5) \times (4.8 \times 10^7)}{3.7 \times 10^5}$

$3 \cdot 37 \times 10^7$

b $(4.6 \times 10^{-4})^2$

c $(8.1 \times 10^7)^3$

OMIT

d $\dfrac{5.9 \times 10^7}{(2.8 \times 10^{-3}) \times (1.6 \times 10^2)}$

8 Use the formula $N = A \div B$ to find the value of N to 3 sf when:
a $A = 6.5 \times 10^{-5}$ $B = 2.906 \times 10^6$
b $A = 1.06 \times 10^4$ $B = 3.27 \times 10^{-9}$
c $A = 4.7 \times 10^{-9}$ $B = 4 \times 10^5$

9 Use the formula $P = \dfrac{R^2}{S}$ to find the value of P to 3 sf when:

a $R = 2.9 \times 10^4$ $S = 6.1 \times 10^2$
b $R = 7.4 \times 10^{-3}$ $S = 2.0 \times 10^{-5}$
c $R = 1.09 \times 10^5$ $S = 3.124 \times 10^{11}$

10 The Earth has a mass of 5.97×10^{21} tonnes and
a radius of 6.4×10^6 metres.
a The volume of a sphere is $\frac{4}{3}\pi r^3$.
Find the volume of the Earth to 3 sf.
b Density = mass ÷ volume
Find the density of the Earth to 3 sf.
c Find the distance around the equator to 3 sf.

11 The distance travelled by light in one year is called a light year.
A light year $= 9.5 \times 10^{12}$ km.
The distance of the star Vega from the Earth is 2.5×10^{14} km.
How many light years is this?
Give your answer to 2 sf.

12 The mass of 7×10^{31} atoms of oxygen is 1.88×10^9 g.
Find the mass of one atom of oxygen.
Give your answer to 2 sf.

To DO.

You also need to be able to do these calculations without a calculator.
To do this, you need to remember the power rules.
When you **multiply** powers of a number you **add** the powers: $10^3 \times 10^4 = 10^7$
When you **divide** powers of a number you **subtract** the powers: $10^3 \div 10^7 = 10^{-4}$

Example   Work these out. Do not use your calculator.

    a $(3 \times 10^4) \times (6 \times 10^8)$
    b $(6 \times 10^4) \div (4 \times 10^{-3})$

    a $(3 \times 10^4) \times (6 \times 10^8)$
       The easiest way to do this is to multiply the
       3 by the 6 and then the 10^4 by the 10^8.
       $3 \times 6 = 18$ and $10^4 \times 10^8 = 10^{12}$
       So $(3 \times 10^4) \times (6 \times 10^8) = 18 \times 10^{12}$

       This is not in standard form because 18 is
       bigger than 10.
       To change it into standard form think about
       18 as 1.8×10
       So $18 \times 10^{12} = 1.8 \times 10 \times 10^{12} = 1.8 \times 10^{13}$.

    b $(6 \times 10^4) \div (4 \times 10^{-3})$
       This time work out $6 \div 4$ and $10^4 \div 10^{-3}$
       $6 \div 4 = 1.5$ and $10^4 \div 10^{-3} = 10^{4--3} = 10^7$
       So $(6 \times 10^4) \div (6 \times 10^{-3}) = 1.5 \times 10^7$

Exercise 22:6   To Do

1 Work these out.
Do not use your calculator.

    a $(4 \times 10^4) \times (2 \times 10^3)$ 8×10^7
    b $(3 \times 10^3) \times (2 \times 10^7)$
    c $(6 \times 10^5) \times (7 \times 10^3)$ 42×10^8 4.2×10^9
    d $(4 \times 10^4) \times (2 \times 10^{-2})$ $4.2 \times 10^?$
    e $(2.1 \times 10^{21}) \times (3 \times 10^7)$
    f $(2.5 \times 10^4) \times (4 \times 10^9)$
    g $(7 \times 10^{-6}) \times (3 \times 10^9)$
    h $(5 \times 10^{-7}) \times (2 \times 10^{-8})$

    i $(4 \times 10^9) \div (2 \times 10^3)$
    j $(6 \times 10^{21}) \div (2 \times 10^8)$
    k $(8 \times 10^8) \div (5 \times 10^{-2})$ 1.6×10^{10}
    l $(4 \times 10^7) \div (3 \times 10^3)$
    m $(8.4 \times 10^4) \div (2 \times 10^{-3})$
    n $(2 \times 10^{12}) \div (8 \times 10^3)$ 0.25×10^9
    o $(3.4 \times 10^4) \div (2 \times 10^{-9})$ 2.5×10^8
    p $(3 \times 10^{-5}) \div (8 \times 10^{-9})$

You may want to compare the size of numbers written in standard form.

Example

In each part write down the bigger number.
a 1.6×10^7 and 4.9×10^5
b 5.1×10^{-6} and 7.2×10^{-4}
c 2.7×10^{-9} and 2.3×10^{-9}

Look at the power of 10 first.
The number with the higher power is bigger.
a $7 > 5$ so 1.6×10^7 is bigger than 4.9×10^5.
b $-4 > -6$ so 7.2×10^{-4} is bigger than 5.1×10^{-6}.

If the two powers are the same you look at the rest of the number.
c Both of the numbers have a power of -9
$2.7 > 2.3$ so 2.7×10^{-9} is bigger than 2.3×10^{-9}

Exercise 22:7

1 Which is bigger?
   a 8.2×10^6 or 4.2×10^8 ← *bigger*
   b 5.3×10^{-4} or 2.1×10^3
   c 6.9×10^{-7} or 9.3×10^{-8}
       bigger

   d 3.6×10^7 or 4.2×10^7
   e 4.8×10^{-6} or 4.9×10^{-6} ← *bigger*
   f 1.6×10^{-12} or 4.9×10^{-16}

2 The mass of a hydrogen atom is about 1.67×10^{-24} g.
The mass of an oxygen atom is about 2.7×10^{-23} g.
Which is lighter?
Explain your answer.

3 The table gives the volume of four planets.

Earth	1.1×10^{12} km³
Mercury	6.0×10^{10} km³
Uranus	7.5×10^{13} km³
Neptune	6.3×10^{13} km³

   a Write down the planet with the greatest volume.
   b Write down the planets in order of size.
      Start with the smallest.

1 Work out the value of each of these.
   a 4^3 **c** the square of 7   **e** the square root of 4
   b 5^4 **d** the cube of 10   **f** $\sqrt{81}$

2 Write these numbers in standard form.
   a 400 000   **c** 2 000 000   **e** 300 800
   b 90 000   **d** 630 000   **f** 1 million

3 These numbers are written in standard form.
Write them as ordinary numbers.
   a 7.2×10^6 **b** 3.9×10^5 **c** 7×10^4 **d** 2.18×10^8

4 The speed of sound is about 340 m/s.
   a Write this number in standard form.
      How far does sound travel in
   b 1 hour   **c** 1 week   **d** 1 year?
   Give your answers in standard form.

5 Work these out. Use your calculator.
   a $(2.5 \times 10^5) \times (3.1 \times 10^7)$ **c** $(7.8 \times 10^4) \times (9.5 \times 10^{11})$
   b $(8.4 \times 10^{15}) \div (1.2 \times 10^9)$ **d** $(5.2 \times 10^{12}) \div (1.3 \times 10^6)$

6 Venus has a mass of about 5.184×10^{21} tonnes and a radius of 6×10^3 m.
   a The approximate volume of a sphere is $4r^3$.
      Find the approximate volume of Venus.
   b The approximate distance around Venus is equal to $3 \times$ diameter.
      Find this distance.
   c Density = mass $\div$ volume.
      Use your answer to part **a** to find the approximate density of Venus.

7 Write these numbers in standard form
   a 20 000 000   **d** 0.000 016 3   **g** 0.000 001   **j** 0.002
   b 0.0007   **e** 2 500 000   **h** 0.8   **k** 800 500
   c 306 000   **f** 0.040 056   **i** 10 000   **l** 5 million

8 These numbers are written in standard form.
Write them as ordinary numbers.
   a 6.3×10^4 **d** 2.5×10^{-3} **g** 7×10^6 **j** 1.782×10^4
   b 7.41×10^{-5} **e** 6.12×10^{-7} **h** 2.76×10^{-2} **k** 2.37×10^{-2}
   c 8×10^{-11} **f** 8.02×10^{-8} **i** 1.003×10^7 **l** 4.3×10^{-6}

9 Work these out. Use your calculator.

    a $(7.1 \times 10^5) \times (4.2 \times 10^{-6})$ **c** $(3.8 \times 10^{-5}) \times (4.5 \times 10^{-4})$

    b $(9.6 \times 10^{-4}) \div (1.6 \times 10^{-11})$ **d** $(2.16 \times 10^9) \div (2.7 \times 10^{-7})$

10 A virus has a diameter of 15 nanometres.

    1 nanometre = 0.000 000 001 metre.

    a Write the diameter of the virus in metres. Use standard form.

    b A bacterium is 120 times as big as a virus.

       Write the diameter of the bacterium in metres. Use standard form.

11 The diameter of an atom is 0.000 000 01 cm.

    How many atoms side by side would measure one centimetre?

12 Work these out. Use your calculator.

    Give your answers to 3 sf.

    a $(7.92 \times 10^{-3}) \times (2.48 \times 10^{-7})$ **c** $(5.06 \times 10^7) \div (8.85 \times 10^9)$

    b $\dfrac{(1.37 \times 10^{-10}) \times (7.4 \times 10^7)}{6.1 \times 10^{-4}}$ **d** $(2.13 \times 10^7)^2$

13 A pollen grain has a mass of 3.5×10^{-4} g.

    Find the number of grains in 1 kg of pollen.

    Write your answer in standard form to 2 sf.

14 These numbers are written in standard form.

    4.5×10^7 4.5×10^{-7} 4.5×10^{-8} 4.5×10^6

    a Write down the largest of these numbers.

    b Write down the smallest of these numbers.

15 The table shows some facts about planets.

	Mercury	Neptune	Saturn	Uranus	Venus
Diameter (km)	4.9×10^3	4.9×10^4	1.2×10^5	5.2×10^4	1.2×10^4
Volume (km³)	6.0×10^{10}	6.3×10^{13}	9.1×10^{14}	7.5×10^{13}	9.3×10^{11}
Mass (tonnes)	3.3×10^{20}	1.0×10^{23}	5.7×10^{23}	8.7×10^{22}	4.9×10^{21}

Write down:

    a the smallest planet   **b** the heaviest planet

    c the planets in order of volume. Start with the largest.

    d the planets in order of mass. Start with the lightest.

1   This is a formula used in a running event to work out the points
    awarded, P.

$$P = 0.112(246 - t)^{1.87}$$

t is the time taken in seconds.
P is always rounded to one significant figure.

   a   Find the value of P when $t = 150$ s
   b   What time gives zero points?
   c   Use trial and improvement to find a time that gives $P = 1000$.

2   The volume of a cylinder is given by

$$V = \frac{\pi d^2 h}{4}$$

   Find the value of V when $d = 3 \times 10^5$ cm, $h = 8 \times 10^9$ cm and $\pi = 3.14$

3   Jupiter has a mass of about 1.372×10^{24} tonnes and a diameter of
    1.4×10^8 metres.

   a   The volume of a sphere is $\frac{4}{3}\pi r^3$.
       Find the approximate volume of Jupiter using $\pi = 3$.
   b   Find the approximate distance around the equator using $\pi = 3$.
   c   Density = mass ÷ volume.
       Find the approximate density of Jupiter.

4   Work these out.
    Give your answers to 3 sf.

   a $\dfrac{(2.7 \times 10^8) \times (3.9 \times 10^{-4})^2}{(5.3 \times 10^6) + (2.3 \times 10^5)}$

   b $\sqrt{8.7 \times 10^6 - 4.3 \times 10^4}$

5   The mass of an electron is 9.1×10^{-28} g.

   a   Find the mass of 5.6×10^{12} electrons.
   b   The mass of a proton is 1.7×10^{-24} g.
       Find the value of k in the formula
       mass of a proton = $k \times$ mass of an electron.
       Give your answer to the nearest whole number.

1 Write each of these numbers in standard form.
  a 450 000
  b 368 300 000
  c 0.0082
  d 0.3751
  e 3 million
  f 0.000 000 06

2 These numbers are written in standard form.
  Write them as ordinary numbers.
  a 6.9×10^4
  b 2.4×10^{-3}
  c 4×10^{-8}
  d 3.618×10^8

3 The table shows the populations of 6 cultures of bacteria.

Culture	Population	Culture	Population
A	6.5×10^{11}	D	9.25×10^{10}
B	7.8×10^{10}	E	7.5×10^{11}
C	8.1×10^{11}	F	8.9×10^{12}

  a Write the cultures in order of size. Start with the smallest number.
  b Find the difference in population between cultures A and F.

4 Water flows through a pipe at a rate of 25 m³ per minute.
  How long will it take to fill a pond of volume 6.34×10^9 m³?
  Give your answer in hours to 3 sf.

5 Work these out. Give your answers in standard form.
  Do not use a calculator.
  a $(7 \times 10^5) \times (5 \times 10^8)$
  b $(1.5 \times 10^4) \div (6 \times 10^{-5})$
  c $(4 \times 10^4) + (6 \times 10^3)$
  d $(3 \times 10^5) - (2 \times 10^4)$

6 Use a calculator to work these out.
  Give your answer in standard form to 3 sf.
  a $(3.82 \times 10^7) \times (2.84 \times 10^9)$
  b $(6.03 \times 10^{-3}) \div (6.221 \times 10^{-15})$
  c $(2.37 \times 10^{-6})^4$

23 Area

1 Counting and estimating
Finding areas by counting squares
Estimating areas of irregular shapes

2 All the formulas
Finding the area of
- a rectangle
- a square
- a triangle
- a trapezium
- a parallelogram
- a kite
- a rhombus
- a circle

Finding the area of more complicated shapes

CORE

3 Nets and surface areas
Drawing nets
Identifying nets
Finding the surface area of solid shapes
Converting square units

QUESTIONS

EXTENSION

TEST YOURSELF

1 Counting and estimating

The Amazon is in South America.
It is one of the world's largest forests.
It covers an area of 2 million square miles.
Every year a large part of the forest is destroyed.

Area

The **area** of a shape is the amount of space it covers.
Area is measured using squares.

This square has sides of 1 cm.
The area of the square is 1 square centimetre.
You write this as 1 cm^2.

This rectangle covers 8 squares.
The area of the rectangle = 8 cm^2

Exercise 23:1

For each of the rectangles in questions **1–4**, write down:
a the number of squares it covers
b the area of the rectangle in cm^2

1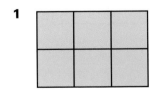

2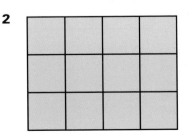

3

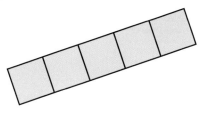

4

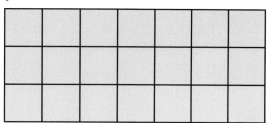

Write down the area of each of the shapes in questions **5–8**.

5

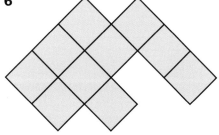

7

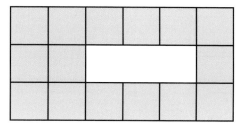

6

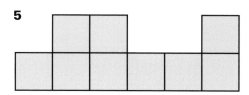

8

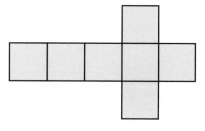

Some areas are more difficult to work out.
This is a drawing of the county of Cheshire.
You can only estimate the area of the drawing.
To estimate the area:

(1) Count whole squares.
There are 5 of these.
(2) Count squares which lie more
than half inside the outline.
There are 4 of these.
(3) Add the two numbers together.
5 + 4 = 9

An estimate of the area is 9 squares.

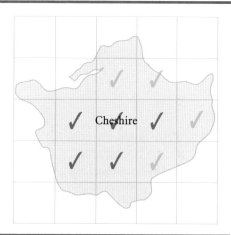

Exercise 23:2

Estimate the area of each country by counting squares.
Give your answers in squares.

1

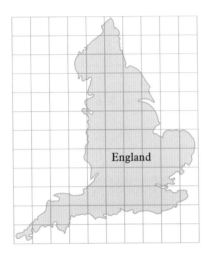

England

3

Scotland

2

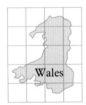

Wales

4

Ireland

5 Write down the country in the British Isles with:
  a the largest area
  b the smallest area.

Squaring the circle

You will need 0.5 cm² paper for this activity.
Draw a circle with a 1 cm radius.
Put the centre on a point where the lines cross.
Estimate the area of the circle in cm².
Calculate the area of a square 1 cm by 1 cm.
Divide the area of the circle by the area of the square.

Now draw a circle with a 2 cm radius.
Put the centre on a point where the lines cross.
Estimate the area of the circle in cm².
Calculate the area of a square 2 cm by 2 cm.
Divide the area of the circle by the area of the square.
Record your results in the best way you can.

Repeat this for circles with radii of 3 cm, 4 cm, etc.
Can you see a pattern in your results?
What do you think would happen to your results if you kept going?

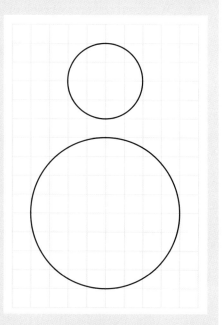

Look at the red shape.
Each small square shows 1 cm².

It covers 6 whole squares and 4 half squares.
The 4 halves make 2 whole ones.
The area of the shape is $6 + 2 = 8$ cm²

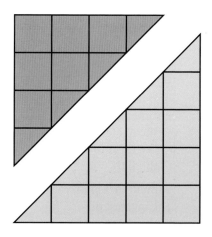

Look at the blue shape.
This shape covers 10 whole squares and 5 half squares.
The 5 halves make $2\frac{1}{2}$ whole ones.
The area of the shape is $10 + 2\frac{1}{2} = 12\frac{1}{2}$ cm²

Exercise 23:3

1 Work out the area of each of these coloured shapes in square centimetres. They are drawn on 1 cm² paper.

a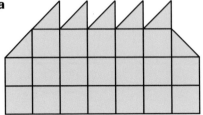

c

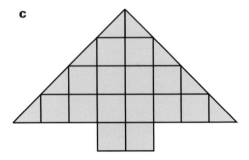

b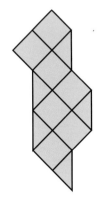

d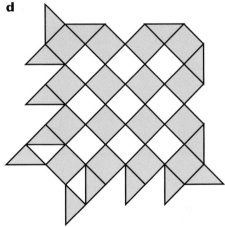

2 Samuel has drawn a plan of his wall on squared paper.
Each square shows an area of 100 cm².
Find the area, in square centimetres, of:
a the poster
b the no smoking sign
c the flag.

Estimate the area, in square centimetres, of:
d the dartboard
e the mirror.

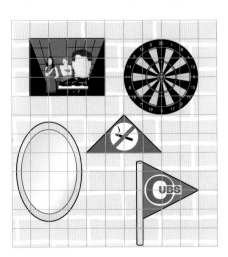

2 All the formulas

This is the Pentagon in Arlington, USA. It is the office building with the largest ground floor area in the world.

29 000 people work in the Pentagon.

There are 7748 windows to be cleaned. Can you estimate the total area of windows to be cleaned?

Area of a rectangle

Area of a rectangle = length × width

This calculates the number of 1 cm squares in this rectangle.

The area of this rectangle = 9 × 8 cm²
$$= 72 \text{ cm}^2$$

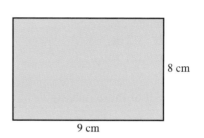

Exercise 23:4

1 Find the area of these rectangles.
Make sure that you use the correct units.

a
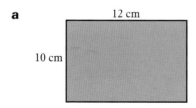
12 cm
10 cm

b
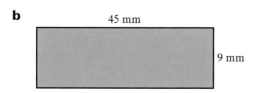
45 mm
9 mm

c
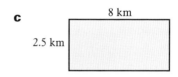
8 km
2.5 km

d
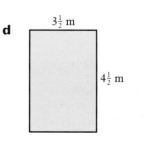
$3\frac{1}{2}$ m
$4\frac{1}{2}$ m

2 Find the area of a rectangle with these measurements:
   a length = 14 cm   width = 6 cm
   b length = 4.2 km   width = 1.8 km
   c length = 6.32 m   width = 14.95 m

3 Find the areas of these squares.

a

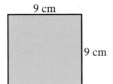

9 cm

9 cm

b

2.5 cm

2.5 cm

c

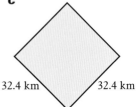

32.4 km   32.4 km

4 Find the area of a square with side:
   a 15 cm
   b 1.2 m
   ● **c** $12\frac{1}{4}$ km

5 All of these rectangles have an area of 306 cm².

   a Find the width of this rectangle.

   34 cm

   c Find the width of this rectangle.

   68 cm

   b Find the length of this rectangle.

   17 cm

   ● **d** Find the length of this rectangle.

   17 mm

● **6** Find the side length of a square with an area of:
   a 4 cm²
   b 64 cm²
   c 289 cm²
   d 729 cm²

Finding the area of a triangle

Look at this triangle.
You can draw a rectangle around it.

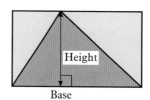

The **length** of the rectangle is the **base** of the triangle.
The **width** of the rectangle is the **height** of the triangle.
The area of the rectangle = length × width
                                      = base × height

The triangle is half the area of the rectangle.
The area of the triangle = area of the rectangle ÷ 2
                                      = (base × height) ÷ 2
If you call the height *h*
and you call the base *b*
Then the area of a triangle is (*b* × *h*) ÷ 2

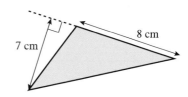

You can write this as $\dfrac{b \times h}{2}$ or $\frac{1}{2}bh$

The area of this triangle = (5 × 12) ÷ 2
                                      = 60 ÷ 2
                                      = 30 cm²

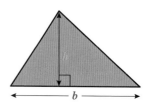

The height of this triangle is outside the triangle.
The area of this triangle = (8 × 7) ÷ 2
                                      = 56 ÷ 2
                                      = 28 cm²

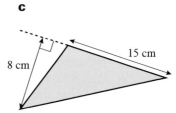

Exercise 23:5

1   Find the area of each of these triangles:

a

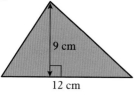

9 cm

12 cm

b

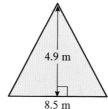

4.9 m

8.5 m

c

8 cm

15 cm

The triangles in questions **2** to **5** are drawn on 1 cm squared paper.
For each triangle:
a write down the base
b write down the height
c work out the area.

2

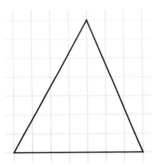

4

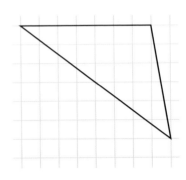

3

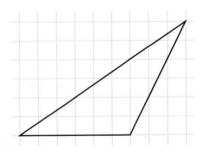

5

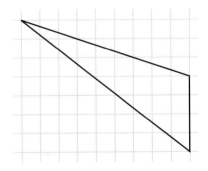

6 Natasha has designed this flag.
  a Find the area of the red triangle.
  b Find the area of the blue triangle.
  c Find the total area of the two triangles.
  d Find the total area of the rectangular flag.
  e Use your answers to **c** and **d** to work out the area of the green section.

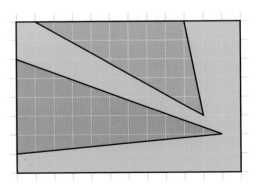

Area of a trapezium

You can split a trapezium into a rectangle and a triangle.

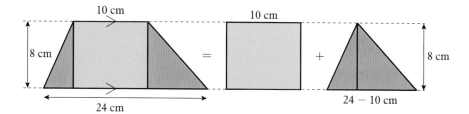

Area of rectangle $= 10 \times 8$ $= 80 \text{ cm}^2$
Area of triangle $= \frac{1}{2} \times 14 \times 8$ $= \underline{56 \text{ cm}^2}$
So the area of the trapezium is $\overline{136 \text{ cm}^2}$

Exercise 23:6

Find the area of each of these trapeziums:

1

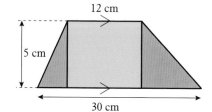

3

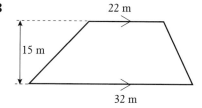

2

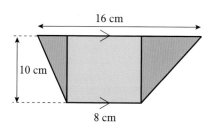

4

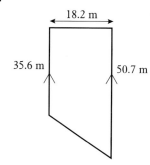

There is another way to find the area
of a trapezium.
You can split it into two triangles.

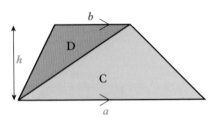

Area of triangle C $= \frac{1}{2} \times a \times h = \frac{1}{2}ah$

Area of triangle D $= \frac{1}{2} \times b \times h = \frac{1}{2}bh$

So the area of the trapezium is $\frac{1}{2}ah + \frac{1}{2}bh$

The expression $\frac{1}{2}ah + \frac{1}{2}bh$ has a common factor of $\frac{1}{2}h$.

So $\frac{1}{2}ah + \frac{1}{2}bh = \frac{1}{2}h(a + b)$

This can be written as $\dfrac{(a + b)}{2} \times h$

which is the mean of the parallel sides times the height.

5 Find the area of this trapezium.

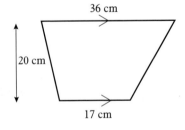

6 Find the area of this trapezium.

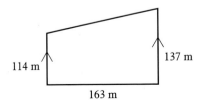

7 This is a field of wheat.
Find the area.

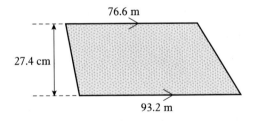

● **8** This is a cross section through a
swimming pool. Find the area.

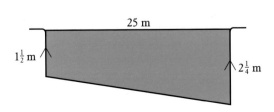

Area of a parallelogram

You can split a parallelogram into two triangles.

Area of triangle S $= \frac{1}{2} \times b \times h = \frac{1}{2}bh$

Area of triangle T $= \frac{1}{2} \times b \times h = \frac{1}{2}bh$

So the area of a parallelogram is bh

You can write Area = base × height or $A = bh$

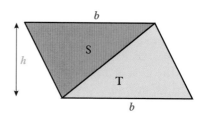

9 Find the area of these parallelograms.

a

8 m

9 m

b

15.8 m

3.2 m

c

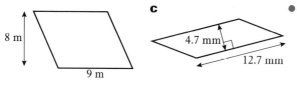

4.7 mm

12.7 mm

d

94 cm

62 cm

● e

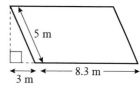

5 m

3 m

8.3 m

Hint: Use Pythagoras
to work out the height

Area of a kite

You can split a kite into two equal triangles.

Area of triangle $= \frac{1}{2}$ base × height

Area of triangle A $= \frac{1}{2} \times x \times \frac{1}{2}y = \frac{1}{4}xy$

Area of triangle B $= \frac{1}{2} \times x \times \frac{1}{2}y = \frac{1}{4}xy$

So the area of a kite is $\frac{1}{2}xy$

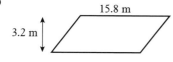

You can write Area $= \frac{1}{2}$ of the diagonals multiplied together or $A = \frac{1}{2}xy$

10 Find the area of these kites.

a

1.9 m

2.4 m

$\frac{1}{2}$ of 1.9 × 2.4

$= 2.28 \text{ m}^2$

b

1.49 m

86 cm

c

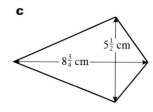

$5\frac{1}{2}$ cm

$8\frac{3}{4}$ cm

Area of a rhombus

A rhombus is a special sort of parallelogram.
It is also a special sort of kite.
So you can use either of these formulas
for the area of a rhombus.
$A = bh$ and $A = \frac{1}{2}xy$

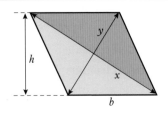

Find the area of each rhombus.

11

a

$A = \frac{1}{2} \times 14 \times 15$
$= 105 \, cm^2$

c

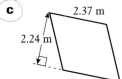

$A = 2.37 \times 2.24$
$= 5.3088 \, m^2$

e

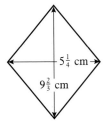

$5\frac{1}{4}$ cm

$9\frac{2}{3}$ cm

b

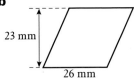

23 mm

26 mm

d

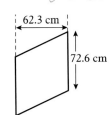

62.3 cm

72.6 cm

● f

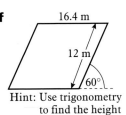

16.4 m

12 m

60°

Hint: Use trigonometry
to find the height

Area of a circle

The **area of a circle** depends on the radius of the circle.
The formula is
Area of circle $= \pi \times radius \times radius$.
This rule is often written $A = \pi \times r \times r$
or $A = \pi r^2$ $(r^2 = r \times r)$

Example   Find the area of this circle.

$A = \pi r^2$
$= \pi \times 4^2$
$= \pi \times 4 \times 4$
$= \pi \times 16$
$= 50.3 \, cm^2$ to 1 dp

4 cm

Exercise 23:7

Give your answers in this exercise correct to 1 dp where appropriate.

1 Find the area of these circles:

a
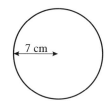
7 cm

d
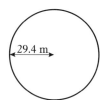
29.4 m

b
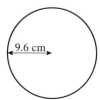
9.6 cm

e
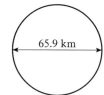
65.9 km

c
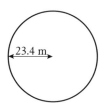
23.4 m

f
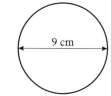
9 cm

2 Find the area of these shapes.

a
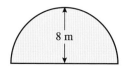
8 m

b

12 mm

3 Use $\pi = 3$ to *estimate* the areas of the circles in question **1**.

4 The radius of a roundabout is 32 metres. What is the area of the circle?

5 The diameter of a £2 coin is 28.5 mm.
Find the area of one face of the coin.

6 Find the area of this circular helicopter landing pad.
Use $\pi = 3\frac{1}{7} = \frac{22}{7}$

14 m

7 Find the area of each of these portholes.
Use $\pi = 3\frac{1}{7} = \frac{22}{7}$

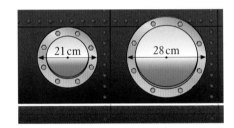

21 cm   28 cm

8 A tarmac path runs around a circular park.
The path is 5 m wide.
The outer radius of the path is 70 m and
the radius of the park is 65 m.
  a Find the area of the park.
  b Find the area of the park and the path.
  c Use your answers to **a** and **b** to find
     the area of the path.

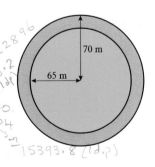

70 m

65 m

[handwritten:] 13273.22896   13273.2 (1dp)
$\pi r^2 = \pi \times 65 \times 65 = 13273.2$ (1dp)
$\pi \times 70 \times 70$
15393.804
15393.8 (1d.p)
= b − a
= 2120.575043
= 2120.6 (1dp)

9 The diagram shows a circular go-kart track.
The area of the grass in the centre is 2500 m².
  a Rearrange the formula $A = \pi r^2$
     to make r the subject of the formula.
  b Use your new formula to find the radius of
     the grass area.
The area of the track is 1400 m².
  c Work out the area of the grass and track.
  d Find the radius of the outer edge of the track.
  e How wide is the go-kart track?

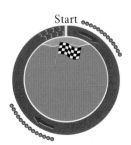

Start

Finding the areas of more complicated shapes

To find these areas you need to:

(1) Decide how to split the shape into parts.
(2) Give each part a letter.
(3) Find any missing lengths.
(4) Work out the area of each part.
(5) Add all these areas to get the total area.

Look at this shape.
The shape is made from a rectangle and a triangle.

Area of rectangle A is $12.5 \times 8.4 = 105$ cm^2

For triangle B you need to find
the base and height.
The base of triangle B is $12.5 - 7 = 5.5$ cm
The height of triangle B is $14 - 8.4 = 5.6$ cm

Area of triangle B is $(5.5 \times 5.6) \div 2 = 15.4$ cm^2

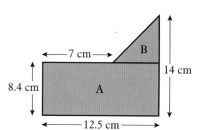

So the total area of the shape = area of A + area of B
$$= 105 \text{ cm}^2 + 15.4 \text{ cm}^2 = 120.4 \text{ cm}^2$$

Exercise 23:8

1 Two rectangles have been joined to
make this shape.
  a Find the area of C.
  b Find the area of D.
  c Find the total area of the shape.

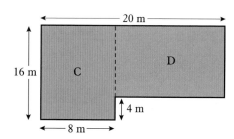

2 Find the total area of each of these shapes:
  a

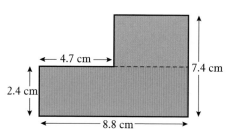

  b

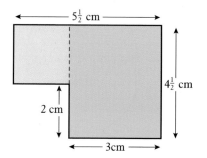

3 Find the areas of these shapes:

a

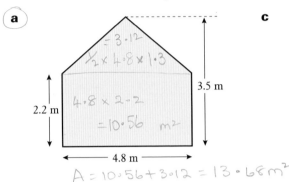

$= 3.12$
$\frac{1}{2} \times 4.8 \times 1.3$

4.8×2.2
$= 10.56 \ m^2$

3.5 m

2.2 m

4.8 m

$A = 10.56 + 3.12 = 13.68 m^2$

c

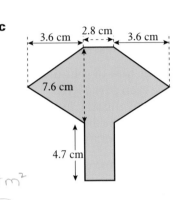

3.6 cm   2.8 cm   3.6 cm

7.6 cm

4.7 cm

b

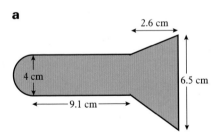

8 cm

14 cm

d

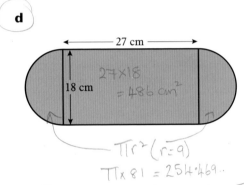

27 cm

27×18
$= 486 \ cm^2$

18 cm

$\pi r^2 \ (r = 9)$
$\pi \times 81 = 254.469..$
$TOTAL = 486 + 254.5 = 740.5 \ cm$

4 Find the areas of these shapes:

a

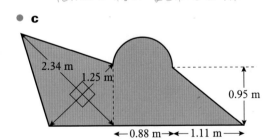

2.6 cm

4 cm

6.5 cm

9.1 cm

c

2.34 m

1.25 m

0.95 m

0.88 m   1.11 m

b

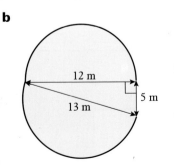

12 m

13 m

5 m

$x^2 = 2.99^2 + 1.97^2$
$= 12.821$
$\therefore x = \sqrt{12.821}$
$= 3.580..$

d

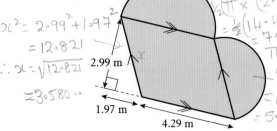

$\pi \frac{r}{2}^2 \ (r = 2.145$
$\frac{1}{2} (\pi \times (2.145)^2)$
$= \frac{1}{2} (14.4....)$
$= 7.0$

πr^2
$(r = 1.07$

$= 10.06 \div$
$= 5.0347$

2.99 m

1.97 m

4.29 m

Area of parallelogram $= 4.29 \times 2.99$
$= 12.8271 \ m^2$

TOTAL $25.0891681 \ \simeq 25.1 \ m^2$

5 The customer area of a restaurant has a floorplan like this.

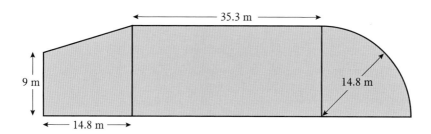

Work out the area available for seating.

6 This door has five glass panels.

    a Find the total area of the glass panels.

    b Find the area of the whole door.

    c Use your answers to **a** and **b** to find the area of wood in the door.

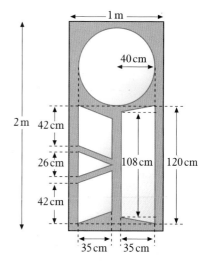

7 A castle has a plan like this. The dark line round the outside shows the castle wall. The castle grounds are shown in green. The castle keep is shown with a blue line.

    a Find the floor area of the keep.

    b Find the area of the castle grounds.

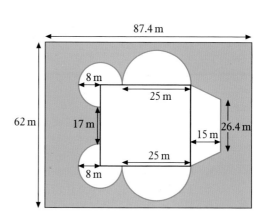

3 Nets and surface areas

Maltesers come in boxes of different shapes and sizes. Each of them has to be made from a single piece of card. Think about how they do it.

Net

When a solid is opened out and laid flat, the shape that you get is called a **net** of the solid.

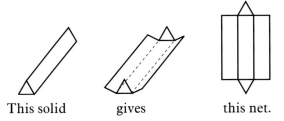

This solid   gives   this net.

You can have more than one net for a solid. This is also a net of the same solid.

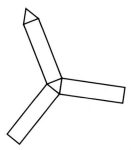

Exercise 23:9

1 Here are some patterns of shapes. Some of them are nets of cubes.
  a Draw the patterns on to squared paper.
  b Cut them out.
  c Fold them up to see if they make a cube.
  d Write down the letters of the ones that make cubes.

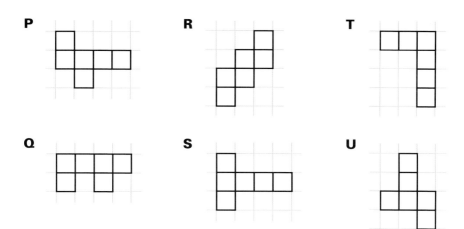

P **R** **T**

Q **S** **U**

2 **a** Copy this net on to 1 cm squared paper.

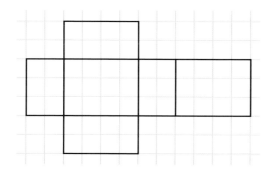

  b Cut out the net. Fold it to make a solid.
  c Write down the name of the solid.
  d The length of the solid is 4 cm.
     Write down the width and the height of the solid.

3 **a** Copy this net.
     Cut it out.
  b Fold it along the lines.
  c Write down the name of
     the solid that it makes.

4 Sketch the net of this square-based pyramid.

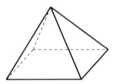

5 Match each solid with its net.

a

b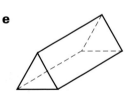

c

d

e

f

g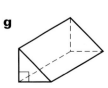

P

Q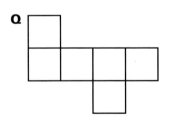

R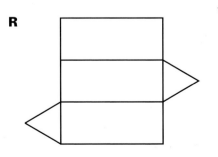

S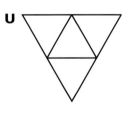

T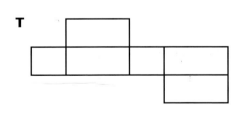

U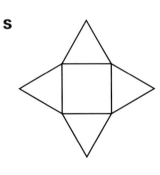

V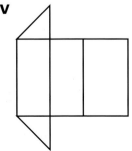

Finding the surface area of a solid

A simple way to do this is to sketch the net.
Then you will not miss any faces.

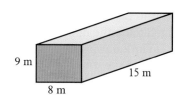

To find the surface area of a solid:
(1) Sketch the net
(2) Work out the areas of the different faces
(3) Find the total of all the areas.

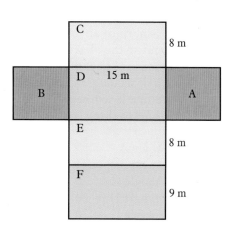

In this cuboid, there are 3 pairs of faces
the same size.
They are A and B, C and E and D and F.

Area of rectangles A and B $= 2 \times 8 \times 9\ \ = 144\,\text{m}^2$
Area of rectangles C and E $= 2 \times 15 \times 8 = 240\,\text{m}^2$
Area of rectangles D and F $= 2 \times 15 \times 9 = 270\,\text{m}^2$
Total surface area $\qquad\qquad\ \ = 654\,\text{m}^2$

Exercise 23:10

Work out the surface areas of the solids in questions **1–3**.

1
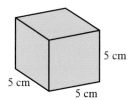
5 cm
5 cm
5 cm

3 This is a square-based pyramid.
All the triangular sides are the
same size.

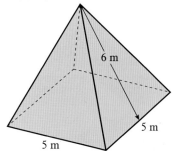
6 m
5 m
5 m

2
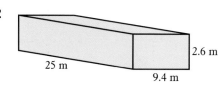
2.6 m
25 m
9.4 m

Finding the surface areas of prisms

To find the surface area of a prism:
(1) Sketch the net,
(2) Work out the areas of the different faces,
(3) Find the total of all the areas.

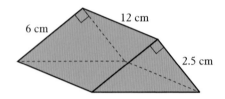

For this prism, right angled triangles A and B
are congruent so they have the same area.
The hypotenuse of triangle A
is the width of rectangle C.
The hypotenuse is worked out by Pythagoras:
$h^2 = 6^2 + (2.5)^2$ so that $h = 6.5$ cm

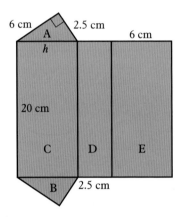

Area of triangle A $= \frac{1}{2} \times 6 \times 2.5 = 7.5$ cm^2
Area of triangle B $= \frac{1}{2} \times 6 \times 2.5 = 7.5$ cm^2
Area of rectangle C $= 20 \times 6.5 \quad = 130$ cm^2
Area of rectangle D $= 20 \times 2.5 \quad = 50$ cm^2
Area of rectangle E $= 20 \times 6 \quad\; = 120$ cm^2
Total surface area $\qquad\qquad = \underline{\underline{315 \text{ cm}^2}}$

4 Work out the surface area of these prisms. You will need to use Pythagoras.

a

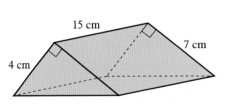

c

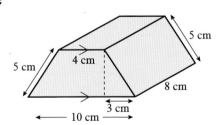

b

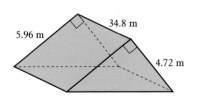

d

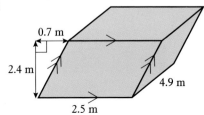

This is a square millimetre.

1 mm
1 mm □

This is a square centimetre.

1 cm
1 cm

There are 10 mm in every 1 cm.
So the square centimetre
    is   10 mm across
  and 10 mm down.
So there are $10 \times 10 = 100$ mm² in 1 cm².

10 mm
10 mm

A square metre is too big to draw here!
This is a diagram of one.
There are 100 cm in every 1 m.
So the square metre
    is   100 cm across
  and 100 cm down.
So there are $100 \times 100 = 10\,000$ cm² in 1 m².

100 cm
100 cm

There are 1000 m in every 1km.
So there are $1000 \times 1000 = 1\,000\,000$ m² in 1 km².

This diagram shows you how to convert square units.

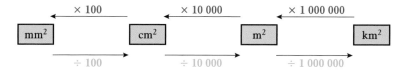

× 100	× 10 000	× 1 000 000

| mm² | cm² | m² | km² |

| ÷ 100 | ÷ 10 000 | ÷ 1 000 000 |

Exercise 23:11

1 Draw a square 2 cm by 2 cm. Find the area in square millimetres.

2 Change each of these areas into square centimetres.
    a 2 m²   **c** 12 m²   **e** 0.43 m²   **g** 128 mm² **i** 2050 mm²
    b 8 m²   **d** 0.9 m²   **f** 400 mm² **h** 672 mm² **j** 25 mm²
    8 0p 00 cm² 900 0 cm²   1·28 cm²

3 Change each of these areas into square metres.
    a 40 000 cm²   **b** 7900 cm²   **c** 0.4 km²   **d** 8.95 km²
                    0·79 m²   8,950,000 m²

4 Change each of these areas into square kilometres.
    a 10 000 m²   **b** 7 500 000 m²   ● **c** 10⁹ m²   ● **d** 2.3 × 10⁷ m²
                      7·5 km²   2·3 × 10⁷ ÷ 10⁶ 10⁹
                                               = 2·3 × 10¹ = 23 km²

1 Write down the area of each of these shapes.
They are drawn on 1 cm squared paper.

   a   **b**   **c**

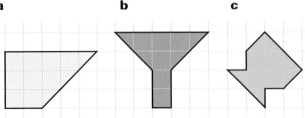

2 Estimate the area of each of these shapes.
They are drawn on 1 cm squared paper.

   a   **b**   **c**

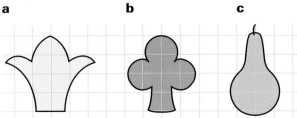

3 Find the area of each of these shapes:

a

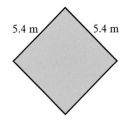

5.4 m   5.4 m

d

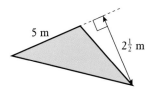

5 m $2\frac{1}{2}$ m

b

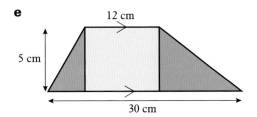

22.3 cm

14.9 cm

e

12 cm

5 cm

30 cm

c

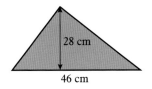

28 cm

46 cm

f

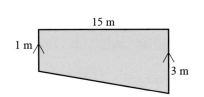

15 m

1 m

3 m

4 Find the area of each of these shapes:

a

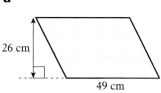

26 cm

49 cm

b

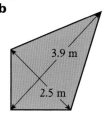

3.9 m

2.5 m

c

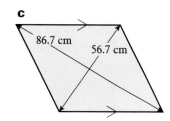

86.7 cm

56.7 cm

5 Find the area of each of these shapes:

a

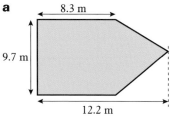

8.3 m

9.7 m

12.2 m

b

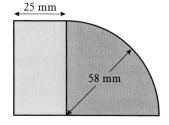

25 mm

58 mm

6 This is a rectangular-based pyramid.
  a Draw the net.
  b Work out the surface area.

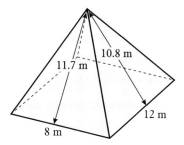

10.8 m

11.7 m

12 m

8 m

7 Farmer Smith has 5 fields in a
piece of land called Flowerdown.
Each field is a trapezium.
He grows vegetables in each field.
  a Work out the area of each field.
  b Work out the area of Flowerdown.

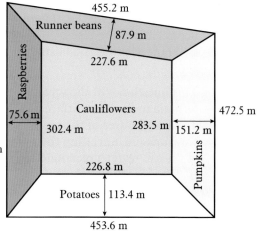

455.2 m

Runner beans

87.9 m

227.6 m

Raspberries

Cauliflowers

472.5 m

75.6 m

302.4 m

283.5 m

151.2 m

510.3 m

226.8 m

Pumpkins

Potatoes | 113.4 m

453.6 m

1 Look at this rectangle.
The area is the same as the perimeter.
Find another two rectangles like this.
You will need to use trial and improvement.

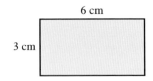
6 cm

3 cm

2 The points A, B, C, D and E have co-ordinates:
A (1, 2), B (5, 1), C (6, 4), D (6, 6) and E (2, 5).
a Copy these axes. Plot the points A, B, C, D and E.
Join them up to get a pentagon.
b Plot the points S (1, 0), T (2, 0), U (5, 0) and
V (6, 0).
c Find the area of the trapeziums:
(1) ABUS   (2) BCVU   (3) SAET   (4) TEDV
d Use your answer to **c** to work out the area
of the pentagon ABCDE.
e Write down another way you could work out
this area.

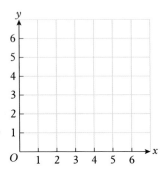

3 Alan's school has just got a new tartan track!
The diagram shows the 400 m track.
There are 8 lanes.
Each lane is 1.5 m wide.
Alan wants to work out some distances
and areas. He calls you in to help.

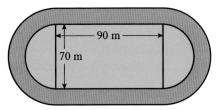
90 m
70 m

a Work out the distance round the inside of each lane.
b Work out the maximum length across the grass area.
c Work out the area of the grass inside the tartan track.
d Work out the area of the tartan track.
At a presentation ceremony Alan wants to fit the whole school into one
of the grass semicircles. There are 880 pupils and 47 staff. Each person
needs 1.2 m² of space.
e Show whether Alan can do this or not.

4 This question will show you how to find a
formula to find the surface area of a cylinder.
a Find the area of the top and bottom.
Now imagine unrolling the side
of the can to get a rectangle.
b What is the length of the rectangle?
c Find the total surface area of the can.
Use r for the radius and h for the height.
d Work out a formula for the surface area.

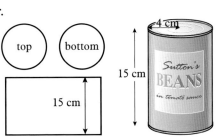
top   bottom
4 cm
15 cm
15 cm
15 cm
Sutton's
BEANS
in tomato sauce

1 These shapes are drawn on 1 cm squared paper.

a Write down the area of this shape.

b Estimate the area of this shape.

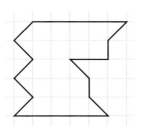

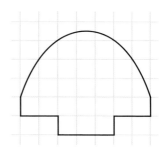

2 Find the area of each of these shapes.

a

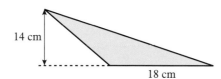

14 cm

18 cm

d

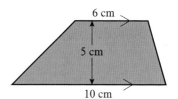

6 cm

5 cm

10 cm

b

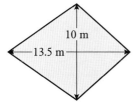

10 m

13.5 m

e

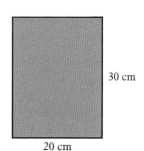

30 cm

20 cm

c

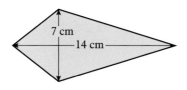

7 cm

14 cm

f

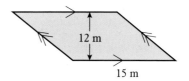

12 m

15 m

113

3 Find the area of each of these shapes.

a

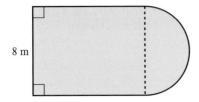

8 m

c

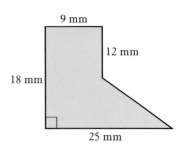

9 mm

12 mm

18 mm

25 mm

b

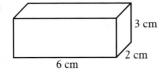

27 cm

18 cm

31 cm

12 cm

d

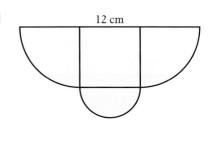

12 cm

4 For each of these solids   (1) Sketch the net.
                                (2) Work out the surface area.

a

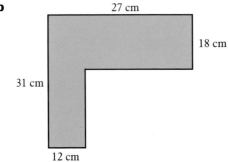

3 cm

2 cm

6 cm

b

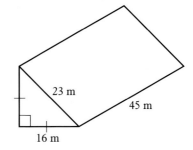

23 m

45 m

16 m

5 Change

  a 3 cm² into mm²

  b 4 m² into cm²

  c 750 000 mm² into cm²

  d 5 × 10¹² m² into km²

24 Pattern power

1 Time for a change
Changing old money
Working with weird and wonderful units!

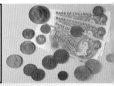

CORE

2 Sequences
Looking at number sequences
Finding missing terms
Using the formula for a sequence
Finding the formula when differences
between terms are the same
Finding the formula when the second
differences are the same

QUESTIONS

EXTENSION

TEST YOURSELF

1 Time for a change

This was the currency in the UK until 1971. It was much more difficult to change between units than it is today.

These are the conversion factors for old money.

4 farthings	= 1 penny	12 pence	= 1 shilling
2 halfpennies	= 1 penny	20 shillings	= 1 pound
1 halfcrown	= 2 shillings and six pence	1 sixpence	= 6 pence
1 florin	= 2 shillings	1 threepennybit	= 3 pence

Example   Change each of these to the units given.

        a £1 to shillings   **b** 1 shilling to farthings

a   There are 20 shillings in every pound.

      So   £1 = 20 shillings

   This diagram shows how to convert from £ to shillings.

      £ ——×20 ——⟶ shillings

b   There are 12 pence in every shilling.

      So   1 shilling = 12 pence

   There are 4 farthings in every penny.

      So   1 shilling = 12 × 4 farthings
                       = 48 farthings

   This diagram shows how to convert shillings to pence and pence to farthings.

      shillings ——×12 ——⟶ pence ——×4 ——⟶ farthings

Exercise 24:1

1 **a** Copy this diagram.
Fill in the missing number.

pence —— × ...... ——→ farthings

b Change 1 penny to farthings.
c Change each of these into farthings:
(1) 3 pence   (2) 7 pence   (3) 11 pence

2 **a** Copy this diagram.
Fill in the missing numbers.

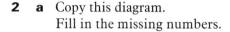

shilling —— × ...... ——→ pence —— × ...... ——→ farthings

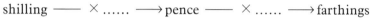

b Change 1 shilling to farthings.
c Change each of these into farthings:
(1) 4 shillings   (2) 8 shillings   (3) 10 shillings

3 **a** Copy this diagram.
Fill in the missing numbers.

£ —— × ...... ——→ shillings —— × ...... ——→ pence

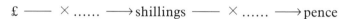

b Change £1 to pence.
c Change each of these into pence:
(1) £2
(2) £5
(3) £10

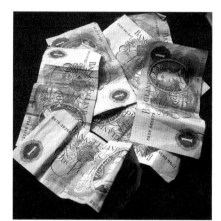

4 Change each of these to pence:
a 1 florin   **c** 7 florins   **e** 2 halfcrowns
b 3 florins   **d** 1 halfcrown **f** 5 halfcrowns

5 Change each of these to farthings:
a 10 shillings   **c** 1 florin   **e** 1 halfcrown
b £1   **d** 6 florins   **f** 4 halfcrowns

6 About 50 years ago the coins used in India
were pies, annas and rupees.
There were 12 pies to an anna and 16 annas
to a rupee.

a Copy this diagram.
Fill it in.   anna ——— × ...... ———→ pies

Draw diagrams to show how to convert:

b rupees to annas
c rupees to pies.

Convert each of these:

d 1 anna to pies   **f** 7 rupees to annas   **h** 4 rupees to pies
e 3 annas to pies   **g** 1 rupee to pies   **i** 48 annas to rupees

7 Some pieces have these values in a game.
1 castle   = 5 cannons
1 cannon = 4 foot soldiers
1 horse   = 2 foot soldiers

a Copy this diagram.
Fill it in.
castles ——— ...... ———→ cannons ——— ...... ———→ foot soldiers

b Change each of these to foot soldiers.
(1) 1 castle   (3) 1 cannon   (3) 1 horse
(2) 12 castles   (4) 7 cannons   (6) 3 horses

c How many horses is 1 castle worth?

8 In a far off land the units of currency are plars, sags, mors and gats.
1 plar = 9 sags, 1 sag = 10 mors and 2 plars = 3 gats.
Convert each of these:

a 5 plars to sags   **c** 3 plars to mors   **e** 6 gats to sags
b 4 plars to gats   **d** 50 mors to sags   • **f** 360 mors to gats

9 The village of Bartwell operates a barter system.
These are the values of some items.
1 hour of manual work   = 2 sacks of potatoes
1 hour of babysitting   = $\frac{1}{2}$ a sack of potatoes
1 hour of skilled work   = 2 hours of manual work
1 week's supply of vegetables   = 3 hours of manual work.
What is the value of:

a 2 hours of manual work in hours of babysitting
b 3 hours of skilled work in sacks of potatoes
c 4 weeks supply of vegetables in hours of skilled work?

2 Sequences

Fibonacci was an Italian mathematician. He knew how important and useful patterns in numbers can be.
He is famous for discovering a special sequence called the Fibonacci numbers.
The Fibonacci numbers are
　　　1, 1, 2, 3, 5, 8, 13, 21, 34, 55, 89, ...
Each number is obtained by adding the previous two.
The amazing thing about the Fibonacci numbers is how many times they appear in nature.
Look for Fibonacci numbers in the pictures.

Number sequence　　A **number sequence** is a list of numbers that follow a rule.

Term　　Each number in a sequence is called a **term**.
The rule tells you how to get from one term to the next.

Example　　**a**　Write down the rule for this sequence
　　　40, 35, 30, 25, 20, ...
　　b　Write down the next two terms.

a
$$40 \xrightarrow{-5} 35 \xrightarrow{-5} 30 \xrightarrow{-5} 25 \xrightarrow{-5} 20$$

Each new term is 5 less than the previous term.
The rule is **subtract 5**.

b　The next two terms are 15 and 10.

Exercise 24:2

For each of questions **1** to **4** write down:
a　the rule for the sequence　　　　　**b**　the missing terms.

1　5, 11, 17, 23, 29, 35　　+ 6

2　7, 3, ..., −5, −9, ..13　　− 4

3　2, 6, 18, 54, ..., 486　　× 3　　162

4　1600, 800, 400, 200, 100, ...　　÷ 2　　50

5 Look at this sequence of numbers: 8, 9, 12, 21 , 48 , 129 .
The rule that has been used to get the sequence is
    'subtract 5 and then multiply by 3'.
Write down the next two numbers in the sequence.

6 The number of dots in these patterns form a sequence.

8   11   14

   a Write down the number of dots in each of these patterns.
   b Write down the rule for the sequence. + 3
   c Write down the next two terms in the sequence. 17 , 20

7 The first term of a sequence is 8.
The rule is 'subtract 3 and multiply by 2'.
Write down the first four terms of the sequence.

8 The formula for this sequence is $4n$:   4, 8, 12, 16, 20, …
Write down the first 5 terms of the sequence with the formula $6n$.
6, 12, 18, 24 , 30

9 Write down the formula for each of these sequences:
   a 2, 4, 6, 8, 10, … $2n$ **c** 12, 24, 36, 48, 60, … $12n$
   b 5, 10, 15, 20, 25, … $5n$ **d** 20, 40, 60, 80, 100, … $20n$.

10 The formula for a sequence is $5n - 1$.
   a Copy this table to find the first three terms. Fill it in.

1st term	$5 \times 1 - 1$ $= 5 - 1$ $= 4$
2nd term	$5 \times 2 - 1$ $= 10 - 1 = 9$
3rd term	$5 \times 3 - 1 = \ldots - 1 = 14$

   b Use the formula to find the 10th term. 49

11 The formula for a sequence is $2n + 4$.
The first three terms are   6, 8, 10.
Find the next two terms. 12 , 14 .

12 A sequence has the formula $6n - 3$.
Write down:
   a the first three terms   **b** the 8th term   **c** the 20th term.
      3, 9, 15   45   117

Finding formulas that contain n

Look at this sequence. Find a formula for the nth term.

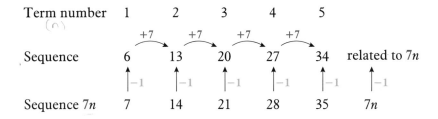

+7   +7   +7   +7
6   13   20   27   34

You can draw a sequence diagram to find the formula for the sequence.
The rule for this sequence is **add 7** so it must be related to $7n$.
Write the sequence $7n$ underneath. Compare the two sequences.

Term number (n)	1	2	3	4	5	
Sequence	6	13	20	27	34	related to $7n$
Sequence $7n$	7	14	21	28	35	$7n$

(with $+7$ steps across the Sequence row and -1 steps between the two sequences)

You need to **subtract 1** from every term in $7n$ to make the sequence.
So the formula for the nth term of the sequence is $7n - 1$.

Exercise 24:3

1 a Copy the sequence diagram for the sequence   4, 7, 10, 13, 16, ...
Fill in the missing numbers.

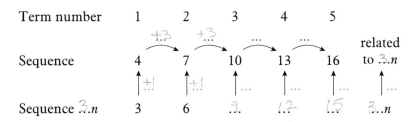

Term number	1	2	3	4	5	
Sequence	4	7	10	13	16	related to $3.n$
Sequence $3.n$	3	6	9	12	15	$3..n$

(with $+3$, $+3$ steps across; $+1$, $+1$ between sequences)

b Copy this. Fill in the spaces.

You need to ...$+1$ to... every term in ...$3n$... to make the sequence.

So the formula for the nth term of the sequence is ...$3n + 1$...

121

2 **a** Copy the sequence diagram for the sequence   3, 8, 13, 18, 23, ...
Fill in the missing numbers.

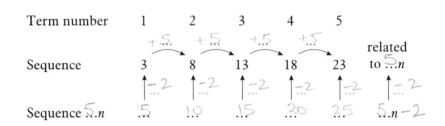

Term number	1	2	3	4	5	
Sequence	3	8	13	18	23	related to $5n$
Sequence $5n$	5	10	15	20	25	$5n-2$

(annotations: $+5$, $+5$, $+5$, $+5$ between sequence terms; -2 arrows between rows)

b Copy this. Fill in the spaces.

You need to ...... -2 from ...... every term in ... $5n$ ... to make the sequence.

So the formula for the nth term of the sequence is ... $5n-2$ ...

For each of the sequences in questions **3–8**:
a draw a sequence diagram   **b** find the formula for the nth term.

3 6, 8, 10, 12, 14, ...   **6** 11, 19, 27, 35, 43, ...

4 3, 7, 11, 15, 19, ...   **7** 4, 14, 24, 34, 44, ...

5 2, 9, 16, 23, 30, ...   **8** 14, 23, 32, 41, 50, ...

9 **a** Write this shape sequence as a number sequence.

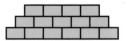

b Use a sequence diagram to work out the formula for the nth term.

10 **a** Write the number of sticks in these patterns as a number sequence.

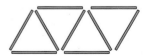

b Write down the next two terms in the sequence.
c Use a sequence diagram to work out the formula for the nth term.

Finding formulas that contain n²

Example   Find a formula for the *n*th term of the number sequence
5, 19, 41, 71, 109, ...

Look at the differences between the terms:
These differences are not the same.
Look at the differences between these numbers:
These are called the **second differences**.

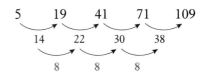

If the **second differences are the same**, the formula for the **nth term contains** n^2.
The number in front of n^2 is **half** the constant difference.

In the example the constant difference is **8**.
The number in front of n^2 is half of **8**, which is **4**.
The first part of the formula is $4n^2$.

Make a table to help you find the rest of the formula.
Fill in the value of $4n^2$ for each term.

Term number	1	2	3	4	5
Sequence	5	19	41	71	109
	+1	+3	+5	+7	+9
Value of $4n^2$	4	16	36	64	100

Now look for what you need
to add to get the sequence.   · 1   3   5   7   9

You now find the formula for this part of the sequence as before

Term number	1	2	3	4	5
Sequence	1	3	5	7	9

The differences are all $+2$ +2   +2   +2   +2   −1

| Value of $2n$ | 2 | 4 | 6 | 8 | 10 |

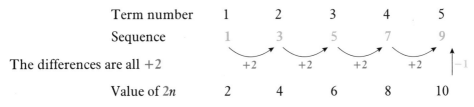

The formula for the second part is $2n - 1$.

You now put the two parts of the formula together.
The formula for the *n*th term of the sequence is $4n^2 + 2n - 1$.
Check the formula by finding term number 5.
$n = 5$, $4n^2 + 2n - 1 = 100 + 10 - 1 = 109$ ✓

Exercise 24:4

1 **a** Copy the sequence diagram for the sequence   8, 18, 34, 56, 84, …
Fill in the missing numbers.

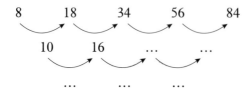

8   18   34   56   84

10   16   …   …

…   …   …

The second differences are the same.

b Copy this. Fill in the missing numbers.
The constant difference is …
The number in front of n^2 is half of …, which is …
The first part of the formula is …n^2.

c Copy this to find the rest of the formula.
Fill in the missing numbers.

Term number	1	2	3	4	5
Sequence	8	18	34	56	84
Value of …n^2	…	…	…	…	…

Now look for what you need
to add to get the sequence.   …   …   …   …   …

To find the formula for this part of the sequence

Term number	1	2	3	4	5
Sequence	…	…	…	…	…

The differences are all …

| Value of …n | … | … | … | … | … |

The formula for the second part is ………………

The formula for the nth term of the sequence is ………………

Check the formula by finding term number 5

$n = 5$, …………… = …………… = ………

2 a Copy the sequence diagram for the sequence 0, 9, 22, 39, 60, ...
Fill in the missing numbers.

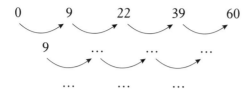

The second differences are the same.

b Copy this. Fill in the missing numbers.
The constant difference is ...
The number in front of n^2 is half of ..., which is ...
The first part of the formula is ...n^2.

c Copy this to find the rest of the formula.
Fill in the missing numbers.

Term number	1	2	3	4	5
Sequence	0	9	22	39	60
Value of ...n^2	...	...	...	...	...

Now look for what you need
to add to get the sequence. ... ...

To find the formula for this part of the sequence

Term number	1	2	3	4	5
Sequence	...	...	...	...	...

The differences are all ...

Value of ...n	...	...	...	...	...

The formula for the second part is ....

The formula for the nth term of the sequence is ....

Check the formula by finding term number 5

$n = 5$, ... = ... = ...

For the number sequences in questions **3** to **10**:

    a Find the formula for the nth term.

    b Find the 5th term using your formula.
       Check to see that it is correct.

3 15, 22, 31, 42, 55, ...   **7** 3, 14, 31, 54, 83 ...

4 4, 13, 26, 43, 64, ...   **8** 6, 23, 48, 81, 122, ...

5 3, 7, 13, 21, 31, ...   **9** 8, 19, 34, 53, 76, ...

6 5, 12, 21, 32, 45, ...   ● **10** 2, 10, 24, 44, 70, ...

11 The formula for a sequence is $5n^2 - 2n + 1$.
    a Copy this table to find the first four terms.
       Fill it in.

1st term	$5 \times 1 - 2 + 1$	$= 5 - 2 + 1$	$= ...$
2nd term	$5 \times 4 - 4 + 1$	$= 20 - 4 + 1$	$= ...$
3rd term	$5 \times ... - ... + 1$	$= ... - ... + ...$	$= ...$
4th term	$5 \times ... - ... + ...$	$= ... - ... + ...$	$= ...$

    b Find the 6th term.
    c Find the 10th term.

12 The formula for a sequence is $3n^2 + n - 3$.
    a Copy this table to find the first four terms.
       Fill it in.

1st term	$3 \times 1 + 1 - 3$	$= 3 + 1 - 3$	$= 1$
2nd term	$3 \times 4 + 2 - 3$	$= 12 + 2 - 3$	$= ...$
3rd term	$3 \times ... + ... - 3$	$= ... + ... - ...$	$= ...$
4th term	$3 \times ... + ... - ...$	$= ... + ... - ...$	$= ...$

    b Find the 10th term.
    c Find the 11th term.
    d Is the number 349 a term in the sequence? Explain your answer.

13 The formula for a sequence is $5n^2 + 4n - 6$.
   a Find the first 4 terms.
   b Find the 10th term.

14 The formula for a sequence is $2n^2 + n - 7$.
   a Find the first 4 terms.
   b Find the 10th term.
   c Use trial and improvement to find which term has the value 734.

15 The formula for a sequence is $5n^2 + 4n - 6$.
   a Find the first 4 terms.
   b Find the 10th term.
   c Use trial and improvement to find which term has the value 5571.

16 Which of these numbers belong to the sequence with the formula $4n^2 + 5n - 12$?
   a 624   **b** 1698   **c** 1229

17 The numbers of planes in these patterns form a sequence.

   a Write down the number of planes in each of these patterns.
   b Write down the special name for this sequence.
   c Write down the first five terms of this sequence.
   d Use a sequence diagram to find the formula for the nth term.
   e Find the 4th term using your formula to check that it is correct.

1 A player can be awarded units of credit in a game.
The units of credit are yings, mangs, rungs and tongs.

$$1 \text{ ying} = 8 \text{ mangs}$$
$$1 \text{ mang} = 5 \text{ rungs}$$
$$1 \text{ rung} = 3 \text{ tongs}$$

Work out the value of:

a 4 yings in mangs
b 5 yings in rungs
c 9 tongs in rungs
d 15 rungs in mangs
e 30 tongs in mangs
f 3 yings in tongs.

2 The first term of a sequence is 256.
The rule is 'divide by 2'.
Write down the first 6 terms of the sequence.

3 The first term of a sequence is 7.
The rule is 'subtract 4 and multiply by 2'.
Write down the first 6 terms of the sequence.

4 The formula for a sequence is $12n - 9$.
Write down:
a the first 4 terms   **b** the 10th term   **c** the 20th term.

5 The formula for a sequence is $20 - 2n$.
Write down:
a the first 4 terms   **b** the 10th term   **c** the 25th term.

6 Which of these are terms of the number sequence $11n + 8$?
a 33   **b** 63   **c** 118

7 A sequence has the formula $3n - 6$.
Use trial and improvement to find which term has a value of 123.

8 A sequence has the formula $15 - 4n$.
a Find the first 5 terms.
b Find the 30th term.
c Use trial and improvement to find which term has a value of -189.

9 a Copy the sequence diagram for the sequence   9, 15, 21, 27, 33, ...
Fill in the missing numbers.

Term number	1	2	3	4	5	
						related
Sequence	9	15	21	27	33	to ...n
Sequence ...n	...	...	...	...	...	...

b Copy this. Fill in the spaces.

You need to .... every term in .... to make the sequence.

So the formula for the nth term of the sequence is ....

10 For each of these sequences:
a draw a sequence diagram   **b** find the formula for the nth term.

(1) 7, 11, 15, 19, 23, ...   (3) 9, 14, 19, 24, 29, ...
(2) 1, 7, 13, 19, 25, ...   (4) −1, 1, 3, 5, 9, ...

11 The formula for a sequence is $6n^2 - 5n + 4$.
a Find the first 4 terms.
b Find the 10th term.
c Use trial and improvement to find which term has a value of 10 883.

For the number sequences in questions **12** to **17**:
a Find the formula for the nth term.
b Find the 5th term using your formula.
Check to see that it is correct.

12 3, 11, 21, 33, 47, ...

13 7, 17, 31, 49, 71, ...

14 1, 11, 27, 49, 77, ...

15 4, 22, 50, 88, 136, ...

16 0, 11, 26, 45, 68, ...

17 −3, 10, 31, 60, 97, ...

1 2 bings $= 5$ bongs   1 bong $= 6$ bangs
 3 bungs $= 4$ bongs   3 bengs $= 10$ bings

Find the value of:
a 8 bings in bongs
b 30 bings in bengs
c 8 bings in bangs
d 96 bangs in bungs
e 75 bongs in bengs
f 15 bungs in bings
g 48 bangs in bungs
h 15 bengs in bangs

2 Find a formula for the nth term of each of these number sequences:
a $-1, 7, 15, 23, 31, \ldots$ **b** $-7, -3, 1, 5, 9, \ldots$

3 The formula for the nth term of a sequence is $2n^3 - 3n^2$.
Which term has the value:
a 27   **b** 175   **c** 3887

4 The formula for the nth term of a sequence is $3n^2 + n - 5$.
a Find the first four terms.
b Find the 15th term.
c Use trial and improvement to find which term has the value 2049.

5 Find a formula for the nth term of the sequence

$$-2, -1, 2, 7, 14, \ldots$$

For the number sequences in questions **6** to **9**:
     a Find the formula for the nth term.
     b Find the 5th term using your formula.
     Check to see that it is correct.

6 $3, 3, 5, 9, 15, \ldots$ **8** $7, 12, 21, 34, 51, \ldots$

7 $2, 6, 16, 32, 54, \ldots$ **9** $0, 12, 34, 66, 108, \ldots$

1 Gary has made a new board game based on the Civil Wars.
Different pieces are used in the game and have different values.

The pieces are: cannon, horse, gun, archer, foot soldier, arrow.

1 cannon = 5 horses   1 horse = 2 guns   1 gun = 20 arrows

1 horse = 3 archers   2 archers = 5 foot soldiers

Find the value of
  a 5 horses in guns   **c** 15 archers in horses
  b 2 cannons in arrows   **d** 4 horses in foot soldiers

2 The first term of a sequence is 10 and the rule is 'multiply by 2 and subtract 12'.
Find the first 5 terms of the sequence.

3 The formula for a sequence is $7n + 3$.
Write down:
  a the first 4 terms   **b** the 10th term

4 A sequence has the formula $250 + 27n$
  a Find the 50th term.
  b Use trial and improvement to find which term has the value 709.

5 **a** Write down the first 5 terms of the sequence with the formula
     (1) $3n$ (2) $4n$ (3) $5n$
  b Write down the formula for each of these sequences
     (1) 7, 14, 21, 28, 35, …
     (2) 11, 22, 33, 44, 55, …
     (3) 15, 30, 45, 60, 75, …

6 These sequences are all related to the sequence $4n$.
Write down the formula for the nth term of each sequence.
  a 5, 9, 13, 17, 21, …
  b 13, 17, 21, 25, 29, …
  c 1, 5, 9, 13, 17, …

7 Copy the sequence diagram for the sequence 2, 8, 14, 20, 26, …
Fill in the missing numbers.

Term number	1	2	3	4	5	
						related
Sequence	2	8	14	20	26	to …n
Sequence …n	…	…	…	…	…	…

You need to ……………… every term in ……… to make the sequence.
So the formula for the nth term of the sequence is …………

8 Look at the sequence 4, 15, 32, 55, 84, …
  a Draw a sequence diagram.
  b Find a formula for the nth term.

9 A sequence has the formula $n^2 - 5n + 10$
  a Find the first 5 terms.
  b Find the 20th term.
  c Use trial and improvement to find the term which has the value 1486.

10 The nth term of a sequence is $\dfrac{16 - 2n}{n + 1}$

  a Write down the first three terms of this sequence.
  b Which term of the sequence has the value 1?

25 Statistics

1 Comparing sets of data
Comparing data using the mean, median and range
Using the interquartile range

2 Cumulative frequency
Using cumulative frequency
Drawing cumulative frequency diagrams
Estimating the median and the interquartile range from a cumulative frequency diagram

CORE

3 Box and whisker diagrams
Reading data from box and whisker diagrams
Drawing box and whisker diagrams
What do you think? – Investigation

QUESTIONS

EXTENSION

TEST YOURSELF

1 Comparing sets of data

Reg is considering a career move.
He wants to compare salaries for other jobs.

You need two values for each set of data to make a comparison.
(1) An average value (use the mean or the median).
(2) A measure of spread.

Mean	To find the **mean** of a set of data: (1) find the total of all the data values (2) divide the total by the number of data values.
Median	To find the median you put all the data values in order of size. The **median** is the one in the middle. When there are two numbers in the middle add them together and divide by 2.
Range	To find the **range** of a set of data you take the smallest value away from the biggest value. The range is always given as a single number. The average and the range give different information about the data. You need both to give the complete picture. You use the mean or the median to compare how big the values are in each set of data. You use the range to compare how spread out the values are in each set of data.

Exercise 25:1

1 Karen and Kath go ten-pin bowling.
The diagram shows their scores after 5 turns each.

	Score										
	0	1	2	3	4	5	6	7	8	9	10
Karen	✓		✓			✓	✓				✓
Kath					✓	✓	✓	✓		✓	

a Look at the pattern of the scores for the two players.
   (1) Who do you think is doing better overall? *Kath*
   (2) Explain how you can tell. *More higher scores*
   (3) Who is the most consistent player? *Kath*
   (4) Explain how you can tell. *Scores closer together / less spread out*
b Find the mean score for each player. *Karen $\frac{23}{5} = 4 \cdot 6$ Kath $\frac{31}{5} = 6 \cdot 2$*
c Find the range for each player. *Karen 10 - 0 = 10   Kath 9 - 4 = 5*
d Explain how you can use the mean and range to compare the two players. *Kath higher Mean, implies better player. Kath's range is smaller, implies more consistent.*

2 Last term Alan had 5 Science tests and 4 Maths tests.
He was given each result as a percentage.
Alan's total score in Science was 335.
Alan's total score in Maths was 284.
   a Alan got a bigger total for science.
   Does this mean that Alan is better at Science? *No - he did one more test in Science*
   b Work out his mean score for Science. *335 ÷ 5 = 67*
   c Work out his mean score for Maths. *284 ÷ 4 = 71*
Alan's worst score in Science was 58%. His best score was 72%.
Alan's worst score in Maths was 36%. His best score was 94%.
   d Use this information to compare Alan's performance in Science and Maths. *Range for Sc 72 - 58 = 14%   Range for Maths = 94 - 36 = 58%   Alan is more consistent in Science, but more likely to score more in Maths*

3 Rachel has six hamsters. These are their ages in months:

   5   8   3   13   15   4

   a Find the mean of their ages.
   b Write down the range of their ages.
   c Rachel also has 14 mice.
   They have a mean age of 6 months and
   the range of their ages is 19 months.
   Compare the ages of the hamsters and
   the mice.

4 These are the ages, in years, of the Adeney quiz team.

     38   61   29   55   52

a Find the mean and the range of their ages.

Adeney have a competition with the Tebbington quiz team.

The mean and range of ages in this team are 51 and 7 years respectively.

b Compare the ages of the people in the two teams.

5 A sports club has facilities for squash and golf.

The tables show the ages of the people who play each sport.

Squash players

Age	17	19	20	21	25	29
Frequency	3	4	5	3	2	1

Golf players

Age	17	24	25	31	45	52
Frequency	1	2	2	3	2	1

Compare the ages of the two groups of players.

6 The table shows the runs scored by
Tom and Ian in their last six innings.

Tom	53	67	40	54	39	125
Ian	55	60	67	59	53	60

a Find the mean and range of Tom's scores.

b Find the mean and range of Ian's scores.

c Comment on the differences between the
two players.

d Which player would you choose if you needed
55 runs to win the match? Explain your answer.

7 The table gives the marks that Angela and Hannah got in the summer exams.

	English	Maths	Science	Art	History	French	Geography
Angela	61	71	52	44	52	39	52
Hannah	52	49	56	61	59	52	56

a Find the mean and range of Angela's marks.

b Find the mean and range of Hannah's marks.

c Comment on the differences between Angela's and Hannah's results.

The range is the simplest measure of spread but it is not always reliable.
These diagrams show two sets of data. The patterns are identical apart from one
extra number in the second set.

Range = 10 − 6 = 4   Range = 10 − 2 = 8

The range of the second set of data has been badly affected by the one extreme value
of 2. Even with much larger sets of data, one extreme value can distort the range.

The interquartile range measures the spread of the middle half of the data. It is not
affected by extreme values.

Lower quartile   The **lower quartile** is the value one-quarter of the way through
the data.

Upper quartile   The **upper quartile** is the value three-quarters of the way
through the data.

Interquartile range   The **interquartile range** = upper quartile − lower quartile

To find the quantities
(1) List the data in order of size, smallest first.
(2) Find the position of the median.
(3) Look at the data to the left of this position.
     The lower quartile is the median of this data.
(4) Look at the data to the right of this position.
     The upper quartile is the median of this data.

Here are the two sets of data used above.

6   7   7   8   9   9   10
       ↑   ↑   ↑
  lower quartile median = 8 upper quartile   interquartile range
     = 7   = 9   = 9 − 7 = 2

2   6   7   7   8   9   9   10
          ↑   ↑   ↑
  lower quartile median = 7.5 upper quartile   interquartile range
     = 6.5   = 9   = 9 − 6.5 = 2.5

The extra number has influenced the interquartile range but not distorted it.
The interquartile range is a more reliable measure of spread than the range.

Exercise 25:2

For questions **1–4** find
a the median   **b** the interquartile range.

1   5, 11, 12, 14, 15, 16, 19

2   8, 10, 10, 11, 12, 23

3   4.2, 4.7, 4.9, 4.9, 5.1, 5.2, 5.2, 7.8 $\text{MEDIAN} = \dfrac{4.9+5.1}{2} = 5, \text{I.R.} = 5.2 - \left(\dfrac{4.7+4.9}{2}\right)$

$= 5.2 - 4.8$

4   27, 33, 34, 34, 35, 35, 35, 37, 39, 39, 39, 40, 40, 41, 41, 41

$\text{MEDIAN} = \dfrac{37+39}{2} = 38, \text{I.R.} = 40 - \left(\dfrac{35+34}{2}\right) = 40 - 34.5 = 5.5 \quad = 0.4$

5   Find the median and the interquartile range of the data in this table.

Value	4	5	6	7	8
Frequency	17	3	18	8	2

6   The table gives the median and the interquartile range of the heights, in centimetres, of sunflowers grown from two types of seed.

	Median	Interquartile range
Type A	110	72
Type B	110	35

   a   Compare the heights of the two types of sunflower.
   b   Which type would you use if you wanted to try to grow a really tall sunflower?
   c   Which type would you use if you wanted to produce flowers all about the same height?

7   Natalie is the manager of a factory.
She needs to buy some new machines
to fill bags of nuts. The bags must
weigh at least 500 grams.
She has two machines to choose from.
She tests the machines by filling
100 packets of nuts with each one
and then weighing the packets.
The table shows her results:

	Median	Interquartile range
Machine A	501	6
Machine B	503	2

Which machine should she choose? Explain your answer.

2 Cumulative frequency

Have you ever wondered how exam grades are worked out?

How many marks does it take to pass or to gain a grade A?

Often this is worked out using percentages and cumulative frequency.
Examiners need to answer questions like, 'How many pupils scored less than 40%?' or, 'How many pupils scored more than 75%?'

To answer questions like these, a cumulative frequency table or a cumulative frequency diagram is very useful.

Exercise 25:3 ALL

1 The table shows the numbers of TVs per household in Parkwell village.

No. of TVs	Frequency	No. of TVs	Frequency
0	2	3	21
1	5	4	9
2	14	5	3

a How many households are shown in the data? 54
b How many households have 2 or fewer TVs? 21
c How many households have more than 3 TVs? 12

2 These are the number of goals scored by Bethesda football team in their last 30 matches.

No. of goals	Frequency	No. of goals	Frequency
0	6	4	2
1	8	5	0
2	7	6	1
3	5	7	1

Write down the number of matches where they scored:
a 3 goals 5
b 5 goals 0
c 2 goals or fewer 21
d at least 3 goals. 9

Cumulative frequency	**Cumulative frequency** is a running total.

3 The table shows the results of a Maths test.

Mark	Frequency	Cumulative frequency	
1	2	2	
2	3	5	$(2 + 3)$
3	1	6	$(5 + 1 = 2 + 3 + 1)$
4	5	11	$(6 + 5)$
5	8	19	
6	11	30	
7	6	36	
8	3	39	
9	1	40	
10	2	42	

a Copy the table. Fill it in.
b How many pupils took the test? 42
c Pupils need to score at least 6 marks to pass the test.
 How many pupils passed the test? 23
d Pupils who score less than 5 marks have to resit the test.
 How many pupils have to resit the test? 11

You can use cumulative frequency to find the median and interquartile range.

Example

A group of pupils were asked how many pieces of homework they had to complete each week. The table shows the results. Find the median and interquartile range.

Number of homeworks completed	Frequency	Cumulative frequency	
3	4	4	
4	15	19	$(4 + 15)$
5	21	40	$(19 + 21)$
6	16	56	$(40 + 16)$
7	4	60	$(56 + 4)$

The median is the value half way through the data.
The total cumulative frequency is 60 so the median is in position $60 \div 2 = 30$.
The first two rows of the table only go as far as the 19th value.
The third row of the table goes as far as the 40th value.
The 30th value must be in the third row of the table.
So the median number of homeworks completed is 5.

The lower quartile is one quarter of the way through the data.
The lower quartile is in position $60 \div 4 = 15$.
The 15th value is in the second row.
So the lower quartile of homeworks completed is 4.

The upper quartile is three quarters of the way through the data.
The upper quartile is in position $15 \times 3 = 45$.
The 45th value is in the fourth row.
So the upper quartile of homeworks completed is 6.

The interquartile range is $6 - 4 = 2$.

Exercise 25:4   ALL

1 The table shows the number of GCSEs passed by Year 11 pupils last year.

Number of GCSEs	Frequency	Cumulative frequency
1	3	3
2	5	8
3	9	17
4	11	28
5	20	48
6	31	79
7	28	107
8	16	123
9	13	136
10	8	144

a Copy the table. Fill in the cumulative frequency column.
b Find the median number of GCSEs passed. $144 \div 2 = 72 \rightarrow$ 6 GCSE's
c Find the interquartile range. $LQ = 36^{th} \rightarrow 5$ $UQ = 108^{th} \rightarrow 8$
    $I.R = 8 - 5 = 3$.

2 This table shows the number of goals scored in a junior football league last season.

Number of goals	Frequency	Cumulative frequency
0	5	5
1	11	16
2	15	31
3	12	43
4	6	49
5	3	52
6	2	54

a Copy the table. Fill in the cumulative frequency column.
b Find the median number of goals scored. $54 \div 2 \to 27 \to$ 2 goals
c Find the interquartile range. L.Q = $54 \div 4 = 13\frac{1}{2}^{th} \to 1$ goal U.Q $= 13\frac{1}{2} \times 3 = 40\frac{1}{2}^{th} \to 3$ goals IR = 3−1 = 2 goals
d How many games had fewer than 4 goals? 43 games
e How many games had more than 3 goals? 54−43 = 11 games
f How many games had between 2 and 4 goals inclusive? up to & incl 4 = 49 −16 less than 2 goals = 16 = 21   33 games

You can also use cumulative frequency when dealing with grouped data.
OR M2 15+12+6 = 33 games

Example   These tables show the number of years employees have spent with one company.
They show the same information in different ways.

Number of years	Frequency	Number of years	Cumulative frequency
1–2	3	2 or less	3
3–4	9	4 or less	12
5–6	11	6 or less	23
7–8	6	8 or less	29
9–10	4	10 or less	33
11–12	5	12 or less	38
13–14	2	14 or less	40

a How many employees are in the survey?
b How many employees have worked for the company for 8 years or less?
c How many employees have worked for the company for more than 10 years?

a The final number in the cumulative frequency column gives you this answer.
(You would need to add up all the frequencies in the table on the left to get the answer.)
40 employees are in the survey.

b The cumulative frequency for 8 or less is 29.
So 29 employees have worked for the company for 8 years or less.
You would need to add the frequencies 3, 9, 11 and 6 in the table on the left to get the answer.

c The cumulative frequency table shows that 33 people have worked for 10 years or less.
The rest of the people surveyed have worked for more than 10 years.
You take 33 from the total number of people surveyed.
The number of employees that have worked for the company for more than 10 years = 40 − 33 = 7.

Exercise 25:5

1 This table shows the ages in years of a sample of cars.

Age in years	Frequency	Age in years	Cumulative frequency
less than 2	18	less than 2	
2 to less than 4	16	less than 4	
4 to less than 6	12	less than 6	
6 to less than 8	9		
8 to less than 10	5		

a Copy the table. Fill it in.
b How many cars were involved in the survey?
c How many cars were less than 8 years old?
d How many cars were 6 or more years old?

2 The table shows the weekly take-home pay of some factory workers.

Wage in £	Cumulative frequency
121–140	15
121–160	36
121–180	71
121–200	82
121–220	88

a Write down how many workers were involved in the survey.
Find how many workers took home:
b £160 or less
c more than £180.

3   This table shows the money spent on food by a number of families.

Amount in £	Cumulative frequency
21–30	4
21–40	16
21–50	39
21–60	67
21–70	83

   a   Write down how many families were involved in the survey.
   b   How many families spent £60 or less?
   c   How many families spent more than £50?
   d   Explain why you can't find how many families spent £45 or less.

Cumulative frequency diagram

A **cumulative frequency** diagram shows how the cumulative frequency changes as the data values increase. The data is shown on a continuous scale on the horizontal axis. The cumulative frequency is shown on the vertical axis.

You plot the upper end of each group against the cumulative frequency. You then join the points with a straight line or a curve.

Example

The table shows the ages of people in a survey.

Age (years)	Cumulative frequency
<20	3
<25	11
<30	28
<35	40
<40	46
<45	50

   a   Draw a cumulative frequency diagram for the data.
   b   Estimate the number of people in the survey who are:
   (1) less than 28 years old   (2) at least 36 years old.

a   The values given in the age column are all at the upper ends of their groups.
You plot these against the values in the cumulative frequency column.
The points to plot are (20, 3), (25, 11) and so on. You could also plot the point (0, 0) since no one is less than 0 years old but, in this case, it is too far from the other points to be helpful.

b (1) Find **28** on the age axis, move up to the graph and across. Read the value off the cumulative frequency scale.

Approximately 20 people.

(2) Repeat the process for **36** but subtract the answer from 50.

Approximately 8 people.

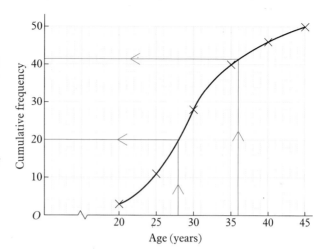

---

4 **a** Draw a cumulative frequency curve for the data in question **2**.
b Use your curve to estimate how many workers took home:
(1) £170 or less (2) more than £190.

5 These are the marks scored by a sample of 750 GCSE students. They are percentages.

Mark	Frequency	Mark	Frequency
1–10	20	51–60	147
11–20	48	61–70	84
21–30	65	71–80	64
31–40	124	81–90	24
41–50	157	91–100	17

a Draw a cumulative frequency table for this data.
b Draw a cumulative frequency curve for this data.

These are the marks needed for certain grades in the exam.

Estimate the following:
c How many pupils scored less than 52%?
d How many pupils scored less than 60%?
e How many pupils gained a grade D?
f How many pupils scored less than 70%?
g How many pupils gained a grade C?
h How many pupils gained a grade B?
i How many pupils gained a grade A?

Grade	Mark
A	76%
B	70%
C	60%
D	52%

You can also estimate the median and quartiles using a cumulative frequency diagram.

To get an estimate of the **median:**
(1) divide the total cumulative frequency by 2
(2) find this point on the cumulative frequency axis
(3) draw a line across to the curve and down to the horizontal axis
(4) read off the estimate of the median.

To get an estimate of the lower quartile:
(1) divide the total cumulative frequency by 4
(2) find this point on the cumulative frequency axis
(3) draw lines as you did for the median
(4) read off the lower quartile.

To get an estimate of the upper quartile:
(1) divide the total cumulative frequency by 4 and multiply by 3
(2) find this point on the cumulative frequency axis
(3) draw lines as you did for the median
(4) read off the upper quartile.

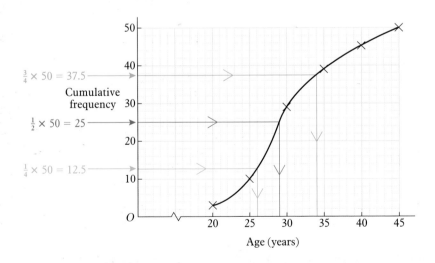

Median = 29 years   Lower quartile = 26 years   Upper quartile = 34 years
Interquartile range = 34 − 26 = 8 years

Exercise 25:6

1 The table shows the scores for players in a golf tournament.

Score	Frequency	Score	Cumulative frequency
61 to 65	5	61 to 65	5
66 to 70	9	61 to 70	14
71 to 75	11	61 to 75	
76 to 80	17		
81 to 85	23		
86 to 90	10		
91 to 95	5		

a Copy the table.
   Fill it in.
b Copy these axes.
   Label them.

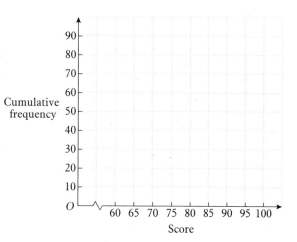

c Draw a cumulative frequency curve.
   The first two points to plot are (65, 5) and (70, 14).

d Use your graph to:
   (1) estimate the median
   (2) find the interquartile range
   (3) estimate how many players scored 78 or less.

2 The table shows the length of time, in minutes, that cars stayed in a short-stay car park.

Time, t	$0 < t \leqslant 20$	$20 < t \leqslant 40$	$40 < t \leqslant 60$	$60 < t \leqslant 80$	$80 < t \leqslant 100$
Frequency	10	25	43	15	7

a Draw a cumulative frequency table for the data.

b Copy these axes.
Label them.

c Draw a cumulative
frequency curve.
The first point to plot
is (20, 10).

d Use your graph to:
(1) estimate the median
(2) find the interquartile
range
(3) estimate how many
cars stayed 30 minutes
or less
(4) estimate how many
cars stayed more
than 90 minutes.

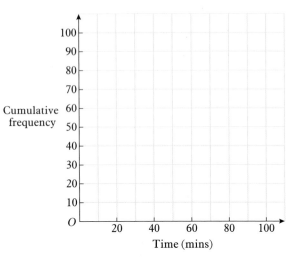

3 The times of treatment for 100 patients at a clinic are shown in the table.

Time (mins)	0–	10–	20–	30–	40–	50–
Frequency	16	30	27	18	9	0

a Draw a cumulative
frequency table for
the data.

b Copy these axes.
Label them.

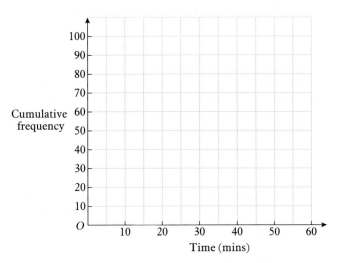

c Draw the cumulative frequency curve.
The first two points to plot are (10, 16) and (20, 46).

d Use your graph to:
(1) estimate the median
(2) find the interquartile range
(3) estimate how many patients had treatment times less than 15 minutes.

4 This table shows the times of treatment for 100 patients at a surgery.

Time (mins)	0–	10–	20–	30–	40–	50–
Frequency	7	42	38	11	2	0

   a Draw a cumulative frequency table for this data.

   b Draw a cumulative frequency curve.

   c Use your graph to:

     (1) estimate the median

     (2) find the interquartile range

     (3) estimate how many patients had treatment times less than 15 minutes.

   d Use your results with those from question **3** to compare the waiting times at the clinic and surgery.

5 Helen has done a survey of two companies, Newmans and Chartwell.
It is on the travelling distances to work of employees.
These are her results.

Newmans

Distance (miles)	0–5	6–10	11–15	16–20	21–25	26–30	31–35
Frequency	3	6	13	10	6	7	3

Chartwell

Distance (miles)	0–5	6–10	11–15	16–20	21–25	26–30	31–35
Frequency	12	9	11	13	2	4	1

   a For each company

     (1) draw a cumulative frequency curve

     (2) estimate the median

     (3) find the interquartile range.

   b Compare the distances travelled to work by the employees of the two companies.

3   Box and whisker diagrams

A cat uses its whiskers to tell how wide an opening is.

In statistics we use a box and whisker diagram to show how wide the data is spread.

Box and whisker diagrams are another way to compare several sets of data.

A box and whisker diagram is sometimes called a box plot or a box and whisker plot.
The box is used to show the middle 50% of the data.
The whiskers are used to show the extreme points of the data.
Here is a box and whisker plot showing train journey times in minutes.

Box and whisker plot showing train journey times in minutes.

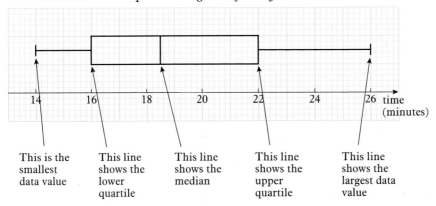

This is the smallest data value

This line shows the lower quartile

This line shows the median

This line shows the upper quartile

This line shows the largest data value

From a box and whisker plot you can read off:

the smallest data value
the lower quartile
the median
the upper quartile
the largest data value
the range of the data.

But you can't tell how many data values there are.

Exercise 25:7

For each of these box and whisker diagrams:

    a Write down the smallest data value.
    b Write down the lower quartile.
    c Write down the median.
    d Write down the upper quartile.
    e Write down the largest data value.
    f Calculate the range of the data.

1

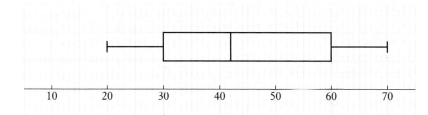

2

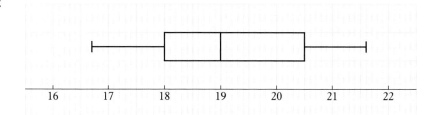

3

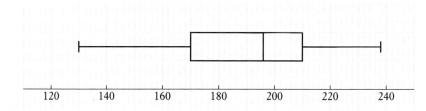

4

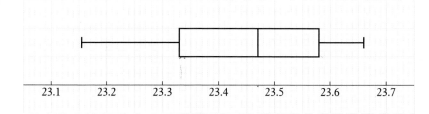

To draw a box and whisker plot you need to work out:

the smallest data value	the median	the largest data value
the lower quartile	the upper quartile	

Example   These are the numbers of pages in 21 editions of a newspaper.

76 82 66 80 92 74 84 70 78 86 84
82 74 68 90 78 64 68 86 70 82

Draw a box and whisker plot to show this data.

First put the data in order of size. Start with the smallest.

64 66 68 68 70 70 74 74 76 78 78
80 82 82 82 84 84 86 86 90 92

Smallest value = 64   Median = 78   Largest value = 92

LQ = median of 64 66 68 68 70 70 74 74 76 78
Lower quartile = 70

UQ = median of 80 82 82 82 84 84 86 86 90 92
Upper quartile = 84

Now you can draw the box and whisker diagram.

First draw the scale and mark on the lower quartile, median and upper quartile.

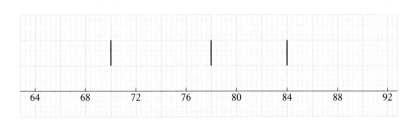

Join these lines to form the box.

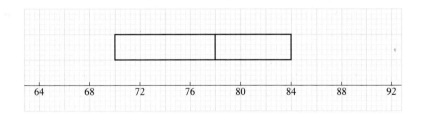

Mark the smallest and highest values and draw in the whiskers.

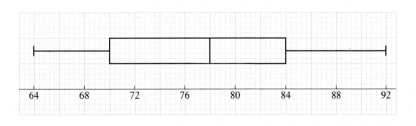

Exercise 25:8

1 Katy measured the length of some caterpillars for a biology experiment.
She measured the lengths in centimetres.
She used her data to work out the following:

smallest data value = 3.4   upper quartile = 4.8
lower quartile = 3.8   largest data value = 5.1
the median = 4.2

Draw a box and whisker diagram to show this data.

2 Andrew did a survey on how much the people in his form earned from
part time jobs in a week.
Here are his results.

£10   £20   £17   £19   £23   £0   £29   £18   £17   £24
£16   £15   £26   £10   £0   £0   £19   £27   £17   £14
£28   £13   £0

a Rewrite the data in order of size. Start with the smallest.
b Find the median earnings.
c Find the lower quartile of the data.
d Find the upper quartile of the data.
e Draw a box and whisker plot to show Andrew's data.

3 Ned is a keen swimmer.
He records the times taken by members of his club to swim 100 m.
These are the times to the nearest tenth of a second.

29.3   26.4   32.4   28.9   27.3   20.7   27.6

25.3   23.5   21.7   24.7   28.9   23.6

a Rewrite the data in order of size. Start with the smallest.
b Find the median time.
c Find the lower quartile of the data.
d Find the upper quartile of the data.
e Draw a box and whisker diagram to show Ned's data.

4 The maximum temperatures in Derby over a period of 14 days in July
were as follows. The temperatures are in degrees Celsius.

16   19   23   25   24   17   18   18   23   24   19   20   25   27

Draw a box and whisker diagram to show this data.

Exercise 25:9

1 These box and whisker plots show the test scores of two different classes.

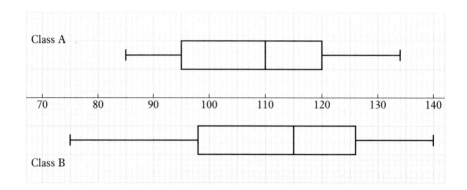

a For each class, write down (1) the range
(2) the interquartile range
(3) the median

b Write a few sentences about the differences between the two sets of marks.

2 This data shows the response times of two ambulance services to 999 calls. The times to get to the emergency are in minutes.

Service A

| 9 | 10 | 13 | 8 | 19 | 12 | 5 | 14 | 13 | 12 |
| 10 | 9 | 12 | 15 | 18 | 7 | 14 | 12 | 13 | 5 |

Service B

| 12 | 13 | 15 | 12 | 14 | 13 | 11 | 14 | 17 | 19 |
| 13 | 14 | 12 | 16 | 15 | 17 | 14 | 11 | 12 | 14 |

a For each ambulance service calculate
(1) the median
(2) the range
(3) the lower and upper quartiles.

b Draw box and whisker plots for both services.
Put them both on the same diagram.

c Write about the differences in the response times of the two services.

d Which service do you think is best? Explain your answer.

What do you think?

The trend in recent years is for girls to do better than boys in most subjects at GCSE. One explanation given for this is that girls' concentration is better in lessons than boys.

Check whether this is true in your school. You need to get permission to watch other lessons. You also need to share your results with others in your group.

 You need a watch, or stopwatch, that allows you to measure 1 minute intervals. You also need Worksheet 25:1. You use this as your observation sheet.

Preparation
(1) Discuss the types of behaviour that you can observe that show concentration.

(2) Plan which groups to visit and how you will select pupils to observe.
     You should be able to observe about 4 pupils at any one time.

(3) Make sure that you know how to complete the observation sheet.
     Practise taking and recording observations in your own group.

(4) Discuss ways of avoiding bias in your observations.

Collecting the data
You need to allow at least 25 minutes for observing pupils in the lesson.

(1) Observe the behaviour of your selected pupils for 1 minute.

(2) Decide whether each one has concentrated for most of this time or not.

(3) Record a ✓ to show concentration or a ✗ to show a lack of concentration.

(4) Repeat steps (1)–(3) to get data for 25 minutes altogether.
     Allow yourself a break after about every 5 minutes. Then carry on.

Worksheet 25:1				
Observation Sheet				
Observation	Boy	Girl	Boy	Girl
1	✓	✗	✗	✓
2				
3				
4				

24				
25				
Total ✓s				
Percentage				

(5) Write down the total number of ✓s for each pupil.

(6) Multiply each total by 4 to give the percentage of time that each pupil concentrated.

Using the collected data

You will probably only be able to collect data on about 4 pupils.
This does not give enough evidence to draw any conclusions.
You need to:

(1) Share your results with others in your group. Ideally you should get data on about 50 boys and 50 girls between you.

(2) Think about how you can use the techniques learned within this chapter to compare the two sets of data.

(3) Make sure that you can justify any conclusions that you state.

Extending the investigation

You might want to adapt the process to make other comparisons. For example you could compare concentration times of pupils of different ages or of pupils in the same group at different times of the day.

1 These are Penny's marks for her tests in five subjects last year.

Maths (%)	65	53	57	71	60	72
English (%)	82	64	51	74	64	49
History (%)	64	50	58	63	59	66
Art (%)	58	64	78	56	71	66
French (%)	57	46	62	49	56	63

a Find the mean mark for each subject.
b Find the range for each subject.
c Use your answers to parts **a** and **b** to decide which is Penny's best subject. Explain your answer.

2 Lisa and Ria are trying to get into the school quiz team.

These are their scores in the last seven practice quizes.

Lisa	70	76	80	78	71	73	77
Ria	85	66	69	79	76	91	59

a Find the mean and range of Lisa's scores.
b Find the mean and range of Ria's scores.
c Which of these two players would you choose for the quiz team? Explain your answer.

3 A clinic collected information on the heights of children of the same age from two different areas.
The table shows the median and interquartile range calculated from their data.

	Median	Interquartile range
Area A height	155 cm	25 cm
Area B height	146 cm	39 cm

Use the data to compare the heights of the children from the two areas.

4 The table shows the results of a survey into the number of hours people spend exercising each week.

Time (hours)	0–2	3–5	6–8	9–11	12–14	15–17
Frequency	16	26	37	21	11	5

  a Draw a cumulative frequency table for this data.
  Find how many people exercised for:
  b 11 hours or less
  c more than 5 hours.

5 The height distribution of Year 11 pupils in a class is shown in the table.

Height (cm)	160–164	165–169	170–174	175–179	180–184	185–189
Frequency	2	3	6	10	7	2

  a Draw a cumulative frequency table for the data.
  b Draw a cumulative frequency curve for the data.
  c Use your graph to:
    (1) estimate the median
    (2) find the interquartile range
    (3) find the number of pupils with heights less than 167 cm
    (4) find the number of pupils with heights greater than 180 cm.

6 These are the marks scored by a sample of 500 GCSE pupils.
  They are percentages.

Mark	Frequency	Mark	Frequency
1–10	13	51–60	98
11–20	32	61–70	56
21–30	43	71–80	43
31–40	83	81–90	16
41–50	105	91–100	11

  a Draw a cumulative frequency table for the data.
  b Draw a cumulative frequency curve for the data.

  These are the marks needed for certain grades
  in the exam.
  c Work out how many pupils gained each grade.

Grade	Mark
B	74%
C	69%
D	58%
E	51%

7 Keith measured the weight of some baby mice as part of a project.
He measured the weights in grams.
He used his data to work these out.

smallest data value = 16   upper quartile = 29
lower quartile = 22   largest data value = 36
the median = 24

Draw a box and whisker diagram to show this data.

8 There are 20 glassblowers on a factory floor.
The manager records the number of glasses each makes during a period
of one hour. This is her data.

| 34 | 29 | 41 | 27 | 19 | 30 | 25 | 33 | 42 | 39 |
| 17 | 34 | 40 | 44 | 17 | 23 | 31 | 33 | 28 | 22 |

a Rewrite the data in order of size. Start with the smallest.

b Find the median number of glasses.

c Find the lower quartile of the data.

d Find the upper quartile of the data.

e Draw a box plot to show the data.

9 The data shows the response times, in minutes, of two fire depots to
emergency calls.

| Greenwall | 6 | 23 | 17 | 19 | 21 | 13 | 10 | 9 |
| | 7 | 17 | 10 | 11 | 20 | 29 | 16 | 8 |

| Barkworth | 11 | 15 | 13 | 19 | 20 | 17 | 15 | 9 |
| | 18 | 16 | 11 | 19 | 20 | 16 | 15 | 10 |

a For each fire depot calculate
  (1) the median
  (2) the range
  (3) the lower and upper quartiles.

b Draw box and whisker plots for both depots on the same diagram.

c Compare the response times for the two depots.

1　200 pupils at Barking School took a maths test and a science test.
The results are shown on these cumulative percentage frequency curves.

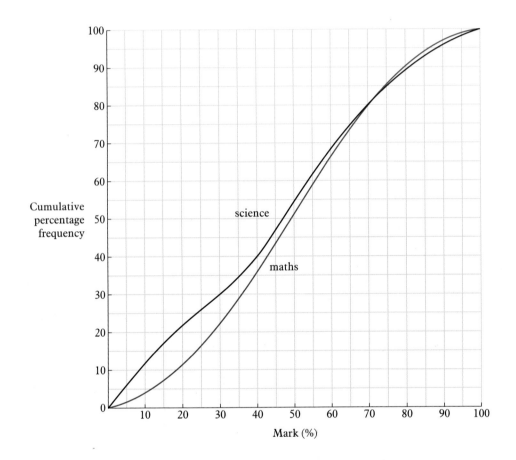

a Say whether these statements are true or false:
  (1) Most pupils scored more than 40% in science.
  (2) 35 pupils scored 40% or less in maths.
  (3) Most people scored more than half marks in both tests.

b What is the median mark for maths?

c Is the median mark in science higher or lower than the median for maths?
  Explain how you could tell this from the graph.

d Copy this sentence. Fill in the gaps.

  .... % of pupils scored .... % or less in both tests.

1 Mike and Sam are practising the long jump for the school sports day.
These are the lengths of their last 8 jumps.
All the lengths are in cm.

Mike	245	239	220	218	248	233	219	226
Sam	232	235	225	231	230	236	228	229

    a Find the mean and range of Mike's lengths.
    b Find the mean and range of Sam's lengths.
    c Comment on the differences between Mike's and Sam's lengths.

2 Look at this data.

14, 15, 16, 16, 18, 19, 21, 23, 26, 31, 33

Find
    a the median   **c** the upper quartile
    b the lower quartile   **d** the interquartile range.

3 Aman has done a survey on the ages of people attending a cinema and a bowling alley.
She has put the results into a table.

Age (in years)	1–10	11–20	21–30	31–40	41–50	51–60
Frequency – cinema	1	15	24	17	32	11
Frequency – bowling	8	29	28	13	8	2

    a For both the cinema and the bowling alley
        (1) Draw a cumulative frequency curve
        (2) Estimate the median
        (3) Find the interquartile range.
    b Compare the ages of the people attending the two places.

4 Mary measured the height of some plants as part of a project.
She measured the heights in centimetres.
She used her data to work these out.

smallest data value = 28   upper quartile = 44
lower quartile = 34   largest data value = 51
the median = 40

Draw a box and whisker diagram to show this data.

5 Cara records the time it takes to drive to work each day.
She does this for 20 working days.
This is her data. The times are in minutes.

21	17	34	20	39	19	27	31	24	33
19	41	36	38	26	17	20	27	23	37

a Rewrite the data in order of size. Start with the smallest.

b Find the median time.

c Find the lower quartile of the data.

d Find the upper quartile of the data.

e Draw a box plot to show the data.

Rudi drives the same distance to work.
He records the time for 20 days like Cara.
This box plot shows his data.

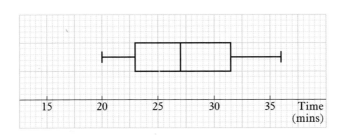

f Find Rudi's values for
   (1) the median   (3) the smallest data value
   (2) the interquartile range   (4) the largest data value.

g Compare the two sets of times.

26 Angles and bearings

1 Angles
Measuring and drawing angles
Calculating angles – on a straight line
          – around a point
Calculating opposite angles
Calculating angles in triangles and
   quadrilaterals
Looking at angles on parallel lines
Calculating angles in circles
Discovering the circle theorems

CORE

2 Get your bearings
Calculating bearings
Solving bearings problems
Drawing to scale

QUESTIONS

EXTENSION

TEST YOURSELF

1 Angles

The angles in this bike frame are very important to its strength.

Designing all sorts of structures involves calculating angles. Look at the entrance to the Louvre in Paris on the cover of this book!

Here are some angle rules that you might remember.

Full turn There are 360° in a **full turn**.

Half turn There are 180° in a **half turn**.

Quarter turn A **quarter turn** is 90°.
This is known as a **right angle**.

Acute angle An **acute angle** is an angle less than 90°.

Obtuse angle An **obtuse angle** is between 90° and 180°.

Reflex angle A **reflex angle** is bigger than 180°.

Exercise 26:1

1 Look at each of these angles.
Write down whether they are acute, right, obtuse or reflex angles.

a   **c**   **e**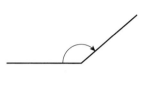

b    **d**    **f**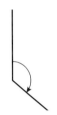

2 Use an angle measurer or protractor to draw each of these angles.
Write under each one whether it is an acute, right, obtuse or reflex angle.
  a 30°   **b** 135°   **c** 210°   **d** 342°   **e** 193°

3 Use an angle measurer or protractor to measure each of these angles.

a 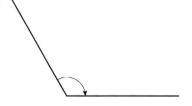   **c**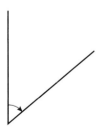

b 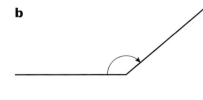   **d**

4 Estimate the size of each of these angles.
Measure them afterwards to check your answers.

a   **b**    **c**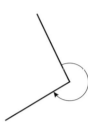

Angles on a straight line add up to 180°.
This is because a half turn makes a
straight line.

You can use this rule to calculate angles.

Example   Work out the angle marked $a°$.

The angles add up to 180°.
So $a° = 180° - 70°$
       $= 110°$

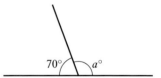

Exercise 26:2

Calculate the angles marked with letters.

1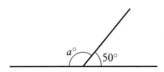

4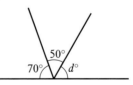

2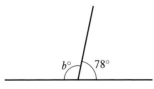

5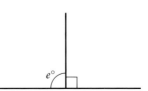

3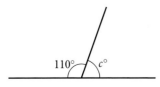

● **6**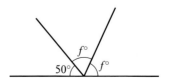

Angles around a point add up to 360°.
This is because they make up a full turn.

Example   Work out the angle marked $b°$.

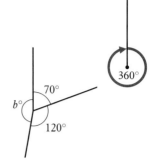

The angles add up to 360°.
So $b° = 360° - 70° - 120°$
      $= 170°$

Calculate the angles marked with letters.

7

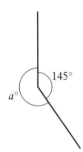

145°

$a°$

10

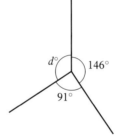

$d°$ 146°

91°

8

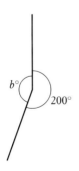

$b°$

200°

11

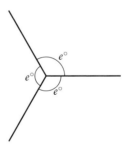

$e°$
$e°$
$e°$

9

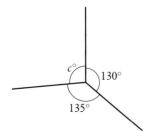

$c°$ 130°

135°

12

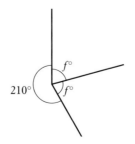

$f°$
210° $f°$

Opposite angles Angles that are opposite each other in a cross are equal.
They are known as **opposite angles**!

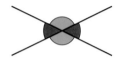

Example Find the angles marked with letters.

$b°$ is opposite $a°$ and so it is the same angle:
$b° = 56$

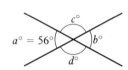

$c°$ makes a straight line with $a°$.
This means that $a° + c° = 180°$.
$c° = 180° - 56° = 124°$

$d°$ is opposite $c°$ and so it is the same angle:
$d° = 124°$

Exercise 26:3

Calculate the angles marked with letters.

1

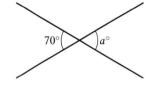

2

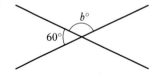

3

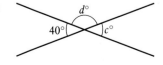

4

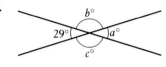

5

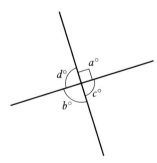

6

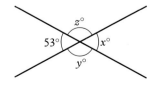

| Angles in a triangle | **Angles in a triangle** add up to 180°. |

Example

Find the angle marked $x°$.

The angles add up to 180°.
So $x° = 180° - 73° - 46°$
$\quad x° = 61°$

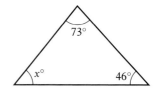

Exercise 26:4

Calculate the angles marked with letters.

1

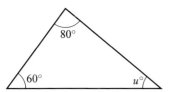

4

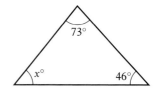

2

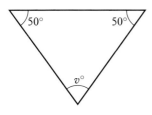

5

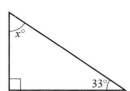

3

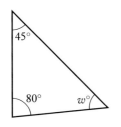

6

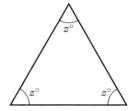

All quadrilaterals are made up of two triangles.

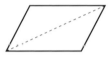

Because the angles in a triangle add up to 180°, the angles in a quadrilateral add up to 2 × 180° = 360°.

Example   Find the angle marked $x°$.

$x° = 360° - 140° - 45° - 55°$
$x° = 120°$

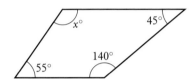

Exercise 26:5

Calculate the angles marked with letters.

1
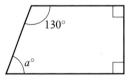

4
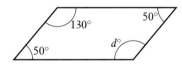

2
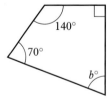

5
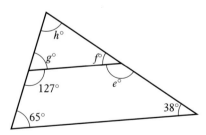

3
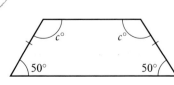

6
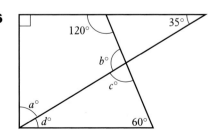

You can use the opposite angles rules to work out **angles on parallel lines**.

$a°$ and $b°$ are equal because they are opposite angles.

The sloping line crosses the bottom line at the same angle that it crosses the top line. This means that $p°$ and $q°$ are the same as $a°$ and $b°$.

Angles $c°$, $d°$, $r°$ and $s°$ are all equal in the same way.

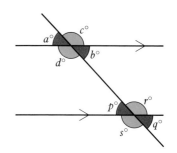

Exercise 26:6

1 **a** Copy this diagram. The angles do not need to be exact.
   b Colour all the angles **red** that are equal to $a°$.
   c Colour all the angles **blue** that are equal to $b°$.

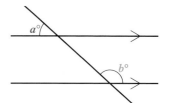

2 **a** Write down the letters of all the angles that are 70°.
   b Write down the letters of all the angles that are 110°.

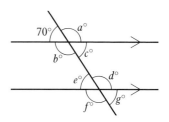

3 Calculate the angles marked with letters.

   a

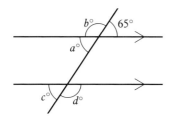

   c

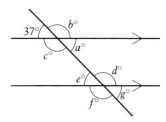

   b

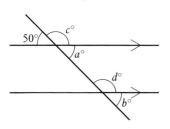

   d

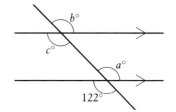

e

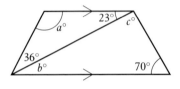

g

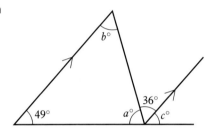

f

h

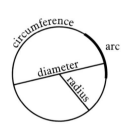

Angles in circles

There are some special angle rules for circles.
Before you learn these, you need to make sure
that you know the names of parts of the circle.

You should already know these:
radius, diameter, circumference.

Also an **arc** is part of the circumference.

Now you need to know these:

| Chord | A **chord** is a straight line going from one point on the circumference to another and *not* going through the centre. |

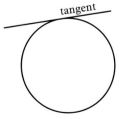

| Tangent | A **tangent** is a straight line that just touches the circle. |

Here are the rules you need to know.

Angle in a semi-circle

The **angle in a semi-circle** is the angle made by joining both ends of a diameter of a circle to a point on the circumference.
The **angle in a semi-circle** is 90°.
In this diagram, angle APB is 90°.

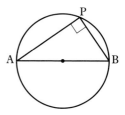

Tangent and radius

A **radius** drawn to the point where a **tangent** touches the circle is at right angles to that tangent.

Midpoint of a chord

A line drawn from the centre of a circle to the **midpoint of a chord** is always at right angles to the chord.

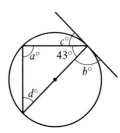

Example   Find the angles marked with letters. Write down the rules that you use.

$a° = 90°$ because it is an angle in a semi-circle.
$b° = 90°$ because it is formed by a radius joining a tangent.
$c° = 180° - 43° - b°$
$\quad = 180° - 43° - 90°$
$\quad = 47°$
because angles on a straight line add up to 180°.
$d° = 180° - 43° - a°$
$\quad = 180° - 43° - 90°$
$\quad = 47°$
because angles in a triangle add up to 180°.

Exercise 26:7

Calculate the angles marked with letters.

1

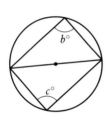

6

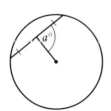

2

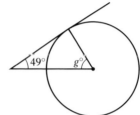

7

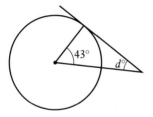

3

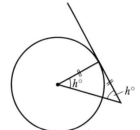

8

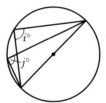

4

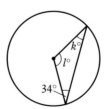

9

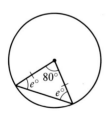

5

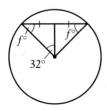

10

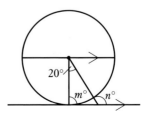

You can draw two tangents to a circle from any point outside the circle.

There are two tangents from the point P to this circle.

They touch the circle at the points A and B.
PA and PB are the two tangents from P to the circle.
The two tangents are equal.

So   PA = PB.

This is an important result to remember.
This means that triangle ABP is an isosceles triangle.
So the angles PÂB and PB̂A are equal.

The centre of the circle is O.
OA is a radius of the circle. OB is also a radius.

So   OA = OB.

This means that triangle AOB is also an isosceles triangle.
So the angles OÂB and OB̂A are equal.

Exercise 26:8

1 Find the angles marked with letters in each part.
You might need to draw extra lines to help you solve the problem.

a

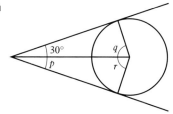

c

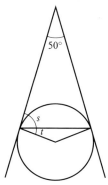

b

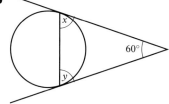

d

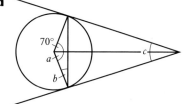

e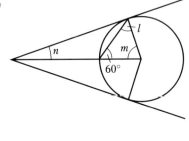

f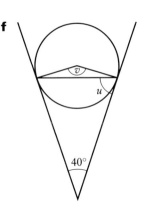

Cyclic quadrilateral

If you draw 4 points on a circle and join them together like this you get a **cyclic quadrilateral.**
ABCD is a cyclic quadrilateral.

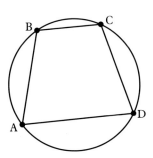

---

2 **a** Draw a circle with radius 5 cm.
   b Draw any cyclic quadrilateral ABCD using your circle.
        You need to label the vertices so that A is opposite C and B is opposite D.
   c Copy this table.

A	C	B	D

Measure the angles inside the cyclic quadrilateral at A, B, C and D.
Fill in your results in the first row of the table.
   d Draw two more cyclic quadrilaterals. Label them ABCD.
        Measure the angles. Fill in the other two rows of the table.
   e Look at your angles.
        Find a rule that connects the angles A and C, and the angles B and D.
        Write down the rule.
        You need to know the rule before you can do the next question.

3 Find the angles marked with letters in each part.

a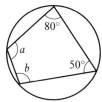

b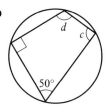

c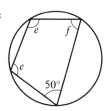

If you draw a chord in a circle you split the circle into two segments.

The red segment is bigger than the blue segment.

The red segment is called the **major segment**.

The blue segment is called the **minor segment**.

You can draw angles in a segment by joining both ends of the chord to a point on the circumference.

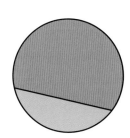

This is an angle drawn in the major segment.

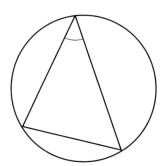

This is an angle drawn in the minor segment.

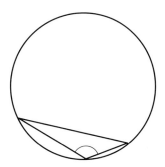

Exercise 26:9

1 **a** Draw a circle with radius 5 cm.
b Draw a chord AB in your circle.
c Draw three angles in the *major* segment in your diagram.
d Measure each of the angles you have drawn.
e Copy this. Fill it in.

The angles in the major segment are ....

2　**a**　Draw a circle with radius 5 cm.

　　b　Draw a chord AB in your circle.

　　c　Draw three angles in the *minor* segment in your diagram.

　　d　Measure each of the angles you have drawn.

　　e　Copy this. Fill it in.

　　　　The angles in the minor segment are ....

　　f　Write one sentence that summarises the results in the last two
　　　　questions. Check that you have the right answer before you do the
　　　　next question.

3　Find the angles marked with letters in each part.

a
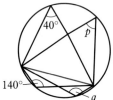

b
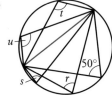

c
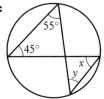

An angle in a segment is
sometimes called an **angle at the
circumference**.

angle at circumference
in major segment

angle at circumference
in minor segment

You can join the ends of the chord
to the centre of the circle.

This gives you two **angles at the
centre**.

There is a connection between the
angle at the circumference and
one of the angles at the centre.

The one that you use depends on
which segment you're looking at.

angle at the centre for
angle at circumference
in major segment

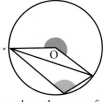

angle at the centre for
angle at circumference
in minor segment

4　**a**　Draw a circle with radius 5 cm.
　　b　Draw a chord AB in your circle.
　　c　Draw an angle in the *major* segment in your diagram.
　　d　Draw the angle at the centre for the angle in the segment you have drawn.
　　e　Measure the angle at the centre and the angle at the circumference. Copy this. Fill it in.

　　　　The angle at the centre is equal to .... the angle at the circumference.

5　**a**　Draw a circle with radius 5 cm.
　　b　Draw a chord AB in your circle.
　　c　Draw an angle in the *minor* segment in your diagram.
　　d　Draw the angle at the centre for the angle in the segment you have drawn.
　　e　Measure the angle at the centre and the angle at the circumference. Copy this. Fill it in.

　　　　The angle at the centre is equal to .... the angle at the circumference.

6　You already know that the angle in a semi-circle is 90°. Explain why this is true using your answers to questions **4** and **5**.

You have now seen all the results that you need to learn about circles!

> **The angle in a semi-circle is 90°.**
>
> **A radius drawn to the point where a tangent touches a circle is at right angles to that tangent.**
>
> **A line drawn from the centre of a circle to the midpoint of a chord is at right angles to the chord.**
>
> **The two tangents to a circle from a point outside a circle are equal in length.**
>
> **The opposite angles in a cyclic quadrilateral add up to 180°.**
>
> **Angles in the same segment are equal.**
>
> **The angle at the centre is twice the angle at the circumference.**

Now you need to be able to use all the results that you've discovered.

Exercise 26:10

Write down the angles marked with letters.

1
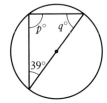

5
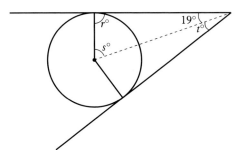

2
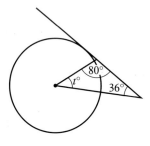

6
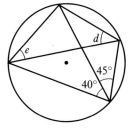

3
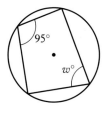

● **7**
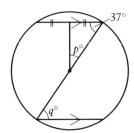

4
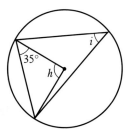

● **8**
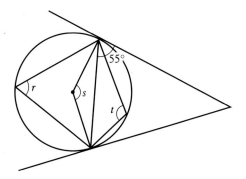

2 Get your bearings

The rescue services need to be able to pinpoint accurately the location of someone in trouble.

They use bearings to help them.

A bearing is an angle.

It is always measured in the same way so that no-one is confused about what the angle means.

Bearing

A **bearing** is an angle.
Bearings are *always* measured clockwise starting from north.
A bearing must always have 3 figures.
If the angle is less than 100° put a zero as the first digit.
030° is the bearing for an angle of 30° clockwise from north.

Bearing of B from A

The **bearing of B from A** means that you are at A.

The **bearing of B from A** is the angle in red.
You start at A.
You face north.
You turn clockwise until you are facing B.

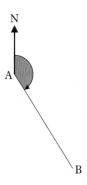

Bearing of A from B

The **bearing of A from B** means that you are at B.

The **bearing of A from B** is the angle in blue.
You start at B.
You face north.
You turn clockwise until you are facing A.

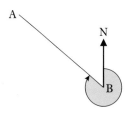

Example

Work out:
a the bearing of B from A
b the bearing of A from B.

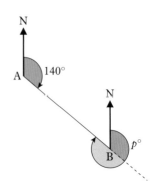

a Draw a north line at A.
Join A to B with a straight line.
Measure clockwise from North
to the line joining A to B.
The bearing is 140°.

b Draw a north line at B.
You must measure the bearing clockwise from this North line.
You want angle $p°$.
Angle $p°$ is 320°.
It is made up of two angles **140°** and 180°
The red angle is 140° because the two north lines are parallel.
The blue angle is 180° because it is on a straight line.
The bearing of A from B is 320°.

Exercise 26:11

1 In each of these find the **bearing of A from B**.

a

c

e

b
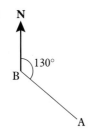

d
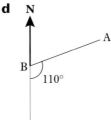

f
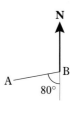

2 For each part of question **1**:
 a Copy the diagram.
 b Draw in a north line at A.
 c Use the angle facts that you know to find the **bearing of B from A**.

3 Asif is in charge of a lifeboat.
These are some of his journeys to rescues.
The lifeboat starts at A. The rescue is at B.
The diagrams show you the bearing that he uses to get to the rescue.

For each part:
(1) Write down the bearing of his journey to the rescue point B.
(2) Work out the bearing for his return journey from B to A.

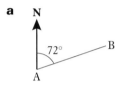

a

b

c

4 Nathan is orienteering.
This diagram shows the route that he takes.

 a Write down the bearing for the first
 part of his journey from A to B.
 b Work out the bearing for the second
 part of his journey from B to C.
 c When Nathan gets to point C, he realises
 that he has left his sandwiches at B!
 Work out the bearing he should use to
 return from C to B.

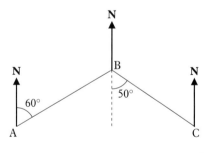

5 This diagram shows the flight
path of an aeroplane.
Find the bearing of R from Q.

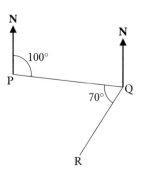

It is often useful to do a scale drawing to solve bearing problems.
An accurate drawing allows you to measure both distances and bearings.

Remember that diagrams should always be drawn in pencil and as accurately as possible.

Example   Charlotte is planning an orienteering course.
Checkpoint A is 500 m from the start on a bearing of 070°.
Checkpoint B is 700 m from B on a bearing of 170°.

  a Make a scale drawing showing the positions of A and B.
Use a scale of 1 cm = 100 m.
  b Find the bearing of the Start from Checkpoint B.

a It is sensible to make a sketch first.
This helps you to plan your sketch on the page.

Now make an accurate scale drawing.
Remember that all bearings are measured
clockwise from **north**.
Make sure that the 0° on your angle measurer
is on the north line.

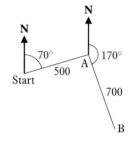

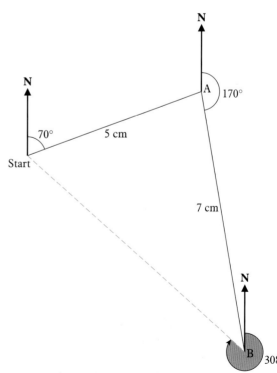

b The bearing of the Start
from B is measured clockwise
from the North line at B.
The bearing is 308°.

Exercise 26:12

1 A plane flies 50 km on a bearing of 050° from Anston to Bridgehope.
It then flies 60 km on a bearing of 140° to Crudgington.
  a Make a scale drawing showing the positions of the three towns.
     Use a scale of 1 cm = 10 km.
  b Use your diagram to find the bearing of Anston from Crudgington.

2 A coastguard is trying to pinpoint a yacht in trouble off the coast.
He measures the bearing from two points A and B.
Point B is due east of A.

The bearing of the yacht from point A is 035°.
The bearing of the yacht from point B is 330°.
Points A and B are 1200 m apart.

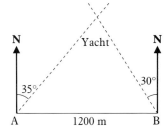

  a Make a scale drawing showing the positions of A, B and the yacht.
     Use a scale of 1 cm = 200 m.
  b Use your diagram to find the distance of the yacht from point A.

3 A ship sails 7 km on a bearing of 150°. It then sails a further 9 km on a
bearing of 230°.
  a Make a scale drawing showing the path the ship takes.
     Use a scale of 1 cm = 1 km.
  b Use your diagram to find the bearing the ship should sail on to
     return to its starting point.

4 Fiona lives in Manchester. Her sister lives in Doncaster which is 70 km
from Manchester on a bearing of 080°. Her brother lives in Derby which
is also 70 km from Manchester but on a bearing of 140°.
  a Draw an accurate scale drawing, showing Manchester, Doncaster and
     Derby.
  b Use your diagram to find the distance from Doncaster to Derby.
  c Find the bearing of Derby from Doncaster.

1 Calculate the angles marked with letters.

a
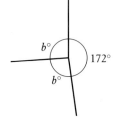

d
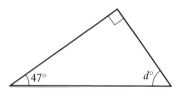

b
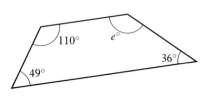

e
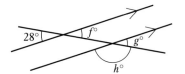

c
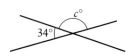

f
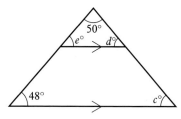

2 Calculate the angles marked with letters.

a
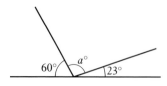

d
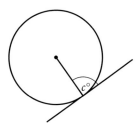

b
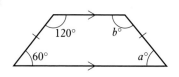

e
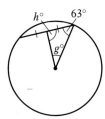

c
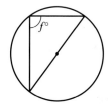

f
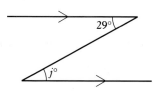

3 A ship sails 5 km on a bearing of 130°. It then sails a further 7 km on a bearing of 215°.

    a Make a scale drawing showing the path the ship takes.
Use a scale of 1 cm = 1 km.

    b Use your diagram to find the bearing the ship should sail on to return to its starting point.

4 A jet flies 220 km due east. It then turns and flies 300 km due south.

    a Draw a sketch of the jet's journey.

    b Make a scale drawing of the jet's journey.
Use a scale of 1 cm = 40 km.

    c Use your diagram to find out how far the jet now is from its starting point.

    d Measure the bearing that the jet should travel on to return to its starting point.

5 This scale drawing shows the position of three islands.
The scale is 1 cm = 10 km.

    a Measure the distance from Black Rock to Puffin Island.

    b Measure the bearing of Black Rock from Puffin Island.

    c Measure the distance from Black Rock to Seal Sanctuary.

    d Measure the bearing of Black Rock from Seal Sanctuary.

1 Calculate the angles marked with letters.

a

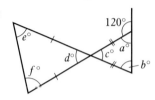

d

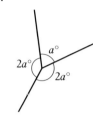

b

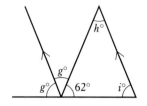

e

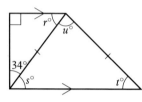

c

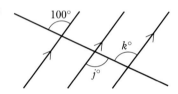

f

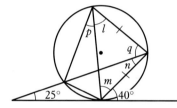

2 Look at this plan of an orienteering course.

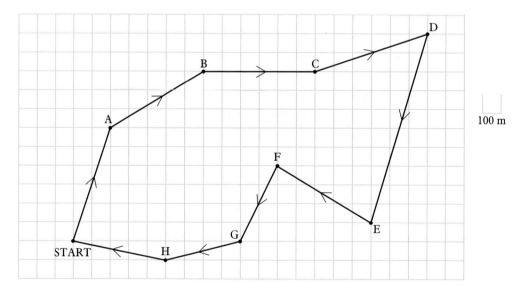

100 m

a Make an accurate copy of the plan.
b Write a list of instructions that could be used to get around the course.
  You need to include distances and bearings.
  You can measure the lengths or calculate them using Pythagoras' theorem.

1 Find the angles marked with letters. Give a reason for each answer.

a

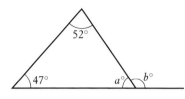

d

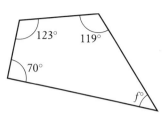

b

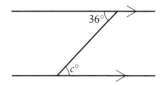

e

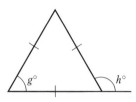

c

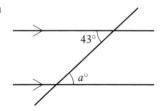

f

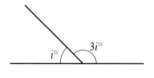

2 For each part, write down the angles marked with letters. Give a reason for each answer.

a

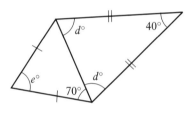

c

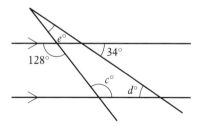

b

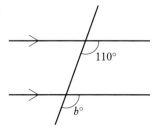

d

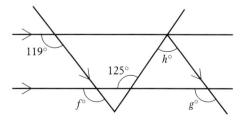

3 For each part, write down the angles marked with letters.
Give a reason for each answer.

a

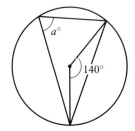

c

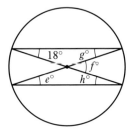

b

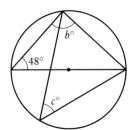

d

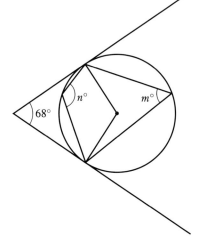

4 For each part, find
(1) the bearing of A from B
(2) the bearing of B from A

a

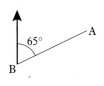

b

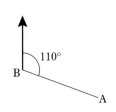

c

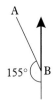

5 A plane flies 20 km from Ampton to Boxford on a bearing of 044°.
It then flies 15 km on a bearing of 102° to Canborough.
  a Draw an accurate scale drawing to show this information.
  b Use your diagram to find the distance of Canborough from Ampton.
  c Use your diagram to find the bearing of Canborough from Ampton.

27 Mainly quadratics

CORE

1 Brackets and factorising
Multiplying out brackets
Looking for common factors
Multiplying out two brackets
Changing the subject

2 Factorising and solving quadratics
Factorising quadratics
Factorising the difference of two squares
Solving quadratic equations
Sketching the graphs of quadratic equations

QUESTIONS

EXTENSION

TEST YOURSELF

1 Brackets and factorising

Alan sometimes took removing brackets too far!

First, a quick recap on how to multiply a bracket by a number.

Example

Multiply out these brackets.

a $3(2x + 7)$ **b** $-6(5y - 2)$ **c** $7(3x^2 + 9x - 8)$

a To work out $3(2x + 7)$ multiply both the $2x$ and the 7 by the 3.
$$3(2x + 7) = 3 \times 2x + 3 \times 7$$
$$= \quad 6x \quad + \quad 21$$

b Notice that there is a minus sign outside the bracket.
$$-6(5y - 2) = -6 \times 5y + (-6) \times (-2)$$
$$= \quad -30y \quad + \quad\quad 12$$

c It doesn't matter how many terms there are in the bracket.
$$7(3x^2 + 9x - 8) = 7 \times 3x^2 + 7 \times 9x + 7 \times (-8)$$
$$= \quad 21x^2 \quad + \quad 63x \quad - \quad\quad 56$$

Exercise 27:1

Multiply out these brackets.

1 $4(x + 6)$ **5** $-3(2x + 9)$ **9** $6(5y^3 - 60y)$

2 $6(2s - 7)$ **6** $7(3x - 1)$ **10** $5(3x^2 - 2x - 7)$

3 $5(4t + 12)$ **7** $-6(7y - 8)$ **11** $-(2x^2 + 2y - z^2)$

4 $9(5x - 5)$ **8** $5(2c^2 - c - 3)$ **12** $-7(3y - 5r + 2w)$

You can also have letters outside the bracket.

Example

Multiply out these brackets.
a $c(2c + 6)$ **b** $f(3f^2 - 5f + 10)$

a To work out $c(2c + 6)$ multiply both the $2c$ and the 6 by the c.
$$c(2c + 6) = c \times 2c + c \times 6$$
$$= 2c^2 + 6c$$

b In this part, remember that $f \times f^2$ gives you f^3.
$$f(3f^2 - 5f + 10) = f \times 3f^2 - f \times 5f + f \times 10$$
$$= 3f^3 - 5f^2 + 10f$$

Exercise 27:2

Multiply out these brackets.

1 $x(2x + 7)$ **4** $x(4x - 8)$ **7** $b^2(b^2 - 5b + 7)$

2 $a(a - 9)$ **5** $x^2(3x + 2)$ **8** $4g(3g^2 + g - 9)$

3 $c(d + 9)$ **6** $y(x^2 - 4x - 3)$ ● **9** $xy(x^2y - xy^3)$

Factorising

Factorising is the opposite of multiplying out brackets.
The first thing to look for is a common factor in the numbers:

Example

Factorise $6x + 10y$

The numbers 6 and 10 both have a factor of 2.
2 is the biggest number that divides exactly into 6 and 10.
You take the 2 outside a bracket as a factor.
$6x + 10y = 2 (\quad)$

Next, you work out what goes inside the bracket.
$2 \times 3 = 6$ and $2 \times 5 = 10$
So inside the bracket you are left with $3x + 5y$

This means that $6x + 10y = 2(3x + 5y)$.

You can check that 2 is the largest factor you could have taken
out by looking at what is left inside the bracket.
3 and 5 have no common factor so the 2 was correct.

Exercise 27:3

Factorise each of these.
Use the hints to help you in questions **1–4**.

1 $4x + 18 = 2 ($)

2 $3x - 27 = 3 ($)

3 $12y - 16 = 4 ($)

4 $35x - 25 = 5 ($)

5 $6x - 36$

6 $8x^2 - 16y$

7 $30t - 40s - 50r$

8 $21y - 49z$

You can also take letters outside brackets as common factors.

The expression $xy + xz$ has a common factor of x.
$xy + xz$ has an x in both terms.
So $xy + xz = x(y + z)$.

The expression $y^2 + y$ has a common factor of y.
$y^2 + y$ has a y in both terms.
So $y^2 + y = y(y + 1)$

Notice the 1 at the end of the bracket. It is very important.
If you multiply the bracket out you must get back to where you started.
$$y(y + 1) = y \times y + y \times 1$$
$$= \quad y^2 \quad + \quad y$$

If you missed the 1 out, you would not get the y term at the end.

Exercise 27:4

Factorise each of these. Use the hints to help you in questions **1–4**.

1 $ax + bx = x ($)

2 $5xy - 6xz = x ($)

3 $5bc - 8bd = b ($)

4 $7x - 9xy = x ($)

5 $6x^2 - 11x$

● **6** $t^3 + t^2$

7 $3x^3 + 5x^2 + 7x$

● **8** $12xy^2 - 13x^2y$

Sometimes you can take out numbers and letters as factors.

Example   Factorise completely $15x^2 - 10x$

15 and 10 have a common factor of 5.
So $15x^2 - 10x = 5(3x^2 - 2x)$

$3x^2$ and $2x$ have a common factor of x.
So $15x^2 - 10x = 5x(3x - 2)$
You could do this all at once by seeing that the common factor is $5x$.

Exercise 27:5

Factorise each of these.

1 $3x^2 + 6x$

2 $15xy - 20xz$

3 $18x^2 - 9x$

4 $45ax - 35bx + 25cx$

5 $16m^2 + 8mn$

6 $14abc - 21acd$

7 $18x^2y + 36xy^2$

8 $9x + 18x^2 - 27x^3$

Now that you can factorise you can use this skill to cancel factors in fractions.

Fractions will cancel when the top line and the bottom line have a common factor.

The 2s cancel because 2 is a factor of the top and bottom lines.

$$\frac{6}{8} = \frac{\cancel{2} \times 3}{\cancel{2} \times 4} = \frac{3}{4}$$

An x cancels because x is a factor.

This leaves an x^2 on the top because $x^3 = x^2 \times x$

$$\frac{4\cancel{x^3}^{x^2}}{7\cancel{x}} = \frac{4x^2}{7}$$

The $(x + 1)$s cancel here once you factorise.

$$\frac{2x + 2}{5x + 5} = \frac{2(\cancel{x + 1})}{5(\cancel{x + 1})} = \frac{2}{5}$$

You can also cancel an $(x + 2)$ here.

$$\frac{2(x + 2)^{\cancel{2}}}{x(\cancel{x + 2})} = \frac{2(x + 2)}{x}$$

This leaves an $(x + 2)$ on the top because $(x + 2)^2 = (x + 2) \times (x + 2)$. You cannot cancel the x's at the end as the x on the top is not a factor of the top line.

Exercise 27:6

Simplify these expressions by cancelling common factors

1 $\dfrac{12}{18}$

2 $\dfrac{3x}{5x}$

3 $\dfrac{2x^2}{3x}$

4 $\dfrac{4(x + 6)}{7(x + 6)}$

5 $\dfrac{3(x - 3)^2}{5(x - 3)}$

6 $\dfrac{4(x + 4)^2}{x(x + 4)}$

7 $\dfrac{2x + 6}{3x + 9}$

8 $\dfrac{x^2 + x}{5x + 5}$

● **9** $\dfrac{3y^2 + 6y}{6y + 12}$

● **10** $\dfrac{x^2y - xy^2}{4xy}$

Multiplying out two brackets

You also need to be able to multiply out two brackets.
You have to remember to multiply *all* the terms in the second bracket
by *all* the terms in the first bracket.

Here is a simple way of remembering how to do this.

Example   Multiply out $(x + 4)(x - 2)$.

1 Multiply the two **First** terms together: $(x + 4)(x - 2)$ x^2

2 Multiply the two **Outside** terms together: $(x + 4)(x - 2)$ $-2x$

3 Multiply the two **Inside** terms together: $(x + 4)(x - 2)$ $+4x$

4 Multiply the two **Last** terms together: $(x + 4)(x - 2)$ -8

5 Collect all the terms together:
$$x^2 - 2x + 4x - 8$$
$$= x^2 + 2x - 8$$

You can remember this using the word **FOIL**.
If you draw lines between the terms as you multiply them, you get a
face! This may also help you to remember to multiply all the terms.

Exercise 27:7

1 a Copy this diagram.
Use it to help you multiply
out $(x + 5)(x + 3)$

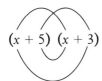

$(x + 5)$ $(x + 3)$

b Copy this diagram.
Use it to help you multiply
out $(x + 9)(x + 10)$

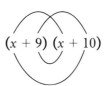

$(x + 9)$ $(x + 10)$

2 Multiply out each of these pairs of brackets.

a $(x + 8)(x + 6)$

b $(x + 7)(x - 8)$

c $(x + 1)(x - 5)$

d $(x - 4)(x + 9)$

e $(x + 8)(x - 1)$

f $(x - 2)(x + 2)$

g $(x - 11)(x - 11)$

h $(x - 5)(x - 15)$

3 Multiply out each of these pairs of brackets.

a $(3x + 1)(x + 2)$

b $(3x + 2)(2x - 7)$

c $(6x - 1)(x + 9)$

d $(x + 5)(\frac{1}{2}x - 6)$

e $(5x + 4)(2x - 7)$

f $(5x - 1)(6x + 1)$

g $(4x - 12)(2x + 7)$

h $(5x - 4)(5x + 4)$

i $(8x - 1)(\frac{1}{2}x + 2)$

j $(7x - 12)(8x + 7)$

k $(10x - 4)(10x + 4)$

l $(10x - 4)(10x - 4)$

4 Multiply these out.

a $(x + 3)^2$

b $(x + 7)^2$

c $(x - 4)^2$

d $(x - 2)^2$

e $(x + 6)^2$

f $(x - 10)^2$

g $(2x - 3)^2$

h $(3x - 8)^2$

i $(2x + 1)^2$

j $(3x - 2)^2$

k $(4x + 1)^2$

l $(7x + 6)^2$

5 Simplify these expressions.

a $(x + 6)^2 + (x + 1)^2$

b $(x + 4)^2 + (2x + 1)^2$

c $(2x + 3)^2 - (x + 1)^2$

d $(4x + 1)^2 - (x + 4)^2$

e $(3x - 1)^2 - (x - 1)^2$

f $(4x - 1)^2 - (x - 2)^2$

Changing the subject

You will need the skills of factorising and multiplying out brackets to solve some changing the subject problems.

You need to re-arrange some formulas in which the new subject appears twice. To do this you need to collect the terms with the new subject in together and then factorise.

Examples   **1** Make t the subject of the formula $\qquad\qquad 8tx = 3ty + s$

First get any terms involving the new subject
onto one side and get any terms not involving
the new subject onto the other side. $\qquad 8tx - 3ty = s$

Now factorise out the new subject. $\qquad\qquad t(8x - 3y) = s$

Finally, divide by the bracket
to leave t as the subject. $\qquad\qquad\qquad t = \dfrac{s}{8x - 3y}$

2 Make r the subject of the formula $\qquad s = \dfrac{r + 4}{r}$

First multiply both sides by r to remove
the fraction. $\qquad\qquad\qquad\qquad\qquad rs = r + 4$
Then move all the r terms to the LHS. $\qquad\quad rs - r = 4$
Now factorise out the r. $\qquad\qquad\qquad\quad r(s - 1) = 4$

Finally divide by the bracket. $\qquad\qquad\qquad r = \dfrac{4}{s - 1}$

Exercise 27:8

Make the **red** letter the subject of each of these formulas.

1 $3xa = 5xb + c$

2 $5yz = 3yx + z$

3 $s = \dfrac{r - 3}{r}$

4 $t = \dfrac{s - p}{2s}$

5 $q = \dfrac{3 + q}{t}$

6 $q + p = 3qt - s$

7 $f = \sqrt{\dfrac{g + 7}{g}}$

8 $y = \sqrt{\dfrac{x - 5}{x}}$

● 9 $f = \sqrt{\dfrac{g^2 + 7}{g^2}}$

●10 $s = \dfrac{t^2 - 7}{3t^2}$

2 Factorising and solving quadratics

The path of a stone thrown in the air is worked out using quadratic equations.

Ben is doing his Maths homework!

Co-efficient

The number in front of a letter is called a **co-efficient**. In $x^2 + 2x - 8$, 2 is called the co-efficient of x.

Constant term

The number on the end of the equation is known as the **constant term**. In $x^2 + 2x - 8$, -8 is the constant term.

Exercise 27:9

1 Multiply out each of these pairs of brackets:

a $(x + 2)(x + 6)$ **d** $(x + 9)(x - 10)$

b $(x + 8)(x - 7)$ **e** $(x - 6)(x + 2)$

c $(x + 4)(x - 7)$ **f** $(x - 10)(x + 10)$

2 Copy this table. Use your answers to question **1** to fill it in. The first one is done for you.

	Number at end of 1st bracket	Number at end of 2nd bracket	Coefficient of x	Constant term
a	2	6	8	12
b	8	−7		
c	4	−7		
d	9	−10		
e	−6	2		
f	−10	10		

In question **2** you should have noticed that when you multiply out two brackets that both start with x:

The **co-efficient of x** is found by *adding* the two numbers at the end of the brackets together.
The **constant term** is found by *multiplying* the two numbers at the end of the brackets together.

Example $(x + 4)(x - 7) = x^2 \quad -3x \quad -28$

$$+4 + -7 = -3 \qquad +4 \times -7 = -28$$

Once you know these facts, you can use them to reverse the process. This means taking a quadratic expression and splitting it back into two brackets.
This process is known as **factorising a quadratic**.

Example Factorise $x^2 + 5x + 6$

The brackets will be $(x + ?)(x + ?)$

The two numbers at the end of the brackets
add together to give 5 and
multiply together to give 6.

The two numbers that do this are 2 and 3.
So $x^2 + 5x + 6 = (x + 2)(x + 3)$
You can write these brackets either way round.

You may also find it helpful to look at the signs in the equation you are factorising.

$x^2 + 5x + 6$	The number at the end is $+6$.
$= (x + ?)(x + ?)$	The numbers must be the same sign so that they multiply to give a $+$.
	They must both be $+$ because they add to give $+5$.
$x^2 - 7x + 10$	The number at the end is $+10$.
$= (x - ?)(x - ?)$	The numbers must be the same sign so that they multiply to give a $+$.
	They must both be $-$ because they add to give -7.
$x^2 + 3x - 10$	The number at the end is -10.
$= (x + ?)(x - ?)$	The numbers must have different signs so that they multiply to give a $-$.
	The $+$ number must be bigger because they add to give a $+$ total of $+3$.

3 Factorise these quadratic expressions.

a $x^2 + 4x + 3$

b $x^2 + 9x + 20$

c $x^2 + 9x + 18$

d $x^2 + 14x + 49$

e $x^2 + 11x + 30$

f $x^2 - 5x + 4$

g $x^2 - 29x - 30$

h $x^2 + 4x - 60$

i $x^2 + 6x + 9$

j $x^2 - x - 2$

k $x^2 - 8x + 15$

l $x^2 - 8x - 33$

m $x^2 + 10x - 24$

n $x^2 + 13x - 30$

o $x^2 + 4x$

p $x^2 - 9$

● **q** $x^2 + 100x + 2100$

● **r** $x^2 + 98x + 2392$

● **s** $x^2 - x - 306$

● **t** $x^2 + x - 600$

Difference of two squares

A quadratic expression which is in the form $x^2 - a^2$ is known as the **difference of two squares**. Difference means subtract. The same rules still work when you are factorising it.

Example

Factorise $x^2 - 16$.
You can think of this as $x^2 + 0x - 16$
The numbers in the two brackets add to give 0 and multiply to give -16.
They are $+4$ and -4
$x^2 - 16 = (x - 4)(x + 4)$

The general rule is $x^2 - a^2 = (x - a)(x + a)$

Exercise 27:10

Factorise these quadratic expressions.

1 $x^2 - 9$

2 $x^2 - 64$

3 $x^2 - 4$

4 $x^2 - 1$

5 $x^2 - 144$

● **6** $x^2 - y^2$

● **7** $x^2 - \frac{1}{4}$

8 $x^2 - 324$

Quadratic equations

Once you can factorise a quadratic expression, you can solve a quadratic equation.

When you have solved a quadratic equation, you can sketch the graph of the quadratic.

Solving the quadratic equation tells you where the graph crosses the x axis.

Example Solve $x^2 + 5x + 6 = 0$

1 **Factorise the quadratic.**

$$(x + 2)(x + 3) = 0$$

You now have two brackets *multiplied* together to give 0.
The only way two things can multiply together to give 0 is if one of them is 0.
It is very important that the quadratic **is always equal to 0.**

2 **Put the two brackets equal to 0.**

This means that either $x + 2 = 0$ or $x + 3 = 0$

3 **Solve these simple equations.**

$$x + 2 = 0 \qquad x + 3 = 0$$
$$x = -2 \qquad x = -3$$

These are both solutions of $x^2 + 5x + 6 = 0$
Quadratic equations always have two solutions.

4 **You can check your answers by putting them back into the original equation.**

Put $x = -2$ into $x^2 + 5x + 6$: $= (-2)^2 + 5 \times (-2) + 6$
$= 4 \quad - 10 \quad +6$
$= 0$

Put $x = -3$ into $x^2 + 5x + 6$: $= (-3)^2 + 5 \times (-3) + 6$
$= 9 \quad - 15 \quad +6$
$= 0$

This shows that both answers are correct.

Exercise 27:11

1 Follow these steps to solve $x^2 - 3x - 18 = 0$

   a Factorise $x^2 - 3x - 18$

   b Put each bracket equal to zero.

   c Solve the equations you wrote down in part **b**.

   d Check your answers by putting them back into the original equation. They should both give 0.

2 Follow these steps to solve $x^2 + 8x + 15 = 0$

   a Factorise $x^2 + 8x + 15$

   b Put each bracket equal to zero.

   c Solve the equations you wrote down in part **b**.

   d Check your answers by putting them back into the original equation. They should both give 0.

3 Solve these quadratic equations.

   a $x^2 + 4x + 3 = 0$ **g** $x^2 + 7x - 30 = 0$

   b $x^2 + 13x + 42 = 0$ **h** $x^2 - 11x + 30 = 0$

   c $x^2 + x - 6 = 0$ **i** $x^2 + 5x + 4 = 0$

   d $x^2 - 7x + 12 = 0$ **j** $x^2 + 12x + 35 = 0$

   e $x^2 + 6x = 0$ ● **k** $x^2 + x = 6$

   f $x^2 - 11x - 26 = 0$ ● **l** $x^2 + 10x = -24$

4 Solve these quadratic equations.

   a $x^2 - 9 = 0$ **g** $x^2 = 16$

   b $x^2 - 25 = 0$ **h** $x^2 = 36$

   c $x^2 - 100 = 0$ **i** $x^2 = 121$

   d $x^2 + 5x = 0$ ● **j** $x^2 = 19$

   e $x^2 - 11x = 0$ ● **k** $x^2 = 24$

   f $x^2 + 10x = 0$ ● **l** $x^2 = 50$

● **5** Solve these quadratic equations.

   a $36 - x^2 = 0$

   b $49 - x^2 = 0$

   c $121 - x^2 = 0$

   d $0.25 - x^2 = 0$

In Chapter 19 you saw how to draw graphs of quadratic equations.
Factorising a quadratic equation allows you to draw a sketch of the graph.
A sketch graph shows the shape of the graph and the points where it
crosses the axes. You can't read off exact values from a sketch graph.

Example

Sketch $y = x^2 - x - 12$.
Show all the points where the graph crosses the axes.

1 Find the points where the graph crosses the x axis.
These are the points where $y = 0$.
To do this, solve the quadratic equal to 0.

$x^2 - x - 12 = 0$
$(x + 3)(x - 4) = 0$
Either $x + 3 = 0$ or $x - 4 = 0$
So $x = -3$ or $x = 4$
The graph crosses the x axis at $x = -3$ and at $x = 4$.

2 Find the point where the graph crosses the y axis.
To do this, put $x = 0$.

$y = x^2 - x - 12$
$ = 0^2 - 0 - 12$
$ = -12$

3 Draw the axes and mark
the crossing points.

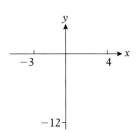

4 Sketch the graph.
Quadratic graphs are always
symmetrical.
The bottom of this curve must be
halfway between the points where
the curve crosses the x axis.

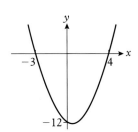

Exercise 27:12

1 Follow these steps to sketch the graph of $y = x^2 - 3x - 10$.

   a Find the points where the graph crosses the x axis.
To do this, solve the quadratic equal to 0.

$$x^2 - 3x - 10 = 0$$
$$(x \quad)(x \quad) = 0$$

Either $x .... = 0$ or $x .... = 0$
So $x = ...$ or $x = ...$

The graph crosses the x axis at $x = ...$ and at $x = ...$

   b Find the point where the graph crosses the y axis.
To do this, put $x = 0$.

$$y = x^2 - 3x - 10$$
$$= ...$$
$$= ...$$

   c Draw the axes and mark the crossing points.

   d Sketch the graph.

2 Follow these steps to sketch the graph of $y = x^2 + x - 12$.

   a Find the points where the graph crosses the x axis.
To do this, solve the quadratic equal to 0.

$$x^2 + x - 12 = 0$$
$$...$$
$$...$$

The graph crosses the x axis at $x = ...$ and at $x = ...$

   b Find the point where the graph crosses the y axis.
To do this, put $x = 0$.

$$y = x^2 + x - 12$$
$$= ...$$
$$= ...$$

   c Draw the axes and mark the crossing points.

   d Sketch the graph.

3 Sketch the graph of each of the following quadratic equations.

a $y = x^2 + 4x + 3$

b $y = x^2 + 2x - 15$

c $y = x^2 + 4x - 12$

d $y = x^2 - 4x - 5$

e $y = x^2 + 3x$

f $y = x^2 - 11x - 26$

g $y = x^2 - 16$

h $y = x^2 - 25$

4 Sketch the graph of each of the following quadratic equations.

a $y = x^2 + 6x + 9$

b $y = x^2 - 4x + 4$

c $y = x^2 - 6x + 9$

d $y = x^2 + 10x + 25$

This is a sketch graph of $y = -x^2$.

When the x^2 term is negative, a quadratic graph is turned upside down.

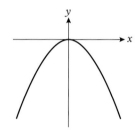

---

5 Sketch the graph of each of the following quadratic equations.

a $y = 9 - x^2$

b $y = 6 + x - x^2$

c $y = -x^2 + 7x - 10$

6 The height of a ball as it travels through the air is worked out using the equation $h = 20t - 5t^2$.
h is the height in metres and t is the time in seconds.

a Sketch a graph of this equation.

b How many seconds is the ball in the air?

1 Multiply out these brackets.

a $4(x + 2)$ **e** $-2(x + 3)$ **i** $y(3y^2 - 7y)$

b $3(y - 3)$ **f** $-4(3x - 4)$ **j** $x(5x^2 - 2x - 6)$

c $6(2x + 3)$ **g** $-3(4x + 1)$ **k** $2x(2x^2 + 3y - y^2)$

d $5(5x - 1)$ **h** $-6(y^2 - 4)$ **l** $3y(4xy - 3x^2z)$

2 Factorise each of these.
Use the hints to help you in parts **a**–**f**.

a $18y - 12$ $= 6 (\qquad)$ **g** $5r - 15s - 50t$

b $15x - 45$ $= 5 (\qquad)$ **h** $21y - 49z$

c $4x^2 + 8x$ $= 4x (\qquad)$ **i** $7m^2 + 8mn$

d $12pq - 20pr$ $= 4p (\qquad)$ **j** $4abc - 6acd$

e $27x^2 - 36x$ $= 9x (\qquad)$ **k** $24x^2y + 36xy^2$

f $12px + 24qx + 48rx = 12x (\qquad)$ **l** $9y + 18y^2 - 27y^3$

3 Multiply out each of these pairs of brackets.

a $(x + 3)(x + 6)$ **i** $(2x - 2)(2x + 3)$

b $(2x + 5)(x + 3)$ **j** $(5x - 6)(6x - 4)$

c $(3x + 2)(x + 2)$ **k** $(3x - 8)(2x - 7)$

d $(x + 3)(x + 6)$ **l** $(2x - 1)(2x - 3)$

e $(2x - 7)(x + 3)$ **m** $(5x + 4)(6x - 4)$

f $(3x + 2)(x - 2)$ **n** $(3x + 1)(2x + 7)$

g $(2x - 8)(x + 3)$ **o** $(5x + 2)(6x - 4)$

h $(3x + 4)(x - 2)$ **p** $(3x + 3)(2x - 7)$

4 Factorise these quadratic expressions.

a $x^2 + 3x + 2$ **j** $x^2 + 14x - 32$

b $x^2 + 6x + 5$ **k** $x^2 + 8x - 48$

c $x^2 + 11x + 24$ **l** $x^2 + 6x$

d $x^2 - 9x + 18$ **m** $x^2 + 7x$

e $x^2 - 14x + 49$ **n** $x^2 - 16$

f $x^2 + 12x + 36$ **o** $x^2 - 0.64$

g $x^2 - 4x + 5$ **p** $x^2 + 8x + 16$

h $x^2 - 29x - 30$ **q** $x^2 + 16x + 64$

i $x^2 - 6x - 7$ **r** $x^2 - 6.25$

5 Solve these quadratic equations.

a $x^2 - 3x + 2 = 0$

b $x^2 - 4x + 3 = 0$

c $x^2 + 5x + 4 = 0$

d $x^2 \quad x - 6 = 0$

e $x^2 + 7x + 12 = 0$

f $x^2 - 4x = 0$

g $x^2 + 12x = 0$

h $x^2 - 5x - 6 = 0$

i $x^2 + 5x - 24 = 0$

j $x^2 - 8x + 20 = 0$

k $x^2 + 15x + 14 = 0$

l $x^2 - 15x + 56 = 0$

m $x^2 + 2x = 3$

n $x^2 - 4x = 5$

6 Follow these steps to sketch the graph of $y = x^2 - 7x + 12$.

a Find the points where the graph crosses the x axis.
To do this, solve the quadratic equal to 0.

$$x^2 - 7x + 12 = 0$$
$$(x \qquad)(x \qquad) = 0$$

Either $x............ = 0$ or $x............ = 0$

So $\qquad x = ...$ or $\qquad x = ...$

The graph crosses the x axis at $x = ...$ and at $x = ...$

b Find the point where the graph crosses the y axis.
To do this, put $x = 0$.

$$y = x^2 - 7x + 12$$
$$= ...$$
$$= ...$$

c Draw the axes and mark the crossing points.

d Sketch the graph.

7 Sketch graphs of these quadratic equations.

a $y = x^2 + 5x + 4$

b $y = x^2 + 5x - 6$

c $y = x^2 + x - 6$

d $y = x^2 - 5x - 6$

e $y = x^2 + 3x$

f $y = x^2 - 11x$

g $y = x^2 - 4x + 3$

h $y = x^2 + 4x - 12$

i $y = x^2 + 9x$

j $y = 9 - x^2$

k $y = x - x^2$

l $y = -x^2 + 4$

1 Look at this rectangle.

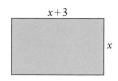

   a Write down and simplify an expression
      for the area of the rectangle.

The area of the rectangle is 10 cm^2.

   b Write down an equation using your answer to **a**.
   c Solve the equation to find two values of x.
   d Explain why only one of the values in **c** is the answer to this problem.

2 p and q are consecutive whole numbers where $p > q$.

   a Write down the value of $p - q$.
   b Factorise $p^2 - q^2$
   c Use your answers to **a** and **b** to prove that $p^2 - q^2 = p + q$.

3 Not all quadratic equations start with just x^2.
Many start with $2x^2$ or $3x^2$ etc.
If you want to solve $2x^2 - 7x + 3 = 0$ you need to start by factorising.
One of the brackets must begin with a $2x$.
This is the only way to get $2x^2$ as the first term.
So $2x^2 - 7x + 3 = (2x - ?)(x - ?)$
The two numbers at the end of the brackets must still multiply together
to give the constant term.
So you need to try different pairs of values at the end of the bracket until
you get the right answer.

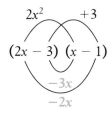

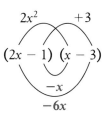

This is wrong because the
$-3x$ and the $-2x$ give you
$-5x$ and you need $-7x$.

This is right. The $-x$ and
the $-6x$ give you $-7x$.

Now you need to solve $(2x + 1)(x + 3) = 0$
Either $2x + 1 = 0$ or $x + 3 = 0$
So $x = -\frac{1}{2}$ or $x = -3$

Solve these quadratic equations.

   a $2x^2 - 5x + 2 = 0$ **d** $5x^2 + 26x + 5 = 0$
   b $2x^2 - 7x + 5 = 0$ **e** $5x^2 - 9x - 2 = 0$
   c $2x^2 + 5x + 3 = 0$ **f** $2x^2 + 3x - 9 = 0$

1 Multiply out each of these brackets.

    a $3(x + 4)$ **c** $-5(3x - 3)$

    b $x(x - 7)$ **d** $x(6x^2 + 2x)$

2 Multiply out each of these pairs of brackets.

    a $(x + 3)(x + 4)$ **c** $(2x - 5)(3x - 3)$

    b $(x + 2)(x - 7)$ **d** $(7x - 4)(6x + 2)$

3 Factorise each of these expressions.

    a $3x + 6y$ **c** $3tx - 9ty$

    b $x^2 + 3x$ **d** $15xyz - 6xz$

4 Factorise these quadratic expressions.

    a $x^2 + 5x + 6$ **c** $x^2 - 3x - 28$

    b $x^2 + 10x + 21$ **d** $x^2 + 7x - 30$

5 Solve these quadratic equations.

    a $x^2 + 8x + 15 = 0$ **c** $x^2 + 2x - 3 = 0$

    b $x^2 - 8x + 12 = 0$ **d** $x^2 - 4x - 12 = 0$

6 Sketch graphs of these quadratic equations.

    a $y = x^2 - 2x - 15$

    b $y = x^2 + 5x - 14$

7 Make the **red** letter the subject of each of these formulas.

    a $6r = 3rt + 4$ **c** $t = \dfrac{r + 4}{r}$

    b $7x + 3y = 3xt$ **d** $3z = \dfrac{4y - 3}{y}$

28 Working with errors

1 Reading scales
Reading whole number scales
Reading decimal scales

CORE

2 Rounding and estimating
Using significant figures
Using sensible accuracy
Estimating
Working out errors
Working out percentage errors

3 Error bounds
Using upper and lower bounds
Combining errors

QUESTIONS

EXTENSION

TEST YOURSELF

1 Reading scales

Police use signs to warn drivers that speed cameras are in use. They do this to stop people speeding.

When a vehicle breaks the speed limit the camera takes two pictures. The pictures show the vehicle in two positions.

Road markings are used as a scale to measure the speed of the vehicle.

Scale

A **scale** has marks on it with gaps in between.
The gaps are called divisions.
You need to work out what each division stands for to be able to read the scale.

There are 5 divisions from 0 to **10** on this scale.
$10 \div 5 = 2$, so each division stands for **2** units.

The pointer is **3** divisions from the start.
$3 \times 2 = 6$

So the number shown by the pointer is 6.

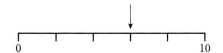

0   10

Exercise 28:1

1 Write down what the divisions stand for in each diagram.

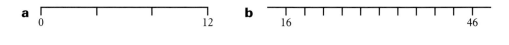

a 0   12   **b** 16   46

c 24   74

d 0   18   **e** 30   70

2 Write down the numbers shown by the pointers.

a

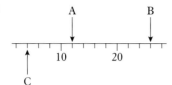

c

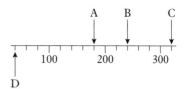

b

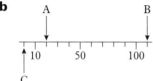

d

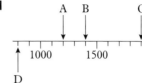

3 A computer game shows you the amount of energy that a player has left.
You start the game with a 100% energy level.
Write down the energy level of each of these players as a percentage.

a

Player A

c

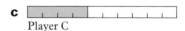
Player C

b

Player B

d

Player D

Example   This scale shows divisions in two different sizes.

0   250 g   500 g   ↓   750 g

Each large division stands for a weight of **250** g.
There are 10 small divisions between each large one.
Each small division stands for a weight of   250 g ÷ 10 = **25** g

The pointer is **4** small divisions after 500 g.

$$= 500\,g + (4 \times 25\,g)$$
$$= 500\,g + 100\,g$$
$$= 600\,g$$

The weight shown by the pointer is 600 g.

---

4 Write down the weights shown by the pointers.

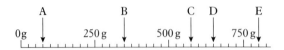

5 A measuring jug is marked with a scale in millilitres.

Some of the numbers have been rubbed off the scale.

Write down the volumes in millilitres shown by the pointers.

Examples **1** Each large division on this scale stands for 1 volt (V).
10 small divisions make 1 large division.
Each small division stands for $1 \div 10 = 0.1$ V
The pointer shows 1.3 V.

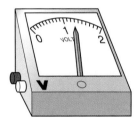

2 Each large division on this scale stands for 1 kg.
5 small divisions make 1 large division.
Each small division stands for $1 \div 5 = 0.2$ kg
The pointer shows 0.8 kg.

Exercise 28:2

In questions **1** to **7** write down the values shown by the pointers.

1

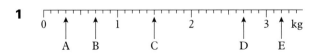

2

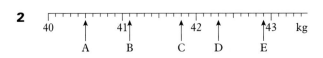

3
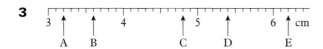

4
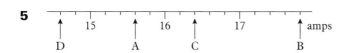

5
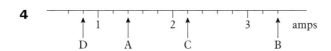

Examples Each large division on this scale stands
for 0.1 amp (A).
10 small divisions make 1 large division.
Each small division stands for
0.1 ÷ 10 = 0.01 A
The pointer shows 0.48 A

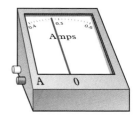

This meter measures very small forces
in newtons.
Each large division on this scale stands
for 0.01 newton (N).
10 small divisions make 1 large division.
Each small division stands for
0.01 ÷ 10 = 0.001 N
The pointer shows 0.017 N

6
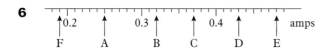

7
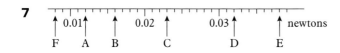

The dashboard of a sports car often has lots of different dials.

8 Write down the reading shown on each of these dials.
Remember to include the units.

a

d

b

e

c

f

2 Rounding and estimating

How tall do you think this building is?

When you answer that question you will probably give your answer to the nearest metre.

Even if you measure it you would probably only give your answer to the nearest centimetre. It would be silly to say that the height of the building is 3.494 632 m!

This would be far too accurate.
This length is given to the nearest ten thousandth of a centimetre!

You already know how to round numbers to a given number of decimal places.
3.494 632 m = 3.49 m to 2 dp. This is a sensible number of decimal places because it gives the answer to the nearest centimetre.
You have also seen how to round numbers to a given number of significant figures.
Most of the time you will be told what accuracy to use in your answers.

Significant figure
In any number the first **significant figure** is the first digit which isn't a 0. For most numbers this is the first digit.
The first significant figure is the digit in red.
21.4   0.00312   45.78   0.801

Rounding to any number of significant figures
To **round to any number of significant figures:**
(1) look at the first unwanted digit
(2) if it is 5, 6, 7, 8 or 9 add one on to the last digit
      that you are keeping
      if it is 0, 1, 2, 3 or 4 ignore it
(3) be careful to keep the number about the right size.

341.4 to 2 sf is 340. It is *not* 34!
The 1 is the first unwanted digit.
This does not change the 4 when you round.

6845.78 to 1 sf is 7000. It is *not* 7!
The 8 is the first unwanted digit.
This changes the 6 to a 7 when you round.

Exercise 28:3

1 Round these numbers to 1 significant figure.

a	18	**d**	849	**g**	8095	**j**	0.0455
b	75	**e**	5684	**h**	9999	**k**	305 567
c	276	**f**	3029	**i**	0.847	**l**	449 999

2 Round these numbers to 3 significant figures.

a	27.36	**c**	408.73	**e**	0.076 49	**g**	0.000 406 09
b	8.923	**d**	0.3462	**f**	4895	**h**	2 098 748

3 Round these calculator displays.

a *3.782497* to 3 sf   **e** *875.543784* to 3 sf

b *27.69256* to 3 sf   **f** *255643.771* to 3 sf

c *422.8673* to 3 sf   **g** *448936225* to 1 sf

d *5678.45454* to 2 sf   • **h** *3.44937 ⁰⁶* to 3 sf

4 Write down the number of significant figures in each of these numbers.

a	472	**c**	3.8457	**e**	0.02468	**g**	0.407 00
b	0.243	**d**	0.9067	**f**	4000	• **h**	$3.449\,37 \times 10^7$

5 Find these percentages. Give your answer to the nearest penny.

a	20% of £406.34	**c**	43% of £19.42	**e**	12.5% of £2189.75
b	11% of £27.89	**d**	17.5% of £98.67	**f**	94% of £81 296.70

6 These are the times that 3 tortoises take to complete a race.
Sonic boom   44.7 s   Hercules   56.4 s   Flying Scotsman   38.9 s
Find their mean time. Give your answer to 3 sf.

7 Norfolk district council has to pave the areas shown by these plans.
Work out the area of tarmac needed. Round your answers to 3 sf.

a

2.69 m

4.96 m

b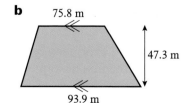

75.8 m

47.3 m

93.9 m

c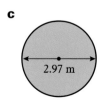

2.97 m

8 Find the lengths of the red lines on these diagrams. You will need to use Pythagoras' theorem or trigonometry. Round your answers to 2 sf.

a

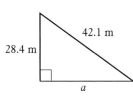

b

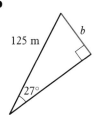

c

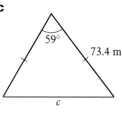

You have also seen how to estimate the answers to problems.
To get an estimate, round each number to 1 significant figure.

Example   Work out 124.9×5.2

Calculation: **1 2 4 . 9 × 5 . 2 =**

Answer: 649.48

Estimate: 124.9 is 100 to 1 sf
5.2 is 5 to 1 sf
124.9×5.2 is about $100 \times 5 = 500$
500 is near to 649.48
So the answer is probably right.

Exercise 28:4

1 Work these out. Write down the answer and an estimate for each one.
a 2.7×6.1 **c** 63×2.7 **e** 34×77 **g** 397×8.52
b 4.8×9.9 **d** 19×8.6 **f** 49×81 **h** 6.95×288

2 Work these out. Write down the answer and an estimate for each one.
a $587 \div 6.2$ **c** $8221 \div 4.31$ **e** $7965 \div 215$ ● **g** $1.9 \div 21.32$
b $901 \div 3.1$ **d** $6211 \div 5.82$ **f** $5847 \div 95.2$ ● **h** $0.0056 \div 0.032$

3 Work these out. Write down the answer and an estimate for each one.

a $\dfrac{8.2 \times 612}{38 \times 29.3}$ **c** $\dfrac{96 + 723}{38 - 29.3}$ ● **e** $\dfrac{(4.002)^3 \times 0.0498}{0.38 \times 45.3 \times 54.7}$

b $\dfrac{5145 + 4949}{4.15 \times 95.9}$ **d** $\dfrac{8199 - 5676}{0.0956 + 3.1}$ ● **f** $\dfrac{4.883\,(18^2 - 184)}{41.5 + 62.6}$

When you are estimating the answer to a question that involves a fraction there is a way of getting a much better estimate than by rounding to 1 sf.

Example   Estimate the answer to $\dfrac{65.9 \times 56.1}{42}$

If you do this question by rounding each number to 1 sf you get

$$\frac{65.9 \times 56.1}{42} \approx \frac{70 \times 60}{40} = \frac{4200}{40} = 105$$

The actual answer is 88.0 to 3 sf.
105 isn't too far from 88 but you can get much closer!
Start by rounding all of the numbers to the nearest whole number.

$$\frac{65.9 \times 56.1}{42} \approx \frac{66 \times 56}{42}$$

Now you need to be clever and see that you can split the 42 in the denominator into 6×7 and cancel the fraction like this:

$$\frac{66 \times 56}{42} = \frac{66 \times 56}{6 \times 7} = \frac{66}{6} \times \frac{56}{7} = 11 \times 8 = 88$$

This gives an excellent approximation!
To do this you must try to cancel parts of the fraction.

Example   Estimate the answer to $\dfrac{78 \times 41}{6.9 \times 8.4}$

The numbers in the denominator round to 7×8 so change the numbers in the numerator to multiples of 7 and 8.

$$\frac{78 \times 41}{6.9 \times 8.4} \approx \frac{77 \times 40}{7 \times 8} = 11 \times 5 = 55$$

For each of questions **4–12**:

a Estimate the answer by rounding so that numbers will cancel.
b Work out the exact answer using your calculator.
    Give your calculator answer to 3 significant figures if you need to round.

4 $\dfrac{24.2 \times 41.8}{42}$ **7** $\dfrac{12.7 \times 102.5}{20}$ **10** $\dfrac{36.1 \times 37.9}{4.1 \times 8.7}$

5 $\dfrac{15.3 \times 27.6}{35}$ **8** $\dfrac{33.1 \times 17}{45}$ **11** $\dfrac{19.1 \times 34.4}{3.56 \times 6.79}$

6 $\dfrac{15.8 \times 41.2}{24}$ **9** $\dfrac{35.1 \times 41.4}{6.3 \times 4.8}$ **12** $\dfrac{46.5 \times 50.8}{7.79 \times 6.25}$

Sometimes you will not be told the accuracy to use for your answers.
You will sometimes need to choose for yourself.
Use your common sense to help you!

For an exact length given in centimetres you would give no more
than 1 dp in your answer.
This would then be correct to the nearest millimetre.
For an exact length in metres you would give no more than 2 dp in your answer.
This would then be correct to the nearest centimetre.

The numbers that you are given in questions will also be a clue.
If a question has non-exact numbers given to 3 sf then you should not give more
than 3 sf in your answers.

Exercise 28:5

In each of these questions give your answer to a sensible degree of accuracy.

1   6 boxes of coloured paper are laid
end to end on a shelf.
They are all the same length.
The shelf is 95 cm long.
Work out the length of each box.

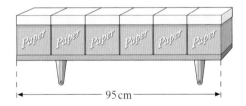

2   This stack of drums is 6 drums high.
The stack is 4 m high.
Work out the height of each drum.

3   9 cyclists are in a relay team. The team has to cycle in a race 85 km long.
Each cyclist rides the same distance. How far does each one ride?

4 For each pair of numbers:
   (1) write down the number of significant figures they have
   (2) work out the calculation.

   a 270×49 **f** $0.009\,82 \div 36.8$
   b $920 \div 75$ **g** $7435 \times 0.086\,27$
   c 4.79×2.36 ● **h** $0.900 \div 0.0450$
   d $86.4 \div 9.86$ **i** $0.001 \div 0.000\,09$
   e 0.0987×4.92 ● **j** $2.3 \times 10^8 \times 3.9 \times 10^4$

5 Jenny invests £122. The interest rate is 7.3% per annum.
Find the amount of money she has at the end of 1 year.

6 Work out the length marked with a letter in each of these.

a
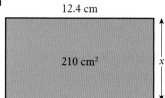
12.4 cm
210 cm²
x

● **b**
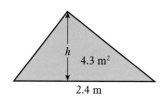
h
4.3 m²
2.4 m

● **7** The diagrams show two parks planned in Adelaide.
Work out the lengths of the paths shown by red dotted lines.
You will need to use Pythagoras' theorem.

a
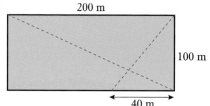
200 m
100 m
40 m

b   O is the centre
    of the circle.
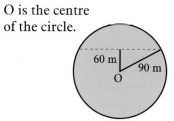
60 m
90 m
O

Error

The difference between an exact answer and an estimate is called an **error**.

Always make the error positive by taking the smaller number away from the bigger number.
It's the size of the error that's important.

Exercise 28:6

1 **a** Estimate the answer to 4.8 × 9.5 by rounding each number to 1 sf.
 b Work out the exact answer using your calculator.
 c Work out the error using your estimate and your exact answer.

2 **a** Estimate the answer to 289 ÷ 17 by rounding each value to 1 sf.
 b Work out the exact answer using your calculator.
 c Work out the error using your estimate and your exact answer.

3 Prasad guesses the number of sweets in a sweet jar.
 He guesses 1000. There are actually 990 sweets.
 a Work out his error.
 Tara guesses the number of sweets in a bag.
 She guesses 100. There are actually 90 sweets.
 b Work out her error.
 c Who has made the bigger error?
 Explain your answer.

4 Cutthroat Colin and Captain Goodfellow
 are having a contest.
 Whoever loses will have to walk the plank!
 They both have to estimate the height of a mast.
 Cutthroat Colin estimates the mizzen mast to
 be 24 feet high.
 It is actually 20 feet high.
 a Work out his error.
 Captain Goodfellow estimates the main mast
 to be 80 feet high.
 It is actually 76 feet high.
 b Work out his error.
 c Who has made the bigger error?
 Should either walk the plank!?

5 **a** Estimate the answer to $\dfrac{84 \times 56}{96}$ by rounding each value to 1 sf.

 b Work out the exact answer using your calculator.
 c Work out the error using your estimate and your exact answer.
 d Estimate the answer to $\dfrac{2.025 \times 0.6}{0.243}$ by rounding each value to 1 sf.

 e Work out the exact answer using your calculator.
 f Work out the error using your estimate and your exact answer.
 g Which estimate gives the bigger error; part **c** or part **f**?
 • **h** Can you think of a better way of measuring the amount of error if
 you make an estimate?

Percentage error The **percentage error** gives you a better idea of the size of an error.

$$\text{Percentage error} = \frac{\text{error}}{\text{exact value}} \times 100\%$$

You always work out a percentage error as a percentage of the exact value.

Example The exact value of a length is 3.473 m.
John measures the length and gets 3.45 m.
Work out his percentage error.

$$\text{Percentage error} = \frac{3.473 - 3.45}{3.473} \times 100\%$$

$$= 0.66\% \text{ to 2 sf}$$

Exercise 28:7

1 The table gives the exact answers and the estimated answers of some calculations. Find (1) the error (2) the percentage error for each part.

	Estimate	Exact answer
a	20	25
b	42	39.8946
c	60 000	66 048
d	0.025	0.024

2 Chris enters a competition at a fete to guess the number of potatoes in a bag. He estimates that there are 384 potatoes. There are in fact 392 potatoes but he still wins the competition with the best estimate. What was the percentage error in his answer?

3 For each shape:
  (1) Estimate the area by rounding each length to 1 sf.
  (2) Calculate the exact answer.
  (3) Work out the percentage error of the estimate.

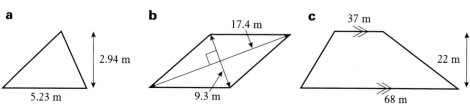

a 2.94 m, 5.23 m

b 17.4 m, 9.3 m

c 37 m, 22 m, 68 m

3   Error bounds

When you put a plug in a plug hole you are happy to assume that it will fit!
When plugs are made they have to be made accurately so that you will not be disappointed!
The plug does not have to be *exactly* the right size.
There is a small error that is allowed.
This is called a tolerance.
A plug would probably fit if it is 0.5 mm too small.
But it won't fit if it is 2 cm too small!

The width of a plug is given as 30 mm to the nearest millimetre.
This does not mean that it is exactly 30 mm.
The width could be anywhere from 29.5 mm right up to but not including 30.5 mm.
You can show this on a number line.

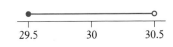

$$29.5 \leqslant \text{width} < 30.5$$

Lower bound   29.5 is called the **lower bound**.
It is the smallest number that will round up to 30.

Upper bound   30.5 is called the **upper bound**.
The largest number that will round down to 30 mm is 30.499 999 99…
You can't use this value as it's too complicated.
So 30.5 is used as the upper bound even though 30.5 would round up to 31 to the nearest whole number.

Exercise 28:8

1   Which of these masses would round to 5 kg to the nearest kilogram?
    a   4.95 kg   **c**   4.5 kg   **e**   4.55 kg   **g**   5.504 kg
    b   5.05 kg   **d**   5.4 kg   **f**   4.45 kg   **h**   4.49 kg

2 To leave the factory, cans must be 454 g to the nearest gram.
These are the masses of some cans. Which are acceptable?

a 454.1 g	**c** 454.4 g	**e** 455 g	**g** 454.06 g
b 450 g	**d** 453 g	**f** 453.49 g	**h** 453.549 g

3 Jean gives a number correct to the nearest unit.
What is the maximum error in her corrected number?

4 Henry has to make some steel cables.
The cables must be 24 m long to the nearest metre.
a What is the greatest error he can make in this measurement?
The cables must be 17 mm in diameter to the nearest millimetre.
b What is the greatest error he can make in this measurement?

5 Each of these numbers is correct to the nearest whole number.
Work out the lower and upper bounds for each number.
Show your answers on a number line.

a 4	**c** 15	**e** 50	**g** 400
b 7	**d** 24	**f** 249	**h** 1004

Example   Write down the lower bound and the upper bound for each of these numbers.

a 240 which is correct to the nearest ten.
b 3.6 which is correct to 1 dp.

a The smallest number that will round up to 240 is 235. So the lower bound is 235. The largest number that will round down to 240 is 244.999 99...
So the upper bound is 245.

b The smallest number that will round up to 3.6 is 3.55
So the lower bound is 3.55
The largest number that will round down to 3.6 is 3.649 99...
So the upper bound is 3.65.

6 Each of these numbers is correct to the nearest ten.
Work out the lower and upper bounds for each number.
- **a** 250
- **b** 40
- **c** 80
- **d** 160
- **e** 100
- **f** 2040
- **g** 4890
- **h** 6000

7 Each of these lengths is correct to 1 decimal place.
Work out the lower and upper bounds for each length.
- **a** 1.8 m
- **b** 5.2 cm
- **c** 6.8 km
- **d** 3.5 mm
- **e** 29.6 mm
- **f** 278.4 cm
- **g** 0.5 km
- **h** 197.0 miles

8 Simon buys a piece of wood at a DIY store.
It is marked as 2.4 m long.
Assume this length is correct to 1 dp.
Write down:
- **a** the lower bound of the length
- **b** the upper bound of the length.

Now take the marked value as the exact
value of the length.
Calculate the percentage error in using:
- **c** the lower bound in part **a**
- **d** the upper bound in part **b**

for the length.
- **e** Write down what you notice about your answers.

9 The radius of the earth is given as 6380 km
to the nearest 10 km.
Write down:
- **a** the lower bound of the radius
- **b** the upper bound of the radius.

Now take the given value as the exact
value of the radius.
Calculate the percentage error in using:
- **c** the lower bound in part **a**
- **d** the upper bound in part **b**

for the radius.
- **e** Write down what you notice about your answers.

10 Work out the lower and upper bounds for each of these masses.
The accuracy of each mass is given in brackets.
- **a** 600 g   (nearest 100 g)
- **b** 3700 g   (nearest 100 g)
- **c** 0.42 mg   (nearest 0.01 mg)
- **d** 25 000 tonnes   (nearest 1000 tonnes)

There is a quick way of remembering how to work out the lower and upper bounds.

If you have a number correct to the nearest 10 then
> the lower bound is 5 less than this number
and the upper bound is 5 more than this number.   5 is half of 10

If you have a number correct to the nearest unit then
> the lower bound is 0.5 less than this number
and the upper bound is 0.5 more than this number.   0.5 is half of 1

If you have a number correct to the nearest 0.1
(which is the same as being correct to 1 dp) then
> the lower bound is 0.05 less than this number
and the upper bound is 0.05 more than this number.   0.05 is half of 0.1

The amount you take away to get the lower bound and add to get the upper bound is half of the place value of the accuracy.

Exercise 28:9

1 Write down the amount that you need to subtract from these numbers to get the lower bound. The accuracy of each number is given in brackets.

a	560	(nearest 10)		**e**	4000	(nearest 1000)
b	3600	(nearest 100)		**f**	278 000	(nearest 1000)
c	25.7	(nearest 0.1)		**g**	0.007	(nearest 0.001)
d	0.04	(nearest 0.01)	●	**h**	480 000	(nearest 10 000)

2 Write down the amount that you need to add to these numbers to get the upper bound. The accuracy of each number is given in brackets.

a	280	(nearest 10)		**e**	8000	(nearest 1000)
b	9200	(nearest 100)		**f**	45 000	(nearest 1000)
c	0.8	(nearest 0.1)		**g**	6.483	(nearest 0.001)
d	0.65	(nearest 0.01)	●	**h**	70 000	(nearest 1000)

3 Work out the lower and upper bounds for each of these populations. The accuracy of each population is given in brackets.

	Town	Population	
a	Gillingham	40 000	(nearest 10 000)
b	Plymouth	300 000	(nearest 100 000)
c	London	7 000 000	(nearest 1 000 000)

Sometimes numbers are given correct to a number of significant figures.
With these look carefully at the last significant figure to see its place value.

Example   Write down the lower and upper bounds of these masses.
Each value is correct to the number of significant figures in brackets.
a 440 g (2 sf)   **b** 0.246 kg (3 sf)

a The place value of the 2nd significant figure is tens.
So 440 g is correct to the nearest 10.
So   the lower bound is 435 g
and   the upper bound is 445 g

b The place value of the 3rd significant figure is thousandths.
So 0.246 kg is correct to the nearest 0.001.
So   the lower bound is 0.2455 g
and   the upper bound is 0.2465 g

4   Work out the lower and upper bounds for each value.
The accuracy of each number is given in brackets.
a   a length of 0.42 cm   (2 sf)
b   a mass of 4260 kg   (3 sf)
c   a diameter of 6.42 km   (3 sf)
d   a population of 20 000   (1 sf)
e   a length of 0.04 m   (1 sf)
f   a capacity of 2100 ml   (2 sf)
g   a distance of 29.6 miles   (3 sf)
h   an area of 400 000 m^2 (1 sf)

5   Write down the amount that you need to subtract from these values to
get the lower bound.
a   a length of 0.006 mm   (1 sf)
● **b**   a diameter of 1.2×10^{-6} m   (2 sf)

6   Write down the amount that you need to add to these values to
get the upper bound.
a   a length of 0.095 cm   (2 sf)
● **b**   a speed of 5.32×10^4 m/s   (3 sf)

Combining errors

When you start doing calculations with lengths that are only
correct to a given accuracy you must be careful!
As soon as you add lengths or multiply lengths together you
make the errors much worse.
You need to be able to work out the combined error.

Example   Terry is the caretaker at a Primary school.
He is making a playground for the pupils.
He needs to cover the ground with
tarmac.
He also wants to put a fence around
the ground.
He has measured the ground as a
rectangle that is 45 m by 33 m.
His measurements are correct to the
nearest metre.

a What are the lower and upper bounds for the length of the fencing?
b What are the lower and upper bounds for the area that needs to be
covered in tarmac?

a The length of the rectangle is 45 m.
length lower bound = **44.5**   length upper bound = 45.5
The width of the rectangle is 33 m.
width lower bound = **32.5**   width upper bound = 33.5

The perimeter is 2 lengths and 2 widths added together.
The lower bound is obtained by finding the smallest possible length.
Perimeter lower bound = 2 × 44.5 + 2 × 32.5 = 154 m.
The upper bound is obtained by finding the largest possible length.
Perimeter upper bound = 2 × 45.5 + 2 × 33.5 = 158 m.

b The area of the ground is the length multiplied by the width.
The lower bound is obtained by finding the smallest possible area.
Area lower bound = 44.5 × 32.5 = 1446.25 m².
The upper bound is obtained by finding the largest possible area.
Area upper bound = 45.5 × 33.5 = 1524.25 m².

Exercise 28:10

1 Each of these plans shows a playground. All lengths are correct to the
nearest metre. For each playground work out:
(1) the lower and upper bounds of each length
(2) the maximum and minimum perimeter
(3) the maximum and minimum area.

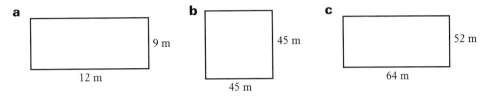

a 9 m 12 m

b 45 m 45 m

c 52 m 64 m

2 Simon has gone back to the DIY store. He buys 2 pieces of wood.
One is marked 3.2 m long, and the other is marked 1.8 m long.
Both lengths are correct to the nearest 0.1 m.
a Write down the lower and upper bounds of each of these lengths.
b What is the maximum value of the lengths added together?
c What is the minimum value of the lengths added together?

3 A football pitch has a length of 102 m and a
width of 72 m.
Each length is correct to the nearest metre.
Jason has to mark the perimeter with white lines.
He also has to re-seed the grass for the next season.
What are the upper and lower bounds for:
a the length of the pitch
b the width of the pitch
c the perimeter of the pitch
d the area that needs to be re-seeded?

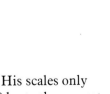

If the original measurements are exact what is
the percentage error in using:
● **e** the lower bound of the area in part **d** for the area?
● **f** the upper bound of the area in part **d** for the area?

● **4** Eddie is loading a van with 40 bags of brussel sprouts. His scales only
weigh to the nearest 2 kg. He is sure that each bag is 20 kg to the nearest
2 kg. What are the lower and upper bounds for
a the mass of each bag
b the total mass in the van?

1 Write down what the divisions stand for in each diagram.

a

```
┌─────┬─────┬─────┬─────┬─────┐
0                             15
```

b

```
      16            40
```

2 Write down the values shown by the pointers.

a

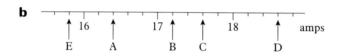

b

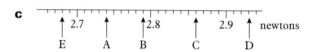

c

```
    ↑ 2.7   ↑   ↑2.8    ↑    2.9  ↑  newtons
    E       A   B       C        D
```

3 Round these calculator displays.

a 58.34497 to 3 sf

b 4097.560836 to 3 sf

c 0.03989898 to 2 sf

d 0.00027366 to 1 sf

e 60.8422611 to 4 sf

f 0.030303030 to 3 sf

g 6.9270909 to 2 sf

h 5.25511 to 3 sf

4 Work these out. Write down the answer and an estimate for each one.

  a 4.9 × 8.2   **c** 807 ÷ 4.1   **e** 46 × 72   **g** 9025 ÷ 317

  b 12.3 × 9.4   **d** 614 ÷ 2.9   **f** 8.69 × 496   **h** 0.0803 ÷ 0.0042

5 This stack of cans is 11 cans high.
The stack is 78 cm high.
Work out the height of each can.

232

6   A bus is designed so that the volume of space for passengers is 40 m³.
Each passenger needs 0.96 m³ of space.
How many passengers can the bus hold?

7   Work out the distances marked with letters.
You will need to use Pythagoras' theorem.

a

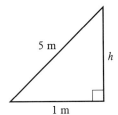

b

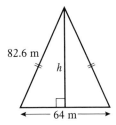

8   **a**   Estimate the answer to 696 ÷ 24 by rounding each value to 1 sf.
  b   Work out the exact answer using your calculator.
  c   Work out the error using your estimate and your exact answer.

9   Planks must be 340 cm long to the nearest centimetre.
These are the lengths of some planks. Which are acceptable?

  a   300 cm   **c**   335 cm   **e**   341 cm   **g**   339 cm
  b   345 cm   **d**   340.4 cm   **f**   339.7 cm   **h**   340.05 cm

10   Give the area of each of these shapes to a sensible degree of accuracy.

  a

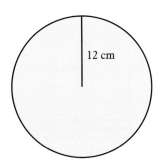

  b

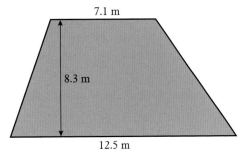

11 Work out the lower and upper bounds for each length.
The accuracy of each length is given in brackets.

    a 5 cm   (nearest cm)   **e** 8.72 mm   (nearest 0.01 mm)

    b 892 m   (nearest m)   **f** 4600 km   (nearest 100 km)

    c 70 m   (nearest 10 m)   **g** 25 000 000 km   (nearest 1 000 000 km)

    d 2.6 cm   (nearest 0.1 cm)   **h** 0.0009 mm   (nearest 0.0001 mm)

12 Work out the lower and upper bounds for each mass.
The accuracy of each mass is given in brackets.

    a 20 g   (1 sf)   **e** 45 mg   (2 sf)

    b 780 kg   (2 sf)   **f** 200 tonnes   (1 sf)

    c 0.05 kg   (1 sf)   **g** 25 000 tonnes   (2 sf)

    d 0.0007 mg   (1 sf)   **h** 2.4×10^7 tonnes   (2 sf)

13 Roger is a weatherman.
He measures the temperature on the weather station thermometer.
He records it in his notebook as −5.2 °C.

    a Show the lower and upper bounds of this temperature on a
       number line.

Now take −5.2 °C as the exact value.

    b Calculate the percentage error in using:
       (1) the lower bound   (2) the upper bound
       for the temperature.

    c Write down what you notice about your answers.

14 This is a plan of a playground.
All of the lengths are correct to the
nearest metre.

    a Work out the lower and upper
       bounds of the length of each side.

    b Work out the maximum and
       minimum perimeter.

    c Work out the maximum and
       minimum area.

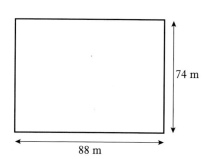

74 m

88 m

1 Write down the values shown by the pointers.

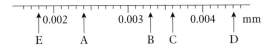

2 Jane enters a competition at a football match
to guess the size of the crowd.
She estimates that there are 22 500 people.
There are in fact 21 756 people but she still
wins a prize for the best estimate.
What was the percentage error in her answer?

3 Bob is loading a trailer with sacks of potatoes. His scales only weigh to
the nearest 2 kg. He is sure each sack is 50 kg to the nearest 2 kg.

  a What are the lower and upper bounds for the mass of each bag?

The trailer will carry a mass of *exactly* 7 tonnes. It has a gauge which
measures the mass on the trailer *very accurately*.

  b What is the greatest number of sacks that Bob can put on the trailer?

4 Robert has a piece of copper piping 3.32 m long to the nearest centimetre.
He cuts a piece of pipe from this 1.24 m long to the nearest millimetre.

  a Give the lower and upper bounds of each piece of pipe.

Use your answers to **a** to work out:

  b the maximum length of the remaining pipe

  c the minimum length of the remaining pipe.

5 Jean has recorded his distances and times for
2 sections of a racing circuit.
(1) 1.5 km   55.4 s   (2) 1.8 km   67.2 s
Each time is correct to the nearest 0.1 s.
Each distance is correct to the nearest 0.1 km.
For each section work out:

  a the greatest and least possible distances

  b the greatest and least possible times

  c Jean's greatest and least possible average speeds.

1 Write down the values shown by the pointers.

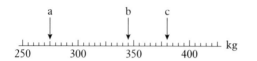
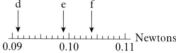

2 Round these numbers.

  a 3.5983 to 2 dp   **c** 346 000 to 2 sf   **e** 0.090 057 42 to 3 sf

  b 0.050 682 3 to 3 sf   **d** 600 070 to 4 sf   **f** 0.899 963 to 3 dp.

3 Work these out. Write down the answer and an estimate for each one. Show clearly how you get your estimates. Use factors for part **b**.

  a $\dfrac{5.085 \times 4.471^2}{32.078 - 19.46}$ **b** $\dfrac{62.83 \times 48.4}{6.71 \times 11.98}$

4 The size of a crowd at a rally is given as 38 000 to the nearest thousand.

  a What is the smallest number of people that could have attended the rally?

  b What is the largest possible number of people?

5 For this triangle:

  a Estimate the area by rounding each length to 1 sf.

  b Calculate the exact answer.

  c Work out the percentage error of the estimate. Give your answer to 2 sf.

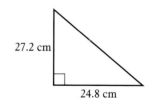

27.2 cm

24.8 cm

6 Jamie is using the formula $v = u - 4t$ in a physics experiment. He measures u as 23 to 2 sf and t as 4.9 to 1 dp. Work out the lower and upper bounds for v.

7 $P = 34$ to 2 sf $Q = 5.71$ to 2 dp $R = 0.5$ to 1 sf
Work out the lower and upper bounds for:

  a $5P$ **c** $Q \div R$

  b $P - Q$ **d** $3P - 4Q$

29 Percentages and decimals

1 Using multipliers
Finding terms of a sequence
Using a calculator to produce sequences
Doing percentage change using multipliers
Increasing and decreasing using multipliers
Reversing percentage change

CORE

2 Finance
Working out tax
Working out compound interest
Working out car insurance payments

QUESTIONS

EXTENSION

TEST YOURSELF

1   Using multipliers

Ivan has a large sheet of paper.

He tears the sheet in half and puts the two pieces on top of each other.
Then he tears the two pieces in half and puts all four pieces on top of each other.

He plans to do this 50 times.

Estimate how high his stack of paper would be.

1000 pieces of paper make a stack that is about 4 inches high.

Multiplier	In the sequence 1, 2, 4, 8, 16, ... each new term is **2 ×** the previous term. The number **2** is the **multiplier** for the sequence.

Example   Write down the first five terms of the sequence with first term 5 and multiplier 3.

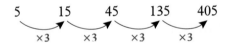

$$5 \qquad 15 \qquad 45 \qquad 135 \qquad 405$$
$$\times 3 \quad \times 3 \quad \times 3 \quad \times 3$$

The first five terms are 5, 15, 45, 135 and 405.

Exercise 29:1

1   For each of these sequences write down:
(1) the multiplier.
(2) the next two terms.

a 7, 14, 28, 56, ...

b 1, 3, 9, 27, ...

c 2, 10, 50, 250, ...

d 0.0003, 0.003, 0.03, 0.3, ...

● **e** 8, 20, 50, 125, ...

f 128, 64, 32, 16, ...

g 81, 27, 9, 3, ...

h 3125, 625, 125, 25, ...

i 1, 0.1, 0.01, 0.001, ...

● **j** 162, 108, 72, 48, ...

2 Find the two missing terms in each of these sequences.
  a 1, ..., 25, ..., 625
  b 8, ..., ..., 64, 128
  c 48, ..., 12, ..., 3
  d 16, 24, ..., 54, ...
  e 50, 55, ..., 66.55, ...
  ● **f** 0.96, ..., 0.24, ...

3 Use the information to write down the first 5 terms of each sequence.
  a first term: 6, multiplier: 5
  b first term: 0.5, multiplier: 4
  ● **c** first term: 9, multiplier: −2
  d first term: 21, multiplier: 3
  e first term: 54, multiplier: $\frac{1}{3}$
  f second term: 16, multiplier 4

You can use your calculator to produce a number sequence.
This is useful if you want to work out a lot of terms.

Example   Use your calculator to produce the sequence 1, 2, 4, 8, 16, ...

You need to enter the first term and the multiplier.

Key in:

 1 **=**

2 **Ans** **=** **=** **=**

You may need to experiment to find the right key sequence.
If the one above doesn't work then try these:

2 **×** **1** **=** **=** **=**

or   **2** **×** **×** **1** **=** **=** **=**

or   **2** **×** **→** **1** **=** **=** **=**

or   **2** **×** **K** **1** **=** **=** **=**

Exercise 29:2

1 The first term of a sequence is 4.
  Find the twentieth term when the multiplier is:
  a 2   **b** 1.2   **c** 0.8   **d** 0.6
  Give your answers correct to 3 sf.

2 The first term of a sequence is 100. Look at the sequence produced on your calculator when the multiplier is:

  a 0.5   **b** 1   **c** 1.5

Write down what is happening to the terms in each sequence.

3 Under ideal conditions a sample of bacteria doubles its population every $\frac{1}{2}$ hour. Use your calculator to produce a sequence to show how the population changes. Start from a single cell.

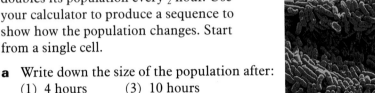

  a Write down the size of the population after:
    (1) 4 hours   (3) 10 hours
    (2) 6 hours   (4) 15 hours

After 1 hour the population can be written as 2^2
After 2 hours the population can be written as 2^4

  b Write the population as a power of 2 after:
    (1) 3 hours   (2) 10 hours   ● (3) n hours

4 Look again at the puzzle given at the start of the chapter. One way to find the number of sheets of paper is to continue the sequence 2, 4, 8, 16, … to find the 50th term. Even with a calculator this can take time but there is a quick way.

  a Write each of the first 4 terms as a power of 2.

  b Write the 50th term in the same way.

  c Use the $\boxed{x^y}$ or $\boxed{y^x}$ key on your calculator to get the value of the 50th term.

The answer is too big for the calculator to display in the usual way so the calculator shows it in standard form.

  d Write down the value of the 50th term. Remember that there is a special way to write a number in standard form. Don't just copy the display.

  e Divide the answer by 1000 and multiply by 4 to find the height of the stack in inches. Write it down.

  f Divide your last answer by 36 to find the height of the stack in yards. Write it down.

  g Divide your last answer by 1760 to find the height of the stack in miles. Write down your answer to the nearest million!

You can use multipliers to help you do percentage calculations.

Example Find the value of:

a 40% of 320 kg **b** 17.5% of £67

a Change 40% to a decimal

$$40\% = \frac{40}{100} = 0.4$$

Use 0.4 as a multiplier

$$40\% \text{ of } 320 \text{ kg} = 0.4 \times 320 \text{ kg}$$
$$= 128 \text{ kg}$$

b Change 17.5% to a decimal

$$17.5\% = \frac{17.5}{100} = 0.175$$

Use 0.175 as a multiplier

$$17.5\% \text{ of } £67 = 0.175 \times £67$$
$$= £11.725$$

Round the answer

$$= £11.73$$

to the nearest penny.

Exercise 29:3

1 **a** Write down the multiplier for working out 12% of an amount.
  b Work out 12% of each of these.

(1) 56 m	(4) £81	(7) 470 m²
(2) 211 kg	(5) £73.50	(8) 8000 cm³
(3) 87.4 cm	(6) £65	(9) 0.49 km

2 **a** Write down the multiplier for working out 7% of an amount.
  b Work out 7% of each of these.

(1) 91 mg	(4) 86.4 m/s	● (7) 1.2×10^{16} miles
(2) 705 m	(5) 2300 mm	● (8) 6.73×10^{19} m
(3) 2.6 km	(6) £18 650	● (9) 5.8×10^{-23} kg

3 Jill earns 9.5% commission on the price of goods that she sells. Work out how much she earns on each of these items. Give your answers to the nearest penny when you need to round.

a	jacket	£39.50	**d**	computer	£1179
b	suit	£174.99	**e**	carpet	£864.43
c	camera	£269.90	**f**	bicycle	£248.75

Questions **4–6** are about endangered species.

4 Black rhinos are hunted for their
valuable horns.
In 1970 there were about 40 000
black rhinos living in Africa.
The population of black rhinos is
now only 5% of this value.
How many black rhinos are left?

5 The blue whale is the largest
mammal on Earth.
The population of blue whales
was about 250 000 at the start of
the 20th century.
The population of blue whales is
now only 0.4% of this value.
How many blue whales are left?

6 In 1975 there were about 24 000
Arctic caribou living in Canada.
By 1985 the number was 35% of
this value.
By 1995 the number was 35% of
the 1985 value.
Copy the diagram below.
Fill in the missing values.
How many Arctic caribou were
left in 1995?

Year	1975		1985		1995
Number of caribou	24 000	$\longrightarrow$ $\times \ldots$	...	$\longrightarrow$ $\times \ldots$	...

To reduce an amount by a percentage the multiplier will always be between 0 and 1.

Example   A chocolate bar weighs 250 g. Ben eats 15% of the bar.
    a Find the multiplier for reducing an amount by 15%.
    b Use the multiplier to work out how much chocolate he has left.

    a Ben starts with 100% of the chocolate bar.
        He eats 15% of the bar so the percentage
        that he has left is 100% − 15% = 85%

$$85\% = \frac{85}{100} = 0.85$$

        so the multiplier is 0.85

    b The amount he has left is 0.85 × 250 g = 212.5 g

Exercise 29:4

1 Write down the multiplier for reducing an amount by:
    a 25%   **c** 68%   **e** 17.5%
    b 30%   **d** 94%   **f** 1.6%

2 Li won a cash prize of £4000. He spent 36% of it and saved the rest.
    a What percentage did he save?
    b How much money did he save?

3 A farmer owns 120 acres of land. He sells 35% to a property developer.
    a What percentage of land does the farmer have left?
    b How many acres of land does the farmer have left?

4 In a sale, all items are reduced in price by 12.5%.
    a Find the multiplier for reducing an amount by 12.5%.
    b Find the sale price for each of these original prices.
        Give your answers to the nearest penny when you need to round.
        (1) £18   (2) £63   (3) £41.50   (4) £149.99

5 Last year Martin earned £24 000. Lisa earned 15% less than Martin.
    Alex earned 15% less than Lisa.
    a Complete this calculation to find out how much Alex earned.

        £24 000 × … × … = …

    b Is it true that Alex earned 30% less than Martin? Explain your answer.

To increase an amount by a percentage the multiplier will be bigger than 1.

Example   **a** Find the multiplier for increasing an amount by 17.5%.
                        b VAT charged at 17.5% is added to a bill of £67.
                        Calculate the total amount to be paid.

a

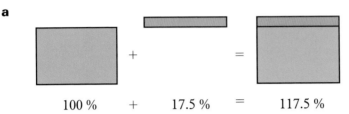

100 %   +   17.5 %   =   117.5 %

The final amount is 117.5% of the original amount

$$117.5\% = \frac{117.5}{100} = 1.175 \text{ so the multiplier is } 1.175$$

b Total paid $= 1.175 \times £67 = £78.725$
                                  $= £78.73$ to the nearest penny.

Exercise 29:5

1 Write down the multiplier to increase an amount by:
    a 3%   **d** 87%   **g** 12.5%
    b 21%   **e** 100%   **h** 37.5%
    c 0.9%   **f** 120%   ● **i** 246%

2 Add VAT at 17.5% to each of these amounts.
    a £14   **b** £98   **c** £2140   **d** £60 000

3 Last year 2500 tickets were sold for a firework display. This year ticket sales increased by 8%. How many tickets have been sold?

4 Jenny earns £1400 each month. How much will she earn per month after a pay rise of 2.6%?

● **5** To qualify for a formula 1 Grand Prix race, a driver must complete the circuit within 107% of the pole position time. In the 1997 Australian Grand Prix, Jack Villeneuve took pole position with a lap time of 1 minute 29.369 seconds. Find the qualifying time to the nearest 1/1000th second.

6 Jason earned £11 400 during his first year at work.
He had a pay rise of 6% for his second year.
Jason then had another pay rise of 8% for his third year.
Complete this calculation to find how much Jason earned in his third year.

$$£11\,400 \times \ldots \times \ldots = \ldots$$

7 In January 1995 the number of computers on
the Internet reached 5 000 000. This number
was increasing at the rate of 9% per month.
Complete this calculation to find the number of
computers on the Internet three months later.

$$5\,000\,000 \times \ldots \times \ldots \times \ldots = \ldots$$

The complete package

PC + Modem + Internet
starter software
Yours for only £699+VAT

Example The cost of a holiday in May is £2000.
The same holiday costs 64% more in August.
The price is then reduced by 52% in September.
How much does the holiday cost in September?

The multiplier for an increase of 64% is 1.64
The multiplier for a reduction of 52% is 0.48

You need to use both multipliers to find the answer.
£2000 × 1.64 × 0.48 = £1574.40

The holiday costs £1574.40 in September.

---

8 The cost of a holiday in July is £1800.
The same holiday costs 25% more in August.
The price is then reduced by 35% in September.
How much does the holiday cost in September?

9 Paula bought her house for £60 000 in 1989.
The value of the house had fallen by 17% in 1992.
The value then increased by 24% in 1995.
What was the value of the house in 1995?

You can use multipliers to undo a percentage change.

Example   The cost of a computer is £1163.25 including VAT at 17.5%.
What was the price before VAT was added?

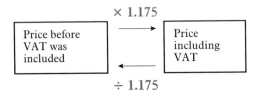

You need to divide to undo a percentage change.

The price before VAT was added = £1163.25 ÷ 1.175 = £990

Exercise 29:6

1 Each of these prices includes VAT at 17.5%
Find the price before VAT was added.
a £58.75   **b** £112.80   **c** £28 200   **d** £399.50

2 All prices are reduced by 15%
in a sale at a computer store.

a Copy the diagram.
Fill in the missing values.
b Find the original price for
each of these sale prices.
(1) £53.72   (2) £84.15   (3) £9.69   (4) £246.16

3 Over a period of 33 years the world record for the long jump had
improved by less than 23 cm. Then one day in 1968, Bob Beamon
improved the record by 6.587% to 8.90 m.
a What was the record that Beamon broke?
b How much further did he jump?

4 When Steve Cram broke the world record for the mile in 1985 he
achieved a time of 3 minutes 46.32 seconds. Cram had reduced the time
set by Roger Bannister in 1954 by 5.464%.
a What was Bannister's time to the nearest tenth of a second?
b Why was Bannister's time so significant?

2   Finance

You pay income tax on money that you earn.

Tax allowance   You can earn a certain amount of money before you start to pay tax. This amount is called your **tax allowance**.

Taxable income   You take your tax allowance from what you earn to find your **taxable income**.

Example   Andy earns £8420 in one year. His tax allowance is £4000. What is his taxable income?

Earnings	£8420
− Tax allowance	£4000
Taxable income	£4420

Exercise 29:7

1   Work out the taxable income on these amounts.

a	Earnings	£8140
	Tax allowance	£5680
	Taxable income	

b	Earnings	£7250
	Tax allowance	£3980
	Taxable income	

2   Copy these. Fill in the gaps.

a	Earnings	£5230
	Tax allowance	£3875
	Taxable income	

c	Earnings	
	Tax allowance	£3980
	Taxable income	£1645

b	Earnings	£6496
	Tax allowance	
	Taxable income	£2671

d	Earnings	£9735
	Tax allowance	
	Taxable income	£4675

There are three rates of income tax: 10%, 22% and 40%.
The amount of tax that you pay depends on your taxable income.

Example   Denise earned £7560 last year. Her tax allowance was £4200.
She paid tax at the 10% rate. How much did she pay?

	£
First you find her taxable income	7560
	−4200
Her taxable income was £3360.	3360

She paid **10%** of this in tax.

Change 10% to a decimal $10\% = \dfrac{10}{100} = 0.1$

Multiply £3360 by **0.1** $10\% \text{ of } £3360 = 0.1 \times £3360$
$$= £336$$

Denise paid £336 in tax.

---

3   Copy the table. Fill in the last two columns.

Name	Earnings	Tax allowance	Taxable income	Tax paid at 10%
Karen	£6842	£4010		
Jo	£5237	£3995		
Noel	£7320	£4689		
Simon	£6107	£4256		
Kath	£11 986	£7482		
Andy	£7965	£5450		

4   Steph and Sally both earn the same amount.
Steph has a tax allowance of £4780. Sally has a tax allowance of £5620.
Who pays more tax? Explain your answer.

If your taxable income is more than £4300 then you start to pay tax at the 22% rate.

Example Jessica earned £18 460 last year.
She had a tax allowance of £7200.
Jessica paid tax at 10% on the first £4300 of her taxable income.
She paid tax at 22% on the rest.

  a How much tax did she pay at the 10% rate?
  b How much tax did she pay at the 22% rate?
  c How much tax did Jessica pay altogether?

a First you find her taxable income.

$$\begin{array}{r} £ \\ 18\ 460 \\ -\ \ 7200 \\ \hline 11\ 260 \end{array}$$

Her taxable income was **£11 260**

She paid tax at the 10% rate on the
first £4300 of this amount.

Multiply £4300 by 0.1

$$10\% \text{ of } £4300 = 0.1 \times £4300 = £430$$

She paid **£430** at the 10% rate

b Find the amount taxed at 22%.

$$\begin{array}{r} £ \\ 11\ 260 \\ -\ \ 4300 \\ \hline 6960 \end{array}$$

She paid tax on **£6960** at the 22% rate.

Write 22% as a decimal.

$$22\% = \frac{22}{100} = 0.22$$

Multiply £6960 by 0.22

$$22\% \text{ of } £6960 = 0.22 \times £6960 = £1531.20$$

Jessica paid **£1531.20** at the 22% rate.

c Add together the amounts paid at the
different rates.

$$\begin{array}{r} £ \\ 1531.20 \\ +\ \ 430.00 \\ \hline 1961.20 \end{array}$$

Jessica paid **£1961.20** altogether.

Exercise 29:8

1 Ben earns £14 760 in one year.
He had a tax allowance of £5700.
Ben paid tax at the 10% rate on the
first £4300 of his taxable income.
He paid tax at the 22% rate on the
rest.
  a How much tax did he pay at
  the 10% rate?
  b How much tax did he pay at
  the 22% rate?
  c How much tax did Ben pay
  altogether?

2 Sonya earned £21 843 in one year. She had a tax allowance of £9450.
Sonya paid tax at the 10% rate on the first £4300 of her taxable income.
She paid tax at the 22% rate on the rest.
  a How much tax did she pay at the 10% rate?
  b How much tax did she pay at the 22% rate?
  c How much tax did Sonya pay altogether?

3 Misha earns £27 641 in one year. He had a tax allowance of £11 256.
Misha paid tax at the 10% rate on the first £4300 of his taxable income.
He paid tax at the 22% rate on the rest.
  a How much tax did he pay at the 10% rate?
  b How much tax did he pay at the 22% rate?
  c How much tax did Misha pay altogether?

4 Sita earned £32 571 last year. She had a tax allowance of £9476.
Liz earned £28 874 last year. Her tax allowance was £5472.
They both paid tax at the 10% rate on the first £4300 of taxable income.
They both paid tax at the 22% rate on the rest.
  a Explain why they paid the same amount at the 10% rate.
  b Explain why Liz paid more tax than Sita altogether.
  c How much more did Liz pay?

Compound interest

When you save money with a bank or building society you earn interest.
This interest is added to your account. You now have more money in
your account and you earn interest on all of it.
This type of interest is called **compound interest**.

Example   Bill opens an investment account with £3000.
The money earns 8% per year compound interest for 5 years.
No money is withdrawn during this time.
a   How much will be in the account at the end of 5 years?
b   How much compound interest will be paid?

a   1.08 is the multiplier for increasing an amount by 8%.
You multiply by **1.08** to find the amount at the end of each year.

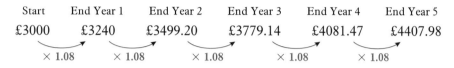

Start	End Year 1	End Year 2	End Year 3	End Year 4	End Year 5
£3000	£3240	£3499.20	£3779.14	£4081.47	£4407.98

$\times 1.08 \quad \times 1.08 \quad \times 1.08 \quad \times 1.08 \quad \times 1.08$

So for the value after 5 years, you multiply by 1.08^5

The value of the account at the end of 5 years $= 3000 \times 1.08^5 = £4407.98$

b   Subtract the original amount invested £4407.98 − £3000 = £1407.98
So £1407.98 compound interest will be paid.

Exercise 29:9

1   Annabel opens an investment account with £5000.
The money earns 7% per year compound interest for 3 years.
a   What is the value of the account at the end of this time?
b   How much compound interest is earned?

2   Leroy puts £8400 in an investment account.
The money earns 8.1% compound interest for 4 years.
a   What is the value of the account at the end of this time?
b   How much compound interest is earned?

3   Richard has £80 000 to invest. One bank offers him 7.5% compound interest and another offers him 8.1% compound interest. How much difference would this make over 5 years?

4   The Meadens have just bought a house for £142 000.
Assume its value increases by 6% each year. Predict its value in:
a   5 years   **b**   10 years   **c**   20 years

Car insurance

The cost of insuring a person to drive a car is worked out using percentage changes. The starting figure is called the **base rate** and this depends on the type of car and the area where it is kept. The base rate is then adjusted up or down depending on a person's age and driving record.

Example   Faye is 19 years old.
She has been driving for 2 years and has not made any insurance claims.
The base rate for the car that she drives is £983.
There is an age loading of 55%.
Faye has a 20% no claims bonus.
She must pay a further 4% IPT (Insurance Premium Tax).
What is the total insurance premium that she has to pay?

The adjustments can be worked out using multipliers.

Adjustment	Change	Multiplier
age loading	+55%	1.55
no claims bonus	−20%	0.8
IPT	+4%	1.04

You can work out the total in one go by using all of the multipliers.

Total premium = £983 × 1.55 × 0.8 × 1.04
= £1267.6768
= £1267.68 to the nearest penny.

Exercise 29:10

1   Steve is 18 years old and has one year's no claims bonus.
The base rate for his car is £1468.
a   Copy the table. Fill it in.

Adjustment	Change	Multiplier
age loading	+65%	
no claims bonus	−10%	
IPT	+4%	

b   Work out the total premium that Steve must pay.

2 Karen is 24 years old and has seven years no claims bonus.
The base rate for her car is £736.

   a Copy the table. Fill it in.

Adjustment	Change	Multiplier
age loading	+5%	
no claims bonus	−65%	
IPT	+4%	

   b Work out the total premium that Karen must pay.

3 Luke is 17 years old and is learning to drive. The base rate for his
car is £860. He wants to pay the insurance in 12 monthly instalments.
To do this he must pay interest charges of 8% of the total premium.

   a Copy the table. Fill it in.

Adjustment	Change	Multiplier
age loading	+75%	
IPT	+4%	
interest	+8%	

   b Work out the total amount that Luke must pay.
   c How much is each instalment?

1 Write down the multiplier and the next two terms in each of these sequences.
    a 5, 10, 20, 40, ...   **c** 240, 120, 60, ...
    b 2, 6, 18, 54, ...   **d** 729, 243, 81, ...

2 Use the information to write down the first 5 terms of each sequence.
    a first term: 8, multiplier: 3   **b** second term: 12, multiplier: 3

3 The first term of a sequence is 4. Find the twentieth term when the multiplier is:
    a 3   **b** 1.5   **c** 0.5   **d** 0.6

4 **a** Write down the multiplier for working out 8% of an amount.
    b Work out 8% of each of these.
       (1) 250 m   (4) 34.5 m/s   (7) 460 cm^2
       (2) 3.68 km   (5) £75   (8) 2400 mm^2
       (3) 745 g   (6) 325.2 kg   (9) £337.50

5 Write down the multiplier to increase an amount by:
    a 2%   **b** 82%   **c** 32.5%   **d** 8.25%

6 Write down the multiplier to reduce an amount by:
    a 25%   **b** 45%   **c** 15.5%   **d** 63.1%

7 Add VAT at 17.5% to each of these amounts. Give your answer to the nearest penny when you need to round.
    a £12   **b** £67   **c** £2250   **d** £10 000

8 Each of these prices include VAT at 17.5%.
    Find the price before VAT was added.
    a £35.25   **b** £89.30   **c** £2937.50   **d** £17 860

9 Copy these. Fill in the gaps.

    a
Earnings	£7230
Tax allowance	£3275
Taxable income	

    b
Earnings	
Tax allowance	£3780
Taxable income	£1845

10 Angela earned £5675 last year. Her tax allowance was £3875.
    She paid tax at the 22% rate. How much tax did she pay?

11 Rebecca earned £15 720 in one year.
She had a tax allowance of £4700.
She paid tax at the 10% rate on the first £4300 of her taxable income.
She paid tax at the 22% rate on the rest.
  a How much tax did Rebecca pay at the 10% rate?
  b How much tax did she pay at the 22% rate?
  c How much tax did Rebecca pay altogether?

12 Liam earned £23 875 in one year. He had a tax allowance of £10 750.
He paid tax at the 10% rate on the first £4300 of his taxable income.
He paid tax at the 22% rate on the rest.
  a How much tax did Liam pay at the 10% rate?
  b How much tax did he pay at the 22% rate?
  c How much tax did Liam pay altogether?

13 Christa invests £5000 at 7% compound interest for 6 years.
  a What is the value of the account at the end of this time?
  b How much interest is gained?

14 A house increases in value by 9% each year for 5 years.
In 1980 the house cost £36 000.

What was its value in 1985?

15 Samir is 19 years old and has two years' no claims bonus.
The base rate for his car insurance is £1638.
  a Copy the table. Fill it in.
  b Work out the total premium that Samir must pay.

Adjustment	Change	Multiplier
age loading	+55%	
no claims bonus	−20%	
IPT	+4%	

1 There is a very old story about the
man who invented the game of chess.
A king promised any prize in his
kingdom to the person who could
invent the greatest game ever.
A wise man invented the game of chess.
When the king saw the game he
realised that this man had won the
prize.
The king promised him any prize he
wanted.

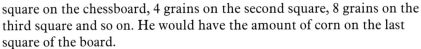

The wise man asked the king to
imagine 2 grains of corn on the first
square on the chessboard, 4 grains on the second square, 8 grains on the
third square and so on. He would have the amount of corn on the last
square of the board.
The king was amazed. "Is that all!" he exclaimed.

a Write a sequence for the amounts of corn on the first 10 squares.
b Write the sequence in part **a** as powers of 2.
c The last square on the board is the 64th square.
Write the amount of corn on that square as a power of 2.
d Use the x^y key on your calculator to work out the number of grains
of corn on the 64th square.
e Assume that 2 grains of corn weigh 1 gram.
Work out how many tonnes of grain the wise man would win.
f Explain why the king was unable to keep his promise and decided
instead to have the wise man executed.

2 During a slump in the property market the value of a house fell by 15%.
What percentage increase will restore the property to its previous value?

3 One year public spending fell by 15%, in the second year it fell by 7%,
in the third year it rose by 3% and in the fourth year it rose again by 8%.
a What is the overall percentage change?
b What percentage change is now needed to return to the original value?

4 Gavin earned £37 640 in one year. He had a tax allowance of £5250.
He paid tax at the 10% rate on the first £4300 of his taxable income.
He paid tax at the 22% rate on the next £22 800 of his taxable income.
He paid tax at 40% on the rest.
How much tax did Gavin pay?

1 **a** Write down the multiplier for working out 8% of an amount.
    b Work out 8% of each of these.
        (1) £67   (3) £49.50   (5) 86.4 kg
        (2) 240 m   (4) 700 cm   (6) 1.9 m²

2 Write down the multiplier for reducing an amount by:
    a 28%   **c** 6%
    b 16.5%   **d** 99.3%

3 Jill earns £1800 each month. She needs 72% of this to pay her bills.
    a What percentage does Jill have left?
    b How much money does she have when the bills are paid?

4 Last year, Tom paid £6520 in tax. This year he will pay 4.2% less.
    How much tax will Tom pay this year?

5 Write down the multiplier for each of these percentage increases.
    a 7%   **c** 0.8%
    b 12%   **d** 150%

6 Add VAT at 17.5% to a garage bill of £96.

7 Andy drove 6420 miles in his van in June.
    He drove 5% further in July.
    How many miles did Andy drive in July?
    Give your answer to the nearest 10 miles.

8 Lisa put £2400 into a savings account.
    In 1 year her savings grew by 7.5%.
    How much did Lisa have in her account at the end of the year?

9 Steve bought a new car for £15 800. It lost 30% of its value during the first year. It then lost a further 25% of its value during the second year. How much was Steve's car worth after 2 years?

10 The diagram shows a rectangle of area 54 cm². Its length is increased by 10%. Its width is reduced by 10%. What is the final area of the rectangle?

Area = 54 cm²

11 The cost of a computer including VAT at 17.5% is £904.75 What was the cost before VAT was added?

12 Simon put £7600 in an investment account 4 years ago. The money has gained 6.7% compound interest each year.
a How much is in Simon's account now?
b How much compound interest has been gained?

13 Jack and Sarah buy a house for £83 000. If it increases in value by 10% each year, how much will it be worth in 5 years time?

14 Alison earned £16 800 in one year. She had a tax allowance of £5300. She paid tax at 10% on the first £4300 of her taxable income. She paid tax at 22% on the rest.
a How much tax did Alison pay at the 10% rate?
b How much tax did Alison pay at the 22% rate?
c How much tax did Alison pay altogether?

30 Solid shapes

1 Drawing shapes
Drawing shapes based on cubes on isometric paper
Completing part drawn cuboids on isometric paper
Drawing missing pieces of cuboids
Plans and elevations

2 Units of mass and capacity
Converting metric units of mass
Converting metric units of capacity
Converting imperial units of mass
Converting imperial units of capacity
Converting between metric and imperial
units of mass and capacity
Estimating masses and capacities

CORE

3 Volume
Introducing volume and capacity
Finding volumes of blocks of 1 cm³ cubes
Volume of a cuboid = length × width × height
Volume of a prism
Volume of a cylinder
Volume of compound shapes

4 Density
Defining density
Using the density formula to find mass and volume

5 Dimensions
Using dimensions to analyse formulas for length,
area and volume

QUESTIONS

EXTENSION

TEST YOURSELF

1 Drawing shapes

Look at this picture carefully.

Can you see what is wrong with it?

You can use isometric paper to help you draw some 3D shapes.
But you must remember to use it the right way up. It must show vertical lines.

Example   Copy the cube on to the grid.

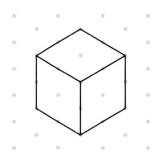

Start at a corner.

Use the grid this way up.

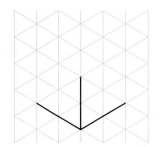

Every line on the grid is in
one of these directions.

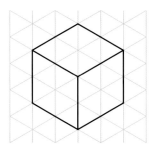

Follow the grid lines to
complete the drawing.

Exercise 30:1

1 Copy these objects on to isometric paper.

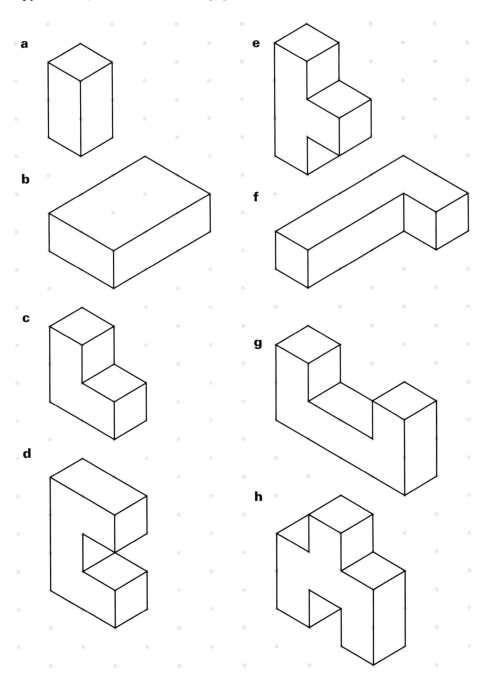

a

b

c

d

e

f

g

h

2 Copy and complete each diagram so that it shows a cuboid.

a

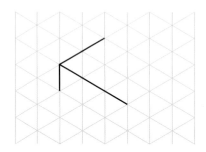

d

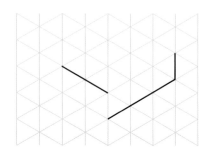

b

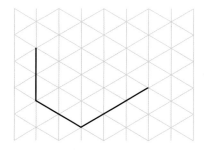

e

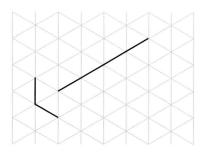

c

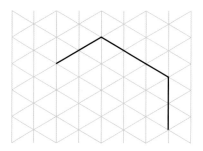

f

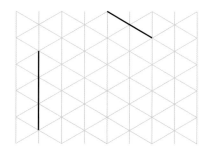

3 Each diagram shows a cuboid with a piece missing.
Draw the missing piece.

a

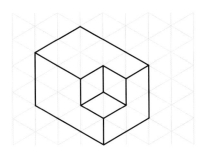

d

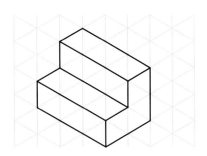

b

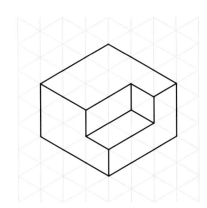

e

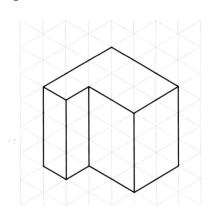

c

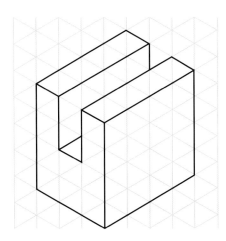

f

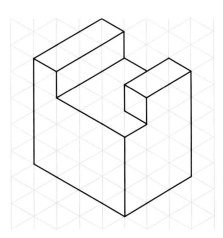

Here is an object made up of cubes.

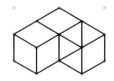

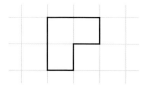

Katie is looking at the object from directly above. This is what she sees.

This is called the plan view of the object.

Exercise 30:2

1 Draw the plan view of each of these objects.

a

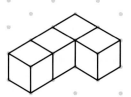

c

b

d

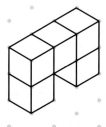

Here is another object.

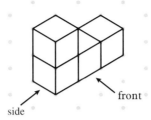

Leah is looking at the object
from the front.
This is what she sees.

Danielle is looking at the object
from the side.
This is what she sees.

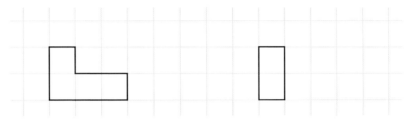

This is called the
front elevation of the object.

This is called the
side elevation of the object.

2 Draw the front elevation of each of these objects.

a

b

3 Draw the front and side elevations of each of these objects.

a

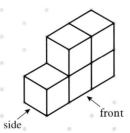

b

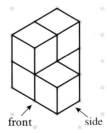

This is what Lee drew for the side elevation in question 3a.

This does not show that the bottom cube isn't directly below the top one.

There is a better way of drawing plans and elevations when the various parts aren't in line with each other.

You use a dashed line to separate the parts that aren't lined up.

The correct elevation for question 3a is

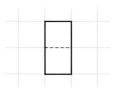

4 Draw the front elevation of each of these objects.

a

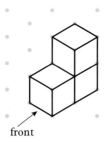

front

b

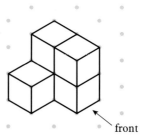

front

5 Draw the front and side elevations of each of these objects.

a

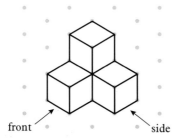

front   side

b

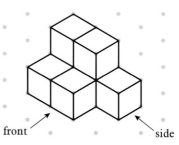

front   side

2 Units of mass and capacity

The weight of an object depends on where it is!
The mass of an object is always the same.
People often talk about the weight of something and most of the time they really mean the mass.

Metric units of mass	The **metric units of mass** are milligrams (mg), grams (g), kilograms (kg) or tonnes (t).

$$1000 \text{ mg} = 1 \text{ g}$$
$$1000 \text{ g} = 1 \text{ kg}$$
$$1000 \text{ kg} = 1 \text{ t}$$

Example Change each of these to the units shown.
 a 0.37 t to kilograms
 b 2400 mg to grams

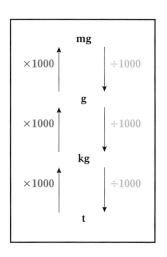

a There are 1000 kg in every tonne
   So $0.37 \text{ t} = 0.37 \times 1000 \text{ kg}$
              $= 370 \text{ kg}$

b Every 1000 mg make 1 g.
   Find how many lots of 1000 mg
   there are in 2400 mg.
       $2400 \div 1000 = 2.4$ so 2400 mg = 2.4 g

Exercise 30:3

1 Change each of these masses into kilograms.
  a 3 t   **b** 7.12 t   **c** 0.5 t   **d** 0.046 t

2 Change each of these masses into grams.
  a 2 kg   **c** 10.5 kg   **e** 0.31 kg   **g** 5.246 kg
  b 3.2 kg   **d** 0.4 kg   **f** 0.302 kg   **h** 2.046 kg

3 Change each of these masses into kilograms.

    a 7000 g   **c** 8450 g   **e** 10 000 g   **g** 960 g

    b 3600 g   **d** 4030 g   **f** 750 g   **h** 45 g

4 Change each of these into the units shown.

    a 25 g to milligrams   **c** 8400 kg to tonnes   ● **e** 10 000 000 g to tonnes

    b 1200 mg to grams   **d** 720 kg to tonnes   ● **f** 7.35 kg to milligrams

5 The largest fish ever caught
on a rod and line was a
great white shark.
The shark's mass was 1537 kg.
Write this mass in tonnes.

6 A gudgeon is a small freshwater fish.
The largest gudgeon ever caught had a mass of 141 g.
Write this weight in kilograms.

Metric units of capacity	The **metric units of capacity** are millilitres (ml), centilitres (cl) and litres (l)

        10 ml   = 1 cl

        1000 ml = 1 l

        100 cl   = 1 l

Example   Change each of these into the units shown.

        a 2.5 l to ml   **b** 750 cl to l

a There are 1000 ml in every l so

        2.5l = 2.5 × 1000 ml

             = 2500 ml

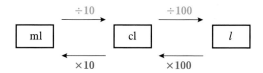

b Every 100 cl make 1 l.

    Find how many lots of 100 cl
there are in 750 cl.

        750 ÷ 100 = 7.5 so 750 cl = 7.5 l

Exercise 30:4

1 Change each of these units into centilitres.

   a 12 *l*   **c** 7.5 *l*   **e** 40 ml   **g** 600 ml

   b 230 *l*   **d** 0.45 *l*   **f** 67 ml   **h** 964 ml

2 Change each of these units into litres.

   a 500 cl   **d** 850 cl   **g** 2800 ml   **j** 400 ml

   b 7000 cl   **e** 4350 cl   **h** 250 ml   **k** 50 ml

   c 20 000 cl   **f** 17 cl   **i** 750 ml   **l** 8 ml

3 Change each of these units into millilitres.

   a 40 cl   **d** 2.4 cl   **g** 7.4 *l*   **j** 0.06 *l*

   b 5 cl   **e** 12.5 cl   **h** 3.124 *l*   **k** 0.075 *l*

   c 9.4 cl   **f** 4.08 cl   **i** 0.8 *l*   **l** 0.0304 *l*

4 Change each of these into the units shown.

   a 200 cl to litres   **c** 2.5 *l* to centilitres   **e** 850 ml to centilitres

   b 550 cl to litres   **d** 0.75 *l* to centilitres   **f** 45 cl to millilitres

5 A 2 litre bottle of Ribena makes 66 servings.
Find the number of ml in each serving.
Give your answer to the nearest whole number.

6 A bottle of milk holds 568 ml.
Len has 50 crates of milk on his milk-float.
Every crate holds 20 bottles.
How many litres of milk are there
on Len's milk-float?

Imperial units of mass	The **imperial units of mass** are ounces (oz), pounds (lb) and stones (st).

$$16 \, oz = 1 \, lb \qquad 14 \, lb = 1 \, st$$

Example

Change each of these into the units shown.

    a 8 st to pounds   **b** 72 oz to pounds

  a There are 14 pounds in every stone.
       So 8 stones $= 8 \times 14 = 112$ pounds

  b Every 16 ounces make 1 pound.
       Find how many lots of 16 ounces there are in 72 ounces.
       $72 \div 16 = 4.5$ so 72 ounces $= 4\frac{1}{2}$ pounds

Exercise 30:5

1 Change each of these to ounces.
    a 3 pounds   **b** 7 pounds   **c** $4\frac{1}{2}$ pounds   ● **d** 6 pounds 3 ounces

2 Change each of these to pounds.
    a 3 stones   **b** 8 stones   **c** $9\frac{1}{2}$ stones   ● **d** 8 stone 12 pounds

3 Change each of these to stones.
    a 98 pounds   **b** 168 pounds   **c** 115.5 pounds   **d** 127.75 pounds

4 Kathryn weighs 10 stone 4 pounds.
    What is her weight in pounds?

5 Alan's grandmother sends him to the shops for $\frac{1}{2}$ stone of potatoes.
    How many pounds of potatoes should he buy?

6 Americans always give their weight in pounds.
    Zak weighs 178 pounds.
    What is his weight in stones and pounds?

Imperial units of capacity	The **imperial units of capacity** are pints (pt), quarts (qt) and gallons (gal).

$$2 \, pt = 1 \, qt \qquad 8 \, pt = 4 \, qt = 1 \, gal$$

Example

A milk churn holds 20 gallons. How many pints is this?
There are 8 pints in every gallon.
$$20 \, gal = 20 \times 8 \, pt$$
$$= 160 \, pt$$

Exercise 30:6

1 Marion buys 1 gallon of milk.
How many pints is this?

2 An elephant drinks about 25 gal
of water each day.
How many pints of water does
an elephant drink each day?

3 An average person uses 160 pt of
water each day.
How many gallons is this?

• **4** Carsington reservoir in Derbyshire holds 7800 million gallons of water.
How many 1 pt bottles could you fill from the reservoir?

Converting between metric and imperial units

It might help you to use conversion
numbers.
You saw this in Chapter 17 where you
converted lengths.

To change from imperial to metric
you **multiply** by the conversion number.
To change from metric to imperial
you divide by the conversion number.

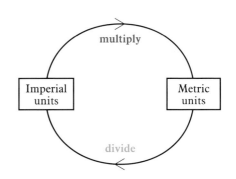

		Conversion number
Mass	1 oz is about 30 g	30
	1 lb is about 450 g	450
	1 lb is about 0.45 kg	0.45
	1 st is about 6.5 kg	6.5
Capacity	1 pt is about 600 ml	600
	1 pt is about 0.6 *l*	0.6
	1 gal is about 4.5 *l*	4.5

You need to remember how to do these conversions.
Your exam paper will not tell you the conversion numbers!

Exercise 30:7

1 Change each of these masses into the units given.
    a 2 oz into grams   **c** 2.3 st into kilograms   **e** 1170 g into ounces
    b 14 lb into kilograms   **d** 3 lb into grams   **f** 2925 kg to pounds

2 Change each of these capacities into the units given.
    a 4 pt into millilitres   **c** 5.7 gal into litres   **e** 30.6 l into gallons
    b 7.3 pt into litres   **d** 4.8 l into pints   **f** 6600 ml into pints

3 An average person should drink 4 pt of liquid each day.
How many litres is this?

4 A recipe asks for 4 kg of sugar. How many pounds is this?

5 Janet's fuel tank has a capacity of 55 l. How many gallons is this?

Estimating

You also need to be able to estimate masses and capacities.
To do this you need to think about things that you know well.
Here are some examples but you may think of others that help you more.

Mass

    30 g or 1 ounce   1 kg or 2.2 pounds   70 kg or 11 stones

Capacity

    250 ml or $\frac{1}{2}$ pint   2 litres or $3\frac{1}{2}$ pints   90 litres or 20 gallons

Exercise 30:8

1 Estimate the mass of each of these in the units shown.

a

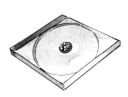

    (1) grams
    (2) ounces

b

    (1) grams
    (2) ounces

c

    (1) kilograms
    (2) pounds

d

    (1) kilograms
    (2) pounds

2 Estimate the capacity of each of these in the units shown.

a

    (1) millilitres
    (2) pints

b

    (1) millilitres
    (2) pints

c

    (1) litres
    (2) gallons

d

    (1) litres
    (2) gallons

3 Volume

Jim is building a garage.
He needs to make a solid base to put the garage on.
This is called the 'footings' for the garage.
He digs out a cuboid shape and fills it with concrete.
He needs to know how much concrete to order.
He needs to be able to work out the volume of the footings.

Volume	The amount of space that an object takes up is called its **volume**.

Volume is measured in cubic units.
These can be millimetres cubed (**mm³**), centimetres cubed (**cm³**) or metres cubed (**m³**).

1 cm³	**1 cm³** is the space taken up by a cube with all its edges 1 cm long.

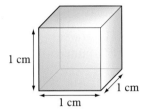

Capacity	The **capacity** of a hollow object is the volume of space inside it.

1 ml	This cube has been filled with water. The volume of liquid inside is **1 millilitre**. This is written **1 ml**.

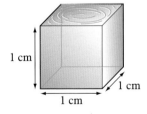

1 litre	Large volumes are measured in **litres**.

      1 litre = 1000 ml   1 litre is written **1 *l***.

A capacity of **1 ml** is the same as a volume of **1 cm³**.
1000 **ml** is the same as 1 litre.

Exercise 30:9

1 Draw a diagram of a cube that has a volume of:
   a 1 cm³   **b** 1 mm³   **c** 1 m³   ● **d** 8 cm³

2 The capacity of a normal can of Pepsi is 330 ml.
Estimate the capacity in millilitres of each of these:

a  **b**  **c**   **d**

3 The capacity of this bottle of lemonade is 2 *l*.
Estimate the capacity in litres of each of these.

a   **b**  **c**   **d**

4 **a** Write down the volume of each drink in centimetres cubed.
b Calculate the volume of Coca-Cola that you get for 1 p for each container.
Give your answers to 2 dp.
c Which container gives the best value for money?

1500 ml 99p
500 ml 59p
330 ml 38p

---

1 cm³

A cube that has sides of 1 cm is called a 1 cm cube.
It has a volume of 1 cm cubed.
This is written as **1 cm³**.

1 cm
1 cm
1 cm

This cuboid has 12 cubes in each layer.
Each cube has a volume of 1 cm³
It has 2 layers.
The volume of the cuboid is
    12 × 2 = 24 cm³

Exercise 30:10

For each of these cuboids, write down:
a the number of cubes in one layer
b the number of layers
c the volume of the cuboid.

1

2

3

4

5

6

7

8

9

10

● **11** Look at this solid.
The yellow cubes go right through
the shape.
  a Find the volume of the red cubes.
  b Find the volume of the yellow cubes.
  c Find the total volume of the shape.

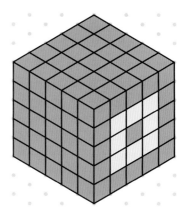

Volume of a cuboid

There is a faster way to find the volume of a block of cubes.
(1) Multiply the length by the width.
    This tells you how many cubes there are in one layer.
(2) Multiply your answer by the height.
    This tells you how many cubes there are altogether.

| **Volume of a cuboid** | You can do this all at once: |

Volume of a cuboid = length × width × height

Example   Work out the volume of this block of cubes.

Volume = length × width × height
       = 6   ×   3   ×   4
       = 72 cm^3

Exercise 30:11

In questions **1**–**8**, find the volume of each of the blocks. Write your
answers in cm^3.

1

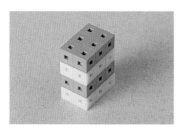

2

3

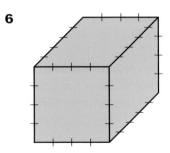

6

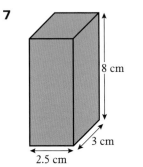

4

7

8 cm

3 cm

2.5 cm

5

● 8

3.5 cm

3.5 cm

←——3.5 cm——→

9 A 750 g cereal box has sides
of length 7 cm, 19 cm and 29 cm.
Find the volume of the box.

10 A 1 litre carton of orange juice
is in the shape of a cuboid.
It measures 5.9 cm by 9 cm by
19.5 cm.
  a Find the volume of the box.
● **b** How much space is there in the
box if it contains exactly 1 *l* of
orange juice?

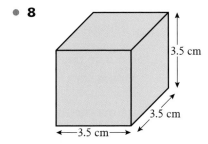

In this exercise you need to use the correct units in your answers.
So far you have only used cm³ for volume.
In this exercise you will need to use m³ and mm³ too.
Look carefully at the units in the question to help you give the right units
in your answer.

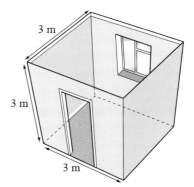

Exercise 30:12

1   Work out the volume of
this boxroom.
It is a cube of side 3 m.

2   **a** Jim dug a hole for his garage
footings.
The hole was 5 m long, 3 m wide
and 0.5 m deep.
Find the volume of earth that he
removed.

     b He had to buy the concrete in
litres.
$$1 \, \text{m}^3 = 1000 \, l$$
How many litres of concrete did
Jim have to buy?

3   A box of computer disks is a cuboid.
The width of the box is 92 mm.
The height is 96 mm.
The depth is 38 mm.
Find the volume of the box.

4   **a** Measure the length, the width and the depth of your *Key Maths GCSE*
book in millimetres to the nearest millimetre.
Write down your answers.

     b Work out the volume of paper in the book.

●   **5**   This cuboid has length x cm,
width y cm and height z cm.
Write down the volume of
the cuboid in terms of x, y and z.

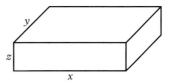

Prism

A **prism** is a solid which is exactly the same shape and size all the way through.

When you cut a slice through the solid it is the same size and shape.

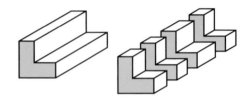

Cross section

The shape of this slice is called the **cross section** of the solid.

The shape of the cross section is often used to name the prism.

This is a triangular prism

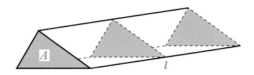

Volume of a prism = Area of cross section × length
You can write this as $V = Al$

Example

Find the volume of this prism.

The cross section is a triangle.
The area of this triangle
$= (5 \times 12) \div 2$
$= 60 \div 2$
$= 30 \text{ cm}^2$

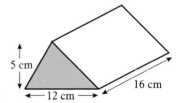

So volume $= 30 \times 16 = 480 \text{ cm}^3$

Exercise 30:13

Work out the volumes of the stage blocks in questions **1–4**.
All the blocks are prisms.
Give your answers to 3 sf when you need to round.

1

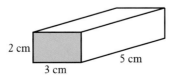

2

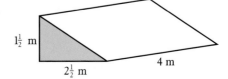

3

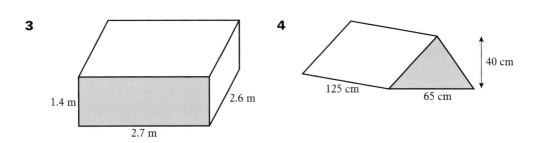

4

Work out the volumes of these prisms.
Give your answers to 3 sf when you need to round.

5

7

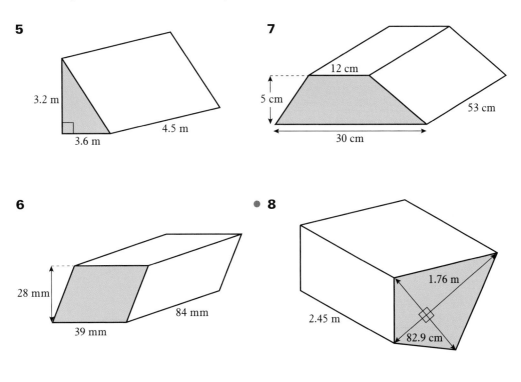

6

● **8**

9 Find the volume of this swimming pool.

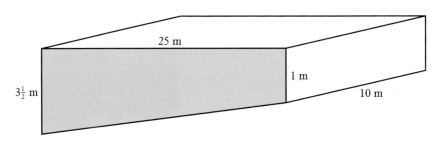

Cylinders

A cylinder is like a prism but it has a circle as its cross section.
The area of the cross section is πr^2 where r is the radius of the circle.
The volume of a cylinder is $V = \pi r^2 h$ where r is the radius and h is the height.

Example   Find the volume of this cylinder.

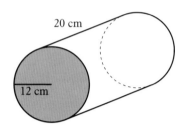

Here $r = 12$ so $A = \pi \times 12^2$
So   Volume $= \pi \times 12^2 \times 20$
                    $= 9047.78 \ldots$
                    $= 9050$ cm^3 to 3 sf

Exercise 30:14

Work out the volumes of the storage tanks in questions **1–4**.
All the tanks are cylinders. Round your answers to 3 sf

1

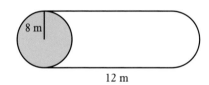

3

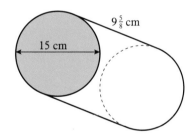

2

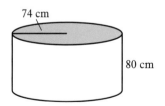

• **4**

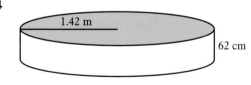

5   The trailer of a wine lorry carries
a cylinder.
The cylinder is 10 m long.
The radius of the cross section is 1.2 m.
How many litres of wine does it carry?
$1000 \, l = 1$ m^3

If you know the volume and length of a prism, you can work out the cross sectional area.

You need to make Area the subject of

$$\text{Volume} = \text{Area of cross section} \times \text{length}$$

You can write this as

$$V = Al$$

Dividing both sides by l gives

$$\frac{V}{l} = A$$

so

$$\text{Area} = \frac{\text{Volume}}{\text{length}}$$

The volume of this prism is 6912 cm³.

$$\text{Area of cross section} = \frac{6912}{24}$$

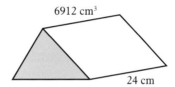

So the blue area is 288 cm².

You can also make length the subject of

$$\text{Volume} = \text{Area of cross section} \times \text{length}$$

Start with

$$V = Al$$

Dividing both sides by A gives

$$\frac{V}{A} = l$$

so

$$\text{length} = \frac{\text{Volume}}{\text{Area}}$$

The volume of this prism is 1080 m³.

$$\text{length} = \frac{1080}{40}$$

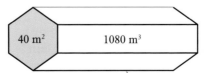

So the green length is 27 m

Exercise 30:15

1 Find the cross sectional areas of the prisms.
Make sure you use sensible units for your answers.

a

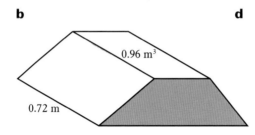

8 m

20 m³

c

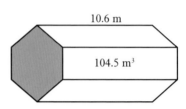

10.6 m

104.5 m³

b

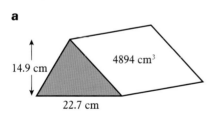

0.96 m³

0.72 m

d

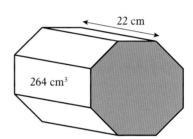

22 cm

264 cm³

2 Find the lengths of these prisms.
Give your answers to 3 sf.

a

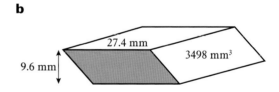

14.9 cm

4894 cm³

22.7 cm

b

27.4 mm

3498 mm³

9.6 mm

3 Tony drives a grain lorry.
The lorry has a trailer in the shape
of an open cuboid.
The width of the trailer is 2.1 m.

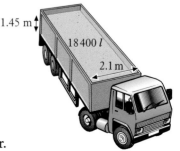

1.45 m

18 400 *l*

2.1 m

The trailer is filled with 18 400 litres
of grain.
The grain is filled to a depth of 1.45 m.
You can assume the surface of the grain is
horizontal and level with the top of the trailer.
Work out the length of the lorry to 3 sf.
1000 litres = 1 m³

If you know the volume and height of a cylinder, you can work out the radius.
You need to make r the subject of $V = \pi r^2 h$

Start with $$V = \pi r^2 h$$

Dividing both sides by π gives $$\frac{V}{\pi} = r^2 h$$

Dividing both sides by h gives $$\frac{V}{\pi h} = r^2$$

Taking the square root of both sides gives $$r = \sqrt{\frac{V}{\pi h}}$$

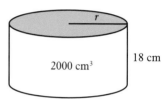

The volume of this cylinder is 2000 cm^3
The height is 18 cm

Substituting these values into the formula for r gives:

$$r = \sqrt{\frac{2000}{3.141... \times 18}}$$

so $r = 5.95$ cm (3 sf)

If you know the radius and volume of a cylinder, you can work out the height.
You need to make h the subject of $V = \pi r^2 h$

Start with $$V = \pi r^2 h$$

Dividing both sides by π gives $$\frac{V}{\pi} = r^2 h$$

Dividing both sides by r^2 gives $$\frac{V}{\pi r^2} = h$$

So for this cylinder $$h = \frac{660}{3.141... \times 5^2}$$

So $$h = 8.4 \text{ cm}$$

4 Find the heights of these cylinders.
Give your answers to 3 sf.

a

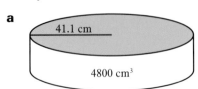

41.1 cm

4800 cm³

c

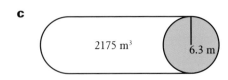

2175 m³

6.3 m

b

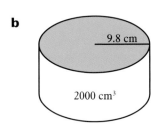

9.8 cm

2000 cm³

d

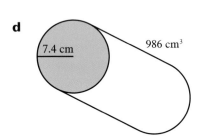

7.4 cm

986 cm³

5 Find the radius of each of these cylinders. Give your answers to 3 sf.

a

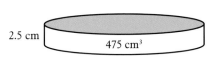

2.5 cm

475 cm³

c

28.2 m

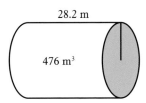

476 m³

b

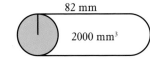

82 mm

2000 mm³

d

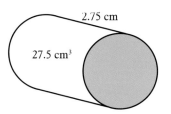

2.75 cm

27.5 cm³

6 An oil drum has a capacity of 900 litres
There are 750 litres of oil in it.
The radius of the drum is 48 cm.
  a Work out the height of the oil drum.
  b Work out the depth of the oil in the drum.

48 cm

900*l*

Finding the volumes of more complicated shapes with constant cross sections

To find these volumes you need to:
(1) decide how to split the cross-sectional area into parts
(2) label each part with a letter
(3) find any missing lengths
(4) work out the area of each part
(5) add all these areas to get the total cross-sectional area
(6) multiply the cross-sectional area by the length.

Look at this cross-sectional area.
The shape is made from a semicircle
and a trapezium.

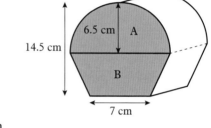

Area of semicircle A $= 0.5 \times \pi \times (6.5)^2$
$= 66.36... \text{ cm}^2$

For trapezium B you need to find
the missing lengths.
The top parallel side of trapezium B is
$$2 \times 6.5 = 13 \text{ cm}$$
The height of trapezium B is $14.5 - 6.5 = 8 \text{ cm}$

Area of trapezium B is $0.5 \times (7 + 13) \times 8 = 80 \text{ cm}^2$

So the cross-sectional area of the shape is area of A + area of B
$$= 66.36... \text{ cm}^2 + 80 \text{ cm}^2 = 146.36... \text{ cm}^2$$

So the volume of the shape is $146.36... \times 12.5 = 1830 \text{ cm}^3 \text{ (3 sf)}$
Don't round the value for the area. Keep it in your calculator and only round at the end.

Exercise 30:16

Find the volumes of these shapes. Round your answers to 3 sf.

1

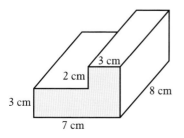

2

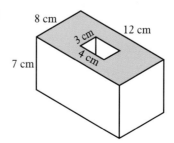

3

47 m

19 m

25 m

● **4**

45 cm

16.4 cm A

30.8 cm

B

21.2 cm

This is a cubic millimetre
All the sides are 1 mm.

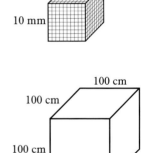

1 cm

1 cm

1 cm

This is a cubic centimetre

There are 10 mm in every 1 cm
    So in the cubic centimetre
    the width is 10 mm
    the length is 10 mm
    the height is 10 mm
    So there are $10 \times 10 \times 10 = 1000$ mm³ in 1 cm³

10 mm

10 mm

10 mm

A cubic metre is too big to draw here!
This is a diagram of one.
There are 100 cm in every 1 m.
    So in the cubic metre
    the dimensions are 100 cm × 100 cm × 100 cm
So there are $100 \times 100 \times 100 = 1\,000\,000$ cm³ in 1 m³

100 cm

100 cm

100 cm

100 cm

This diagram shows you
how to convert cubic units

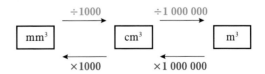

$\div 1000$

$\div 1\,000\,000$

mm³   cm³   m³

$\times 1000$

$\times 1\,000\,000$

---

5 Draw a sketch of a cube 2 cm by 2 cm by 2 cm. Find the volume in mm³.

6 Change each of these volumes into cm³.
    a 6 m³   **b** 0.4 m³   **c** 12.36 m³   **d** 2050 mm³   **e** 672 mm³

7 Change each of these volumes into m³.
    a 40 000 000 cm³   **b** 7 900 000 cm³   **c** 459 000 cm³

4   Density

The density of a neutron star is 10^{14} g per cm³.
The mean density of the earth is only 5.5 g per cm³.

The mass of a solid is proportional to its volume.

This is because $\text{Density} = \dfrac{\text{Mass}}{\text{Volume}}$

The units of density are g/cm³   or   kg/m³.

There is a triangle that can help you to remember how to use this formula.

You remember $D = \dfrac{M}{V}$ then write out the triangle.

Cover up the letter you want. Then what you see is the rule.

Example   A block of steel has dimensions
2 cm by 3 cm by 4 cm
It has a mass of 187.2 grams.
Work out its density.

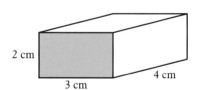

2 cm

3 cm

4 cm

Volume of a cuboid = length × width × height
$$= 2 \times 3 \times 4$$
$$= 24 \text{ cm}^3$$

You need the formula for density:

If you cover D you see $\dfrac{M}{V}$

so $D = \dfrac{M}{V}$

$$= \dfrac{187.2}{24}$$

$$= 7.8 \text{ g/cm}^3$$

Exercise 30:17

1 This diagram shows an ordinary house brick.
It has a mass of 2834 grams
Work out its density.

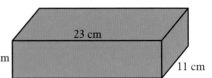

7 cm   23 cm   11 cm

2 Mrs Smowk is a Chemistry teacher.
She has a set of chemical elements. Each of the elements is a cuboid.
Work out (1) the volume and (2) the density of each cuboid.
Give your answers to 3 sf when you need to round.

	Element	Mass (grams)	Dimensions (cm)		
			length	width	height
a	carbon	13.2	3	2	1
b	iron	63.2	2	2	2
c	sulphur	5.3	1.8	1.3	1.1
d	copper	868	3.2	2.3	1.8
e	silver	0.709	0.6	0.45	0.25
f	gold	0.296	0.4	0.24	0.16
g	zinc	121.9	3.7	2.9	1.6
h	lead	10.1	1.4	0.8	0.8

If you know the density and volume of a substance, you can work out the mass.
You need the formula for mass:

If you cover M you see $D\,V$ so $M = D \times V$

The density of this piece of glass is 1.8 g/cm³
It is a cuboid as shown in the diagram.
To find its mass, first you need to work out
its volume.
Change all the units to centimetres.

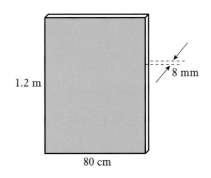

1.2 m   8 mm   80 cm

Volume $= 120 \times 80 \times 0.8$
$= 7680 \text{ cm}^3$

Now put these values in $M = D \times V$

so $\qquad$ Mass $= 1.8 \times 7680$
$= 13\,824 \text{ g}$

Now change this to kilograms
$13\,824 \text{ g} \div 1000 = 13.824 \text{ kg}$

---

3 A brass plate has a density of 8.1 g/cm³
The plate is a cuboid 52 cm by 32 cm by 0.4 cm
Work out the mass of the plate.

4 A load of topsoil has a density of 2 g/cm³.
A lorry is delivering 6 m³ of topsoil to a new house.
  a Change 6 m³ to cm³.
  b Work out the mass of the soil in grams.
  c Work out the mass that the lorry must carry in tonnes.

If you know the mass and density of a substance, you can work out the volume.
You need the formula for volume:

If you cover V you see $\dfrac{M}{D}$ so $V = \dfrac{M}{D}$

The density of mercury is 13.6 g/cm³
A mass of 12.8 grams is in the bulb of this thermometer.
Calculate the volume of the bulb.

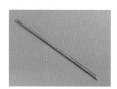

Put these values in $V = \dfrac{M}{D}$

Volume $= \dfrac{12.8}{13.6} = 0.941$ cm³ (3 sf)

---

5 Gold has a density of 19.3 g/cm³.
This wedding ring weighs 18.4 g.
Work out the volume of the wedding ring.

6 George mixes up 30 kg of mortar.
Mortar has a density of 2.2 g/cm³.
  a Work out the mass of the mortar in grams.
  b Work out the volume of the mortar in cm³.
  c Work out the volume of the mortar in m³.

5 Dimensions

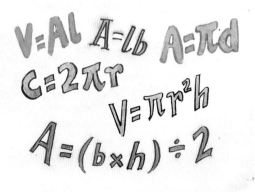

Some of these formulas are for length, some are for area and some are for volume.

You can tell quickly what a formula is for by looking at the dimension of the formula.

Dimension   The **dimension** of a formula is the number of lengths that are multiplied together.

Constant   A **constant** has no dimension. It is just a number.

Length has one dimension
Any formula for length can only involve constants and length.

$C = \pi d$ is a length formula.
π is a constant.
d is a length.

Area has two dimensions
Any formula for area can only involve constants and length × length.

$A = \pi r^2$ is an area formula.
π is a constant.
$r^2 = r \times r$
which is length × length

Volume has three dimensions
Any formula for volume can only involve constants and length × length × length.

$V = \frac{4}{3}\pi r^3$ is a volume formula.
$\frac{4}{3}$ and π are constants
$r^3 = r \times r \times r$
which is length × length × length

Example   Write down the dimension of the expression $\dfrac{3\pi r^2}{4h}$ where r and h are lengths.

The expression is $\dfrac{\text{constant} \times \text{constant} \times \textbf{length} \times \textbf{length}}{\text{constant} \times \textbf{length}}$

This cancels down to give a **length**.
So the dimension is 1.

Exercise 30:18

1 In this question d, e and f are lengths.
Work out the dimension of each of these.

   a de **c** $5df$ **e** $34e$ **g** $12\,e^3$
   b $2f$ **d** def **f** d^2 **h** $4e^2f$

2 In this question p, q and r are lengths, c and k are constants.
Work out the dimension of each of these.

   a pqr **e** $3kp^2q$ **i** $\dfrac{3rp}{q}$ ● **m** $\dfrac{r^2p^2}{q^3}$

   b $3pq$ **f** $5ckr$ **j** $\dfrac{3pr^2}{q}$ ● **n** $\dfrac{4c^2krp^3}{q^2}$

   c $2rq^2$ **g** $3kpq$ **k** $\dfrac{7ckp^3}{q^2}$ ● **o** $\dfrac{5ck\,\pi pq^2r}{p^2q}$

   d $4cpq$ **h** $5ckp$ **l** $\dfrac{ckpqr}{p^2}$ ● **p** $\dfrac{\pi r^3p^2}{ckp^2q}$

3 Sue is trying to find a formula for the volume of a bottle.
She is testing different formulas to see which works best.
The radius of the base of the bottle is r and the height is h.
These are the formulas that she is using.

$$V = \frac{3}{5}\pi r^2 h \qquad V = \frac{3}{5}\pi r^3 h \qquad V = \frac{3}{5}\pi r h^2 \qquad V = \frac{3}{5}\pi r h^3$$

Explain why Sue should only be testing two of these formulas.

Some formulas have more than one part.
When this happens all of the parts must have the same dimension if the formula is
for length or area or volume.
This is a formula for the total surface area of a cylinder.
     $A = 2\pi r^2 + 2\pi rh$

The first part is   constant $\times$ constant $\times$ length^2 which is an area.
The second part is   constant $\times$ constant $\times$ length $\times$ length   which is also an area.

This formula for a volume, V, cannot be right.
   $V = 2\pi r^3 + 2rh$
The first part is   constant $\times$ constant $\times$ length^3 which is a volume.
But the second part is   constant $\times$ length $\times$ length   which is an area.
So it is impossible for this formula to give you a volume.

---

4 In this question a, b and c are lengths.
Write down what each expression could represent.
If an expression cannot be for length, area or volume, explain why.

a $b + c$　　　　　**c** $2ac + 3ab$　　　　　**e** $5abc + 3b^2c$

b $3a + 5bc$　　　**d** $5ab + 3a^2$　　　● **f** $12a + \dfrac{bc}{a}$

5 In this question p, q, r, s and t are lengths, c and k are constants.
Write down what each formula could represent.
If an expression cannot be for length, area or volume, explain why.

a $pqr + s^2t$　　　　**e** $kp^2q + crst$　　　　● **i** $\dfrac{2rp}{q} + \dfrac{r^2p^2}{q^3}$

b $3pq + 5rst$　　　**f** $5ckr + 3cr^2$　　　● **j** $\dfrac{\pi pr^2}{qs} + \dfrac{4crp}{q}$

c $2rq^2 + 4s^2t$　　**g** $kp^2q + cr^3$　　　● **k** $\dfrac{8ckp^3}{q^2} - \dfrac{5\pi pq^2r}{s^2t} + \dfrac{r^2p^2}{q^3}$

d $4cpq + 2ckr$　　**h** $5ckp + cr$　　　● **l** $\dfrac{ckpqr}{t^2} + \dfrac{\pi r^3p^2}{cks^2q} - \dfrac{t^2p^2}{q^3}$

6 Tina is trying to find a formula for the volume of a jar.
r, h and b are lengths.

She thinks that the volume is $V = 3\pi r^2h + \frac{3}{4}\pi rb^2$

Tina's friend Glenda thinks that the volume is $V = 3\pi r^2h + \frac{3}{4}\pi r^2b^2$

Explain why Glenda has to be wrong.

7 Norman thinks that the total surface
area of this cylinder is
$A = 2\pi r(r + h)$
a Explain how Norman can show that
his formula has the right dimension.
b Does this mean that his formula is correct?

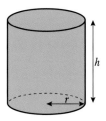

● **8** Cath thinks that the area of material
needed to cover this lampshade is
$A = \pi h(b - a)^2$
Explain why Cath has to be wrong.

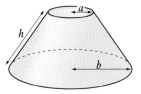

1 Copy each diagram.
Complete it so that it shows a cuboid.

a
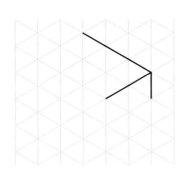

b
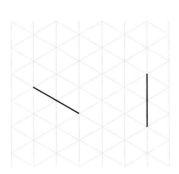

2 Each diagram shows a cuboid with a piece missing.
Draw the missing piece.

a
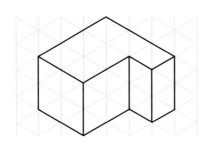

b
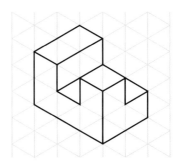

3 **a** Change each of these masses into the units given.
  (1) 60 grams into ounces (2) 10 kg into pounds (3) 4 st into kilograms
 b Change each of these capacities into the units given.
  (1) 5 pints into litres (2) 6 gallons into litres (3) 4500 ml into pints

4 Work out the volume of each of these shapes.

a
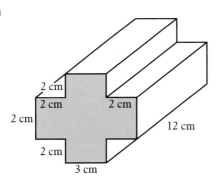

b
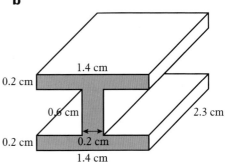

295

5 Find the volumes of these shapes.
Round your answers to 3 sf.

a

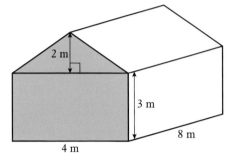

2 m

3 m

8 m

4 m

b

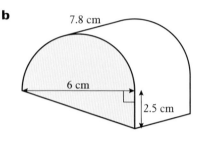

7.8 cm

6 cm

2.5 cm

6 The diagram shows a prism made of aluminium.
It has a mass of 48.6 grams.
Work out its density.

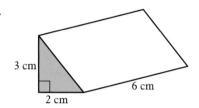

3 cm

2 cm

6 cm

7 A cork float is in the shape of a cylinder.
It has a mass of 784 grams.
Work out its density.

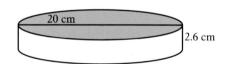

20 cm

2.6 cm

8 A steel girder has a volume of 60 000 cm³
It has a mass of 462 kg.
a Change the mass from kilograms to grams.
b Work out the density of the girder.

9 In this question a, b, c, d and e are lengths. π and k are constants.
Write down what each formula could represent.
If an expression cannot be for length, area or volume, explain why.

a πab

b kb

c $\dfrac{abc}{k}$

d $\dfrac{\pi a}{b}$

e $\dfrac{4dab}{kc} + \dfrac{2\pi bae}{kc}$

f $\dfrac{\pi c^2 e}{ka}$

g $\dfrac{2a^3}{k} + \dfrac{\pi kb^2 e}{c}$

h $\dfrac{5kc^3 d^2}{a^3} - \dfrac{2\pi ka^2 e}{3c}$

i $\dfrac{\pi(kc^2 e - 4bd^2)}{a}$

1 A railway tunnel has this cross section.
The tunnel runs in a straight line for
$3\frac{3}{4}$ miles.
1 mile = 1760 yards
a Work out the length of the tunnel in
yards.
b Find the cross-sectional area.
c Work out the volume of the tunnel
in cubic yards.

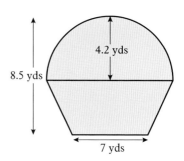

2 Mr Weybridge is moving marble floor tiles in his van.
The floor tiles are cuboids with dimensions
15 cm by 15 cm by 1.4 cm.
The density of marble is 2.7 g/cm³
He has 3400 tiles to move.
The van can only carry a load of 2.2 tonnes at a time.
How many journeys does he need to make?

3 This is the cross-sectional
area of an aircraft hangar.
It is to be built in the year 2020.
The hangar is to be 200 m long.
Find the volume of the hangar.

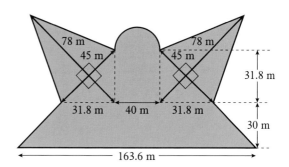

4 A very large concrete pipe has a regular hexagonal
cross section.
Within the pipe 4 cylindrical tubes carry liquid gases.
Each tube has a radius of 82 cm.
a Work out the volume of gas in 100 m of 1 tube.
Now split the hexagon into equilateral triangles.
b Use trigonometry to find the height of an
equilateral triangle.
c Work out the cross-sectional area of the pipe.
d Work out the volume of concrete in 1 km of pipe.

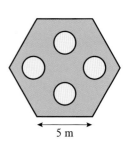

1 Copy and complete the diagram to show a prism.

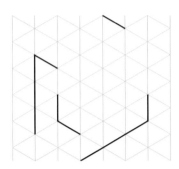

2 Change each of these to the units shown.

  a 37 mm to m   **c** 7600 kg to tonnes   **e** 3.8 cl to l

  b 0.8 km to m   **d** 3.08 m to cm   **f** 478 ml to cl

3 Ivan is a weightlifter. He can lift 450 kg.
How many pounds is this?

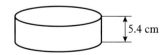

4 Each side of a cube is 8 cm long.
Find its volume.

5 Find the volume of this prism.

6 This cylinder has volume 86 cm³.
Find its radius to the nearest mm.

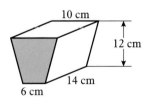

7 In this question l and m are lengths, p and q are constants.
Write down what each formula could represent.

  a $pl + qm$ **c** pql^2 **e** $\dfrac{q(l + m)^2}{l}$

  b plm **d** pml^2 **f** $(p + q)(l + m)$

31 More probability

1 Tree diagrams
Drawing tree diagrams
Finding probabilities from tree diagrams
Only drawing paths that are needed
Drawing tree diagrams where some paths
   end before others

CORE

2 Changing probabilities
Using changing probabilities
Answering questions using the words
   'at least one'

QUESTIONS

EXTENSION

TEST YOURSELF

1 Tree diagrams

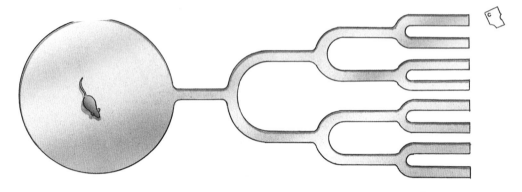

There are many paths that the mouse can take through the maze of tunnels.
Only one of these paths leads to the food.

Tree diagrams

You can use **tree diagrams** to show the outcomes of two or more events.
Each branch represents a possible outcome of one event.
The probability of each outcome is written on the branch.
The final result depends on the path taken through the tree.

Example

The probability that a new company will fail in the first 5 years is 0.6
Two new companies are chosen at random.

a Show all the possible outcomes on a tree diagram.
b Use the diagram to find the probability that both will fail.
c Find the probability that only one company fails.

a The first set of branches of the tree shows what can happen to the first company.

The second set of branches shows what can happen to the second company.

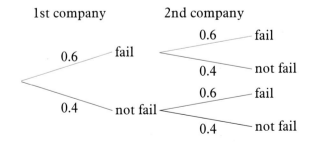

1st company   2nd company

Each path through the tree gives a different outcome.
The tree has four paths so there are four outcomes.

b The blue path gives the outcome 'both companies will fail'.
You *multiply* the probabilities on the branches of this path.
This gives you the probability of this final outcome.

The probability that both companies will fail is $0.6 \times 0.6 = 0.36$

c Each red path gives an outcome of one of the two companies failing.

The top red path gives the probability
of only the first company failing
$$= 0.6 \times 0.4$$
$$= 0.24$$

The lower red path gives the probability
of only the second company failing
$$= 0.4 \times 0.6$$
$$= 0.24$$

Now you *add* the probabilities of each path to find
the probability that only one company fails
$$= 0.24 + 0.24$$
$$= 0.48$$

Remember: You **multiply** the probabilities along the branches.
You **add** the probabilities when more than one path is used.

Exercise 31:1

1 Jenny posts two letters at her local post office. The probability that a
letter posted will be delivered the next morning is 0.96
  a Copy this tree diagram to show all the possible outcomes.
  Fill in the probabilities.

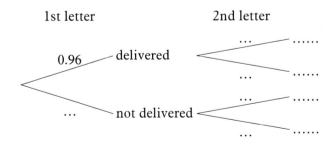

Find the probability that:
  b neither letter will be delivered the next morning
  c only one letter will be delivered the next morning.

2 The probability that Tanya has to do the washing up after dinner on any day is $\frac{2}{5}$.

   a Copy this tree diagram to show all the possible outcomes for one weekend.
Fill it in.

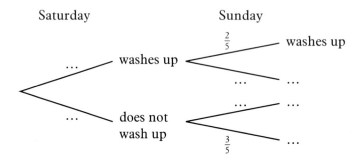

Saturday   Sunday

Find the probability that Tanya washes up:
b on both days
c on neither day
d on Saturday but not Sunday
e on only one of the two days.

3 Gary uses two buses to get to work.
The probability that the first bus is late is 0.2
The probability that the second bus is late is 0.3

   a Copy this tree diagram.
Fill it in.

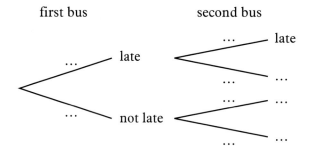

first bus   second bus

Find the probability that:
b both buses are late
c both buses are not late
d the first bus is late but the second bus is not late
e only one bus is late.

4 Tom and Nick are taking their driving tests.
The probability that Tom will pass is 0.7 and the probability that Nick
will pass is 0.6

   a Draw a probability tree to show all the possible outcomes.

Find the probability that:
   b both pass
   c only Nick passes
   d only one of them passes.

5 The probability that a new car will develop a fault in the first six months
is $\frac{1}{10}$. Three new cars are chosen at random.

   a Copy this tree diagram. Finish it off.
   Fill in the probabilities.

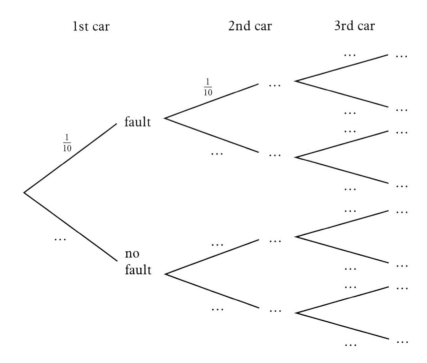

Find the probability that:
   b all three cars will develop a fault
   c none of the cars will develop a fault
   d exactly two cars will develop faults.

● **6** Jenny tosses a coin three times.

   a Draw a tree diagram showing all the possible outcomes.

Use your tree diagram to find the probability that Jenny gets:

   b three heads

   c exactly two heads

   d exactly one head

   e more heads than tails.

Tree diagrams can take a long time to draw if all the outcomes are included.
You can simplify them by only drawing paths that are needed.

Example   Penny rolls a dice three times.
Find the probability that she gets exactly two 6s.

Although the possible outcomes are 1, 2, 3, 4, 5 and 6 the
question only involves 6s.
You only need to draw paths to show 'a 6' or 'not a 6'.

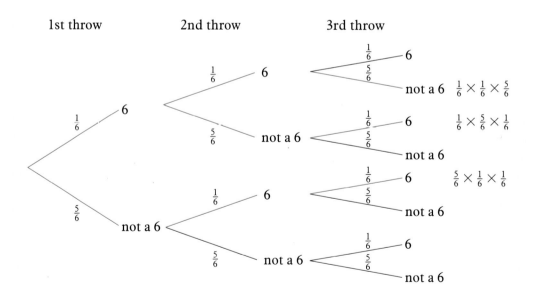

The three red paths give exactly two 6s.

$$P(\text{exactly two 6s}) = (\tfrac{1}{6} \times \tfrac{1}{6} \times \tfrac{5}{6}) + (\tfrac{1}{6} \times \tfrac{5}{6} \times \tfrac{1}{6}) + (\tfrac{5}{6} \times \tfrac{1}{6} \times \tfrac{1}{6})$$

$$= \tfrac{15}{216} = \tfrac{5}{72}$$

Exercise 31:2

1 Graham has a box containing 20 counters. Four are red, six are green and the rest are blue.
Graham picks out one counter at random and then replaces it.
He then picks out a second counter at random.

a Copy this tree diagram.
Fill it in.

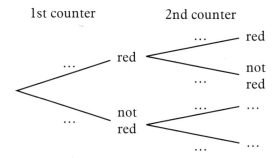

Find the probability that:
b both counters are red
c only one counter is red.

2 Keith uses this spinner twice.

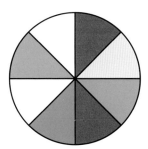

Use a tree diagram to find the probability that Keith gets:
a two blues
b only one blue.

3 Jane chooses one card at random from a pack of cards and then replaces it.
She does this two more times.
Use a tree diagram to find the probability that Jane gets:
a three hearts
b only one heart
c no hearts.

Sometimes one of the paths of a tree diagram stops before the others.

Example   Julia is taking a music exam. The probability of her passing is 0.6
If she fails she resits the exam.
a Draw a tree diagram to show the possible outcomes.
b Find the probability that she passes the exam on the second try.

a

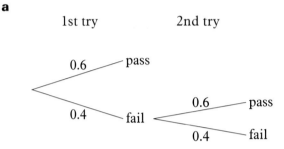

1st try   2nd try

The top path stops because she has passed the exam.
There is no need for her to resit.

b *P*(Julia passes on the second try) = 0.4 × 0.6
                                                   = 0.24

Exercise 31:3

1   Amira has to pass a fitness test before she can join the school athletics team.
The probability that she passes the test is 0.8
Amira resits the test if she fails first time.
a Copy this tree diagram showing all the possible outcomes for two tests.
Fill it in.

1st try   2nd try

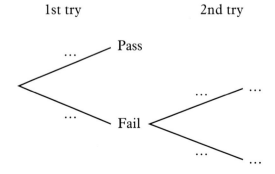

Find the probability that Amira will:
b pass on the second test
c fail both tests.

2 The probability of Gary winning a place on a Tennis course is $\frac{1}{4}$.
If he does not get on the first course then he can try for the second course.
   a Draw a probability tree showing all the possible outcomes for the two courses.

Find the probability that Gary wins a place:
b on the second course
c on neither course.

3 Penel has to throw a six with a dice to win a game.
She is only allowed three throws of the dice.
   a Copy and complete the tree diagram to show all the possible outcomes of the three throws.

1st throw   2nd throw   3rd throw

Find the probability of Penel:
b not getting a six on the first try
c not getting a six on the first two tries
d winning the game on the third try
e not winning the game.

2 Changing probabilities

Sally has just lost her match. She has another match next week and she thinks that she will lose that one too. She has lost confidence in herself.

Example

Sally has two tennis matches to play.

The probability that she wins the 1st match is $\frac{3}{5}$

If she wins the 1st match the probability that she wins the 2nd is $\frac{7}{10}$

If she loses the 1st match the probability that she wins the 2nd is $\frac{2}{5}$

Use a tree diagram to find the probability that Sally:

a wins both matches

b wins only one of her matches.

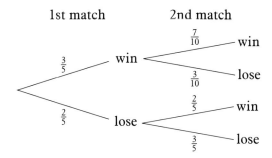

In the top two paths Sally has won the 1st match.

This means that the probability that she wins the 2nd is $\frac{7}{10}$

In the bottom two paths Sally has lost her 1st match.

This means that the probability that she wins the 2nd is $\frac{2}{5}$

a P (Sally wins both matches) $= \frac{3}{5} \times \frac{7}{10} = \frac{21}{50}$

b P (Sally wins only one of her matches) $= (\frac{3}{5} \times \frac{3}{10}) + (\frac{2}{5} \times \frac{2}{5}) = \frac{17}{50}$

Exercise 31:4

1 Phillip has two darts matches to play.
The probability that he wins the 1st match is $\frac{1}{4}$
If he wins the 1st match the probability that he wins the 2nd is $\frac{1}{2}$
If he loses the 1st match the probability that he wins the 2nd is $\frac{1}{6}$

a Copy and complete this probability tree.

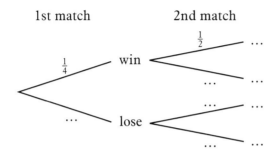

Find the probability that Phillip:
b wins both matches
c loses both matches
d wins the 1st match but loses the 2nd
e wins only one of the two matches.

2 The probability that Ajay passes his driving test first time is 0.5
If he fails, the probability that he passes on the second attempt is 0.6

a Copy this tree diagram showing all the possible outcomes for two tests.

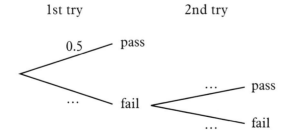

Find the probability that Ajay:
b passes on the second try
c fails both tests.

3 Richard chooses a two course meal from a menu. He chooses either fish or meat for each course.
The probability that he will choose fish for his first course is 0.6, otherwise he chooses meat.
The probability that he chooses fish for his second course is either 0.3 if he has fish for the first course or 0.8 if he has meat for his first course.

a Copy and complete this probability tree.

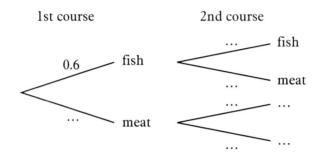

Find the probability that he chooses:
b fish for both courses
c fish for only one course.

4 The probability that Ann is late for lectures is 0.2
When she is late the probability that the car park is full is 0.8
When she is not late the probability that the car park is full is 0.4

a Copy and complete this probability tree.

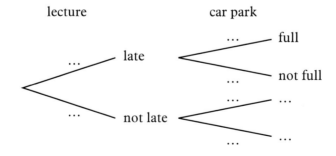

Find the probability that Ann:
b is late and finds the car park full
c finds the car park full.

5 Tom is practising his archery.
He says the probability that he hits the bull with an arrow is 0.4
If there is an arrow already in the bull then the probability that he hits
the bull a 2nd time falls to 0.3

Tom shoots two arrows. Find the probability that:

a both arrows hit the bull
b both arrows miss the bull
c only one arrow hits the bull.

6 The probability of Judy being accepted on a Drama course is $\frac{1}{4}$
If she does not get on the course then the probability that she will be
accepted for the next course is $\frac{3}{5}$
She can only attend one course.
a Draw a probability tree showing all the possible outcomes for 2 courses.

Find the probability that Judy:
b is accepted on the second course
c is not accepted on either course.

7 Sanjay has two chances to lift a set of weights.
The probability of his succeeding on the
first try is 0.8
On the 2nd try the probability that he
succeeds is 0.4
a Draw a tree diagram to show all the
possible outcomes

Find the probability of Sanjay:
b failing on the first try
c failing on both tries
d succeeding on the 2nd try.

You can use mutually exclusive events to find a quick method for finding probabilities which involve the words 'at least one'.

Example　A bag contains 2 yellow and 3 red balls.
A ball is picked out at random and its colour noted.
The ball is then replaced and the process repeated.
Find the probability that **at least one** ball is red.

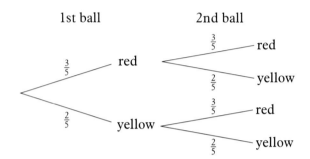

1st ball   2nd ball

The events $P(\text{\textbf{at least one} ball is red})$ and $P(\text{\textbf{no} balls are red})$ are mutually exclusive and nothing else is possible.
Either **no** balls are red or **at least one** of them is red.

$$P(\text{at least one ball is red}) = 1 - P(\text{no balls are red})$$
$$= 1 - \tfrac{2}{5} \times \tfrac{2}{5}$$
$$= 1 - \tfrac{4}{25}$$
$$= \tfrac{21}{25}$$

Exercise 31:5

1　A bag contains 4 green and 3 black cubes.
A cube is picked out at random and its colour noted.
The cube is then replaced and the process repeated.
a　Draw a tree diagram to show all the possible outcomes.
b　Copy this. Use your diagram to fill it in.

$$P(\text{at least one cube is green}) = 1 - P(\ldots\ldots\ldots\ldots\ldots)$$
$$= 1 - \left(\frac{\ldots}{7} \times \frac{\ldots}{7} \right)$$
$$= 1 - \ldots$$
$$= \ldots$$

2 Carl throws two fair dice.

  a Copy this tree diagram. Fill it in.

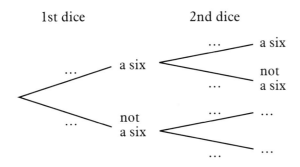

1st dice   2nd dice

... — a six

... — a six

not a six — ... — not a six

not a six

... — ...

... — ...

  b Copy this. Use your diagram to fill it in.

P(at least one six) $= 1 - P(\ldots\ldots\ldots\ldots\ldots)$
$= 1 - (\ldots \times \ldots)$
$= 1 - \ldots$
$= \ldots$

3 Geoff spins two coins.
  a Draw a tree diagram to show all the possible outcomes.

Find the probability that Geoff gets:
  b two heads
  c only one tail
  d at least one tail.

4 Daniel drives through two sets of traffic
lights on his way to work.
The probability that he has to stop at
the first set is $\frac{3}{5}$ and that he has
to stop at the second is $\frac{1}{2}$

Find the probability that he has to stop at:
  a both sets of lights
  b just one set of lights
  c at least one set of lights.

5 Emma is making jewellery with semi-precious stones.
The probability that a stone is flawed is 0.3
Emma makes a pendant using 3 stones.
  a Copy this tree diagram. Fill it in.

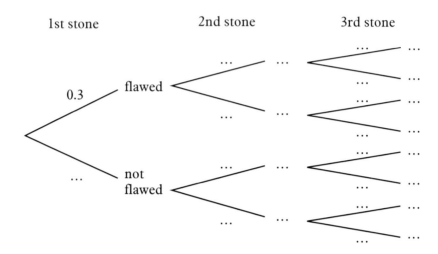

1st stone	2nd stone	3rd stone

0.3 — flawed

... — not flawed

Find the probability that:
  b no stones are flawed
  c only one stone is flawed
  d at least one stone is flawed.

6 Veena is taking exams in Maths, English and History.
The probability that she passes Maths is 0.6
The corresponding probabilities for English and History are 0.8 and 0.3
Find the probability that Veena:
  a passes all three exams
  b fails just one exam
  c passes at least one exam.

7 Cara sorts plates in a china factory.
Of the plates made 70% are perfect,
25% are seconds and the rest are chipped.
The chipped ones are destroyed.
Cara picks out two plates at random.
Find the probability that:
  a they are both perfect
  b they both have to be destroyed
  c at least one is a second.

1 Sally drops two drawing pins.
The probability that a drawing pin lands point up is $\frac{1}{4}$
  a Draw a tree diagram to show all the possible outcomes for the two
    drawing pins.
Find the probability that:
  b both drawing pins will land point up
  c only one drawing pin will land point up
  d neither drawing pin will land point up.

2 The probability that a family has three or more children is $\frac{1}{9}$
Two families are chosen at random.
  a Draw a tree diagram to show all the possible outcomes.
Find the probability that:
  b neither family has three or more children
  c only one family has three or more children.

3 Tarvin tennis club have two matches to play.
One is at home and the other away.
The probability that they will win the home match is $\frac{4}{5}$
The probability that they will win the away match is $\frac{3}{5}$
Use a tree diagram to find the probability that:
  a they win both matches
  b they lose both matches
  c they lose only one of the matches.

4 Faith uses this spinner three times.
  a Draw a probability tree to show
    all the possible outcomes.
Find the probability that Faith gets:
  b three reds
  c only one red
  d exactly two reds.

5 Philip has a 60% chance of getting a place on any one of his school's
ski trips. He is only allowed to go on one trip.
  a Write 60% as a decimal.
    Philip starts trying to get a place this year. If he fails he will try again
    next year and so on. He has just three years left at school.
  b Draw a probability tree to show all the possible outcomes.
Find the probability that Philip:
  c gets a place this year
  d gets a place next year
  e doesn't get a place on any of the three trips.

6 Mary always does the crossword on her way to work on the train.
The probability that she finishes the crossword is 0.7 if the train is late
and 0.55 if the train is not late.
The train is late 20% of the time.

a Copy and complete this tree diagram.

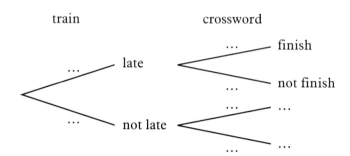

Find the probability that:
b the train is late and Mary finishes the crossword
c Mary finishes the crossword.

7 William has a biased coin.
The probability of a head when it is tossed is 0.6
He tosses the coin three times.
Find the probability that he gets:
a 3 tails
b 3 heads
c at least one tail.

8 The probability that the school team wins their next football match is 0.4
If they win then the probability that they win the following match is 0.5
If they do not win, the probability that they win the following match is 0.3
a Draw a probability tree showing all the possible outcomes of the next
two matches.

Find the probability that, in the next two matches:
b they win both
c they do not win either
d they win only one match
e they win at least one match.

9 A player in the school football team has a probability of 0.2 of suffering an injury during the football season. If a player suffers an injury one season then the probability that they will get an injury next season increases to 0.4
Find the probability that a player gets:
  a one injury in either of his first two seasons
  b his first injury in the second season
  c no injuries in his first two seasons.

10 20% of the calls to a fire station are false alarms.
Find the probability that for the next three calls:

  a all three are false alarms
  b at least one is false
  c only one is false.

11 The probability that a lightbulb will fail in the first year is 0.3
Three bulbs are chosen at random.
  a Draw a tree diagram to show all the possible outcomes.
  Find the probability that:
  b all three will fail in the first year
  c only two will fail in the first year
  d none will fail in the first year
  e at least one will fail in the first year.

1 One lunchtime three times as many men as women ordered meals at a restaurant. 70% of the men and 30% of the women ordered chips.
Find the probability that a diner chosen at random is:
a a woman
b a man who ordered chips
c a person who ordered chips
d a woman who didn't order chips.

2 Rhian has a 60% chance of passing her driving test first time.
If she fails her test the probability of her passing it next time increases by 10%.
Find the probability that Rhian passes her test:
a on her second attempt
b on her third attempt
c on her fifth attempt
d on either the third or the fourth attempt.

3 Tom drives to work and is sometimes late because of traffic jams.
He is late $\frac{1}{5}$ of the time.
The car park is full 90% of the time when he is late.
It is full one quarter of the time when he is not late.
a Copy and complete this tree diagram.

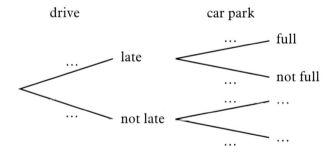

Use the diagram to find the probability that
b he is late and the car park is full
c he is not late and the car park is full
d the car park is full when he gets to work
e the car park is not full when he gets to work.
Tom drives to work 300 times in one year.
f How many times would you expect the car park to be full?

4 Dev does not know the answers to 3 multiple choice questions in a test.
Each question has three possible answers. Dev guesses the answers.
Find the probability that Dev gets
a all three answers correct
b all three answers wrong
c at least one answer correct.

1 Jason spins an octagonal spinner twice.
The sides of the spinner are numbered from 1 to 8.
Each score is equally likely.
a Copy this tree diagram. Fill it in.

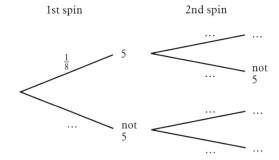

Find the probability that:
b Jason scores a 5 on both spins.
c Jason scores a 5 with just one of the spins.

2 Selena serves three balls in a game of tennis.
The probability that she serves an ace on any one serve is 0.15
a Copy and complete the tree diagram to show all the possible
outcomes of the three serves.

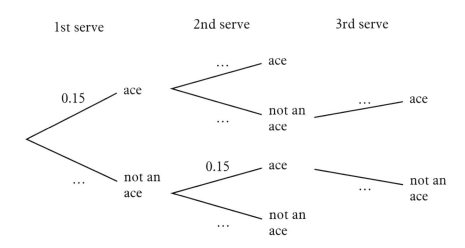

b Find the probability that Selena will serve:
   (1) three aces
   (2) at least one ace
   (3) just two aces
   (4) less than three aces.

3 Tom has an interview for a job.
Successful candidates attend a second interview.
The probability that Tom is successful in the first interview is 0.6
The probability that he is then successful in the second interview is 0.7
  a Copy the tree diagram. Fill it in.

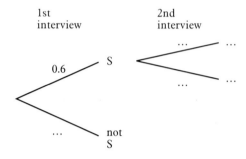

  b What is the probability that Tom is successful in both interviews?
  c What is the probability that Tom attends both interviews but is not successful in the second?

4 A spinner has two possible outcomes: red or blue.

The probability of obtaining red is $\frac{5}{8}$.

Cherie uses the spinner three times.
Use a tree diagram to find the probability that Cherie gets:
  a three reds
  b at least one blue
  c two reds and one blue.

5 Jack has a biased coin.
The probability that it shows heads when tossed is 0.7
He tosses the coin three times.
Find the probability that he gets:
  a 3 heads
  b at least one tail
  c at least one head.

32 Inner space

1 Identical shapes
Defining congruence
Looking at congruence
Counting lines of symmetry
Completing patterns with symmetry
Drawing reflections in a line of symmetry
Using planes of symmetry in 3D

CORE

2 About turn
Looking at rotational symmetry
Finding angles inside and outside of polygons
Looking at tessellations

3 Similar triangles
Introducing similar triangles
Using the rules for similar triangles to find
missing sides

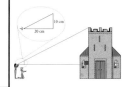

QUESTIONS

EXTENSION

TEST YOURSELF

1 Identical shapes

These twins are said to be identical. There may be very small differences but most people can't tell them apart.

In maths, if two shapes are identical they are called congruent.

Congruent   Two shapes are **congruent** if they are identical.
They have to be the same size *and* the same shape.

Shapes do not have to be drawn the same way round to be congruent.
All these triangles are congruent.

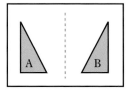 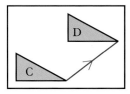 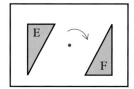

You reflect triangle A to get triangle B.
You translate triangle C to get triangle D.
You rotate triangle E to get triangle F.

Exercise 32:1

1 Look at these shapes. Which shapes are congruent?
Write down their letters in pairs.

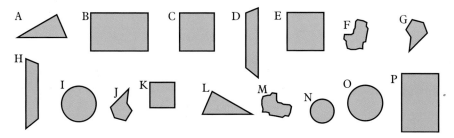

2 Look at these shapes. Which shapes are congruent?
Write down their letters in pairs.

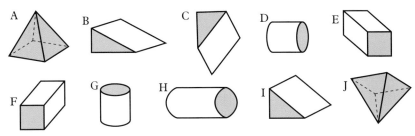

3 You need tracing paper for this question.
  a Can shape C be mapped on to shape A by a transformation?
  b Can shape D be mapped on to shape A by a transformation?
  c Can shape B be mapped on to shape A by transformation?
  d Describe fully any transformations you have found in **a** to **c**.
  e Which of the shapes are congruent?

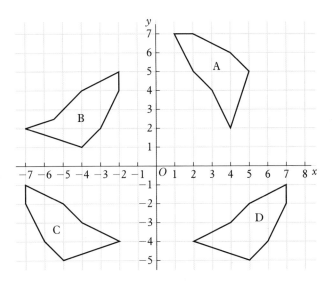

4 Are these shapes congruent? Explain your answer.

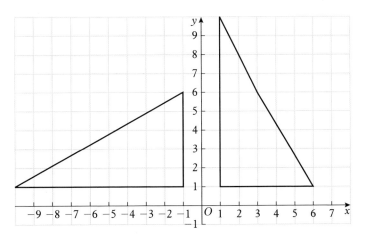

| Line of symmetry | A **line of symmetry** divides a shape into two identical halves. Each part is a reflection of the other. If you fold a shape along this line, each part fits exactly on top of the other. |

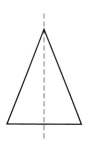

This isosceles triangle has one line of symmetry. You draw a line of symmetry with a dashed line.

Exercise 32:2

1 How many lines of symmetry does each of these shapes have?

a

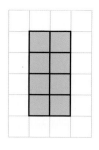

b

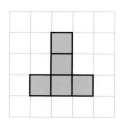

2 Copy these shapes on to squared paper.
Mark on all the lines of symmetry.

a

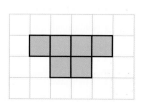

b

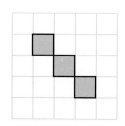

Example   Complete this pattern so that the
red line is a line of symmetry.

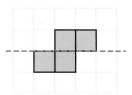

You need to shade in the squares
that complete the pattern.
There are two squares needed.

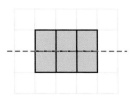

This is the completed pattern.

3   Copy these shapes on to squared paper.
Shade in two more squares so that the **red** line is a line of symmetry.

a

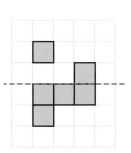

b

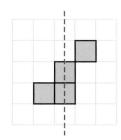

4   Copy these shapes on to squared paper.
Shade in two more squares so that the **red** line and the **blue** line are both
lines of symmetry.

a

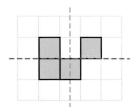

b

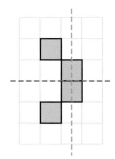

Example

Draw the reflection of the shape in the **red** line.

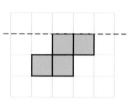

You need to draw what you would see in a mirror if you put a mirror on the red line.
You can use a mirror to help you.

This is the completed picture.
The red line is a line of symmetry.

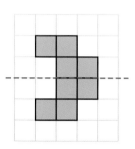

5 Copy these shapes on to squared paper.
Draw the reflection of each shape in the line of symmetry.

a

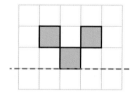

b

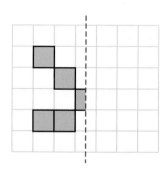

6 Copy these shapes on to squared paper.
Use the **red** lines of symmetry to complete each picture.

a

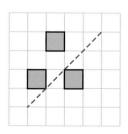

b

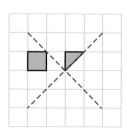

You can also have symmetry in 3 dimensions.

Instead of having a mirror line you can now think about putting a whole mirror into the shape.

This is a cuboid.

You can see the three possible places to put a mirror so that the two halves are symmetrical.

When you can put a mirror into a shape like this the mirror is called a plane of symmetry.

Exercise 32:3

1 How many planes of symmetry does each of these shapes have?

a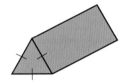

c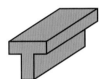

e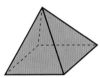

b

d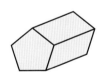

f

2 How many planes of symmetry does

   a a cube have

   ● **b** a sphere have?

W You need worksheet 32:1

2 About turn

The Three Legs of Man is the national symbol of the Isle of Man.

It is based on an earlier design that was a symbol of pagan Sun worship.

Rotational symmetry	A shape has **rotational symmetry** if it fits on top of itself more than once as it makes a complete turn.
Order of rotational symmetry	The **order of rotational symmetry** is the number of times that the shape fits on to itself. This must be two or more.
Centre of rotation	The **centre of rotation** is the point that stays still as the shape makes a complete turn.

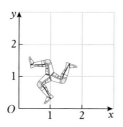

The Three Legs of Man symbol has rotational symmetry of order 3 about its centre at (1, 1).

Exercise 32:4

1 Look at these shapes.
Write down the letter of each one that has rotational symmetry.

a 　　b 　　c 　　d

Write down the order of rotational symmetry of each of the shapes in questions **2** and **3**.

2 a

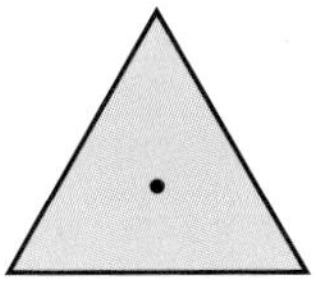

c

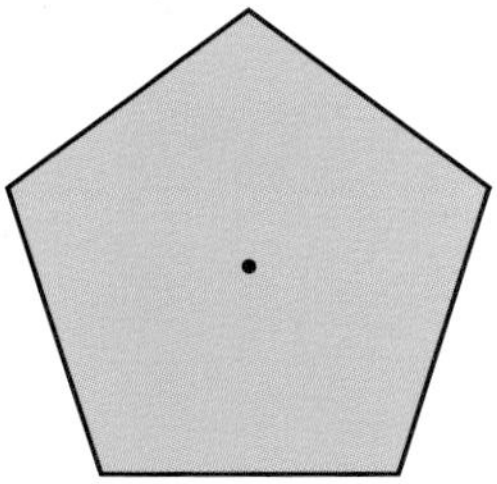

e

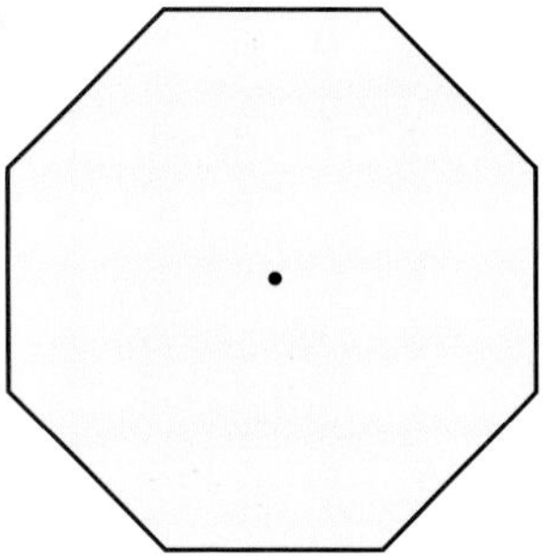

b

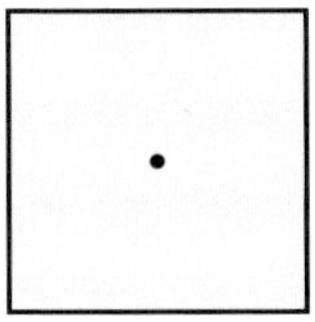

d

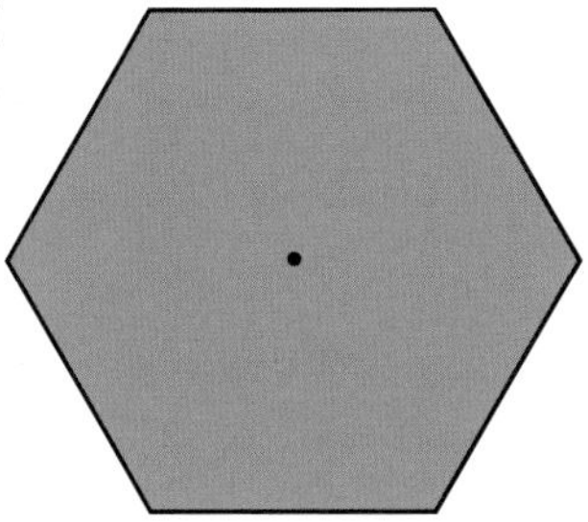

f

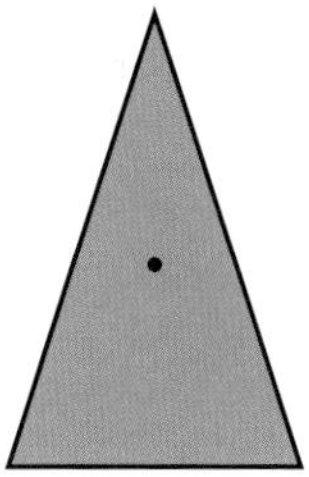

3 a

c

b

d

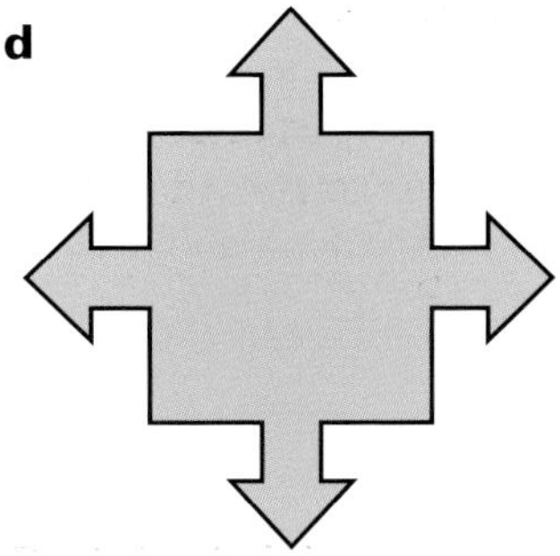

4 Describe the rotational symmetry of each of these graphs.
You will need to give the order of the rotational symmetry and the
co-ordinates of the centre of rotation for each one.

a $y = x^3$

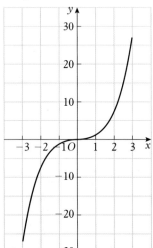

● **c** $y = (x - 2)^3 + 1$

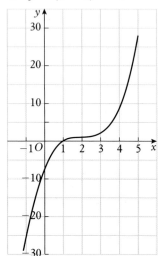

b $y = \dfrac{1}{x}$

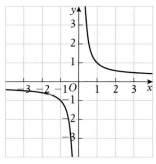

d $y = \dfrac{1}{x - 3} + 2$

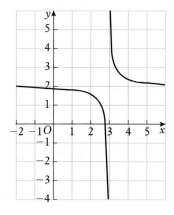

5 Copy the diagram.
Complete it so that it
has rotational symmetry
of order 4 about C.

Exterior angles To find an **exterior angle**:
(1) Make one side longer.
(2) Mark the angle between your line and the next side.
(3) This is the exterior angle. The blue angles are all exterior angles.

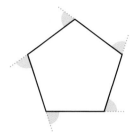

The diagram shows a regular pentagon. It has rotational symmetry of order 5 about the point C.

The pentagon fits onto itself 5 times in one rotation.

The size of each turn is $360° ÷ 5 = 72°$. This is the size of the exterior angle.

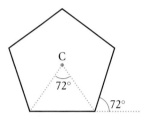

If a regular polygon has n sides then:

1 it has rotational symmetry of order n

2 the exterior angle $= \dfrac{360°}{n}$

3 $n = \dfrac{360°}{\text{the exterior angle}}$

Exercise 32:5

1 Work out the exterior angle of a regular hexagon.

2 Work out the exterior angle of a regular decagon.

3 The exterior angle of a regular polygon is 12°.
How many sides does it have?

4 The exterior angle of a regular polygon is 15°.
How many sides does it have?

5 a Write down which of these is not an exterior angle of a regular polygon.
(1) 40°   (2) 22.5°   (3) 50°   (4) 8°
b Explain how you were able to decide.

6 Each diagram shows two sides of a regular polygon.
Work out the number of sides for each one.

a

24°

c

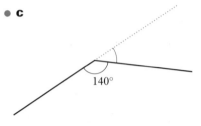

140°

b

10°

d

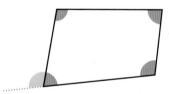

157.5°

Interior angles   An **interior angle** is the
angle inside a shape where
two sides meet. The red
angles are all interior angles.

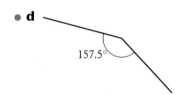

The interior angle always makes a straight line with the exterior
angle.

This means that interior angle + exterior angle = 180°.

---

7 Write down the interior angle when the exterior angle is:
   a 72°   **b** 9°   **c** 60°   **d** 3°

8 A regular polygon has 30 sides.
   a Find the size of the exterior angle.
   b Write down the interior angle.

9 The interior angle of a regular polygon is 172°.
   a Write down the exterior angle.
   b Work out how many sides the polygon has.

You can find the sum of the interior angles of any polygon.

(1) Draw the polygon.

(2) Join one vertex to all the others.
You divide the shape into triangles.
All the interior angles are now inside one of the triangles.

(3) Count the number of triangles.
Multiply by 180° to find the total.

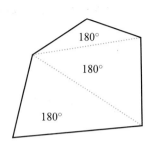

Example   Find the sum of the interior angles of a pentagon.
The pentagon splits into 3 triangles.

Total = 3 × 180° = 540°

The sum of the interior angles of a pentagon is 540°.
This is true for all pentagons.

Exercise 32:6

1   Calculate the size of the missing angle in each of these pentagons.

a

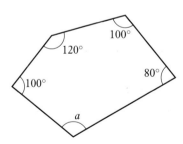

c

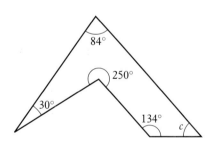

b

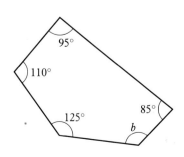

d

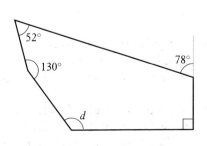

2 **a** A hexagon has 6 sides. Draw a hexagon.
   b Join one vertex to all of the others.
   c Count the number of triangles.
   d Find the sum of the interior angles of a hexagon.

3 **a** A heptagon has 7 sides. Draw a heptagon.
   b Join one vertex to all of the others.
   c Count the number of triangles.
   d Find the sum of the interior angles of a heptagon.

4 **a** An octagon has 8 sides. Draw an octagon.
   b Join one vertex to all of the others.
   c Count the number of triangles.
   d Find the sum of the interior angles of an octagon.

5 **a** A nonagon has 9 sides. Draw a nonagon.
   b Join one vertex to all of the others.
   c Count the number of triangles.
   d Find the sum of the interior angles of a nonagon.

6 **a** A decagon has 10 sides. Draw a decagon.
   b Join one vertex to all of the others.
   c Count the number of triangles.
   d Find the sum of the interior angles of a decagon.

7 **a** Copy the table. Fill it in.

Name of polygon	Number of sides	Number of triangles	Sum of interior angles
	5	3	$3 \times 180°$
	6		
	7		
	8		
	9		
	10		

   b Use the results in your table to find a formula for the sum of the interior angles of a polygon with n sides.

The sum of the interior angles of a polygon with n sides is $(n - 2) \times 180°$.

The sum of the exterior angles of any polygon is $360°$.

8   The exterior angles of a pentagon are $64°$, $78°$, $80°$, $36°$ and $x°$.
   Find the value of x.

9   The exterior angles of a hexagon are $x°$, $x°$, $2x°$, $2x°$, $3x°$, $3x°$.
   a   Find the value of x.
   b   How many of these angles are right-angles?
   c   How many of the interior angles are obtuse? Explain your answer.

10   Find the sum of the interior angles of a polygon with 22 sides.

11   The sum of the interior angles of a polygon is $3240°$.
   a   Use n to stand for the number of sides. Write an equation for n.
   b   Solve your equation. How many sides does the polygon have?

Tessellation   A **tessellation** is a pattern made by repeating the same shape
over and over again.

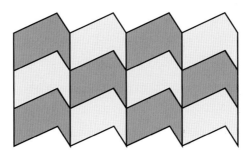

There are no gaps in a tessellation.

Exercise 32:7

1 The diagram shows 2 congruent trapeziums joined along one side.
   a Copy the diagram.
   b Draw another 10 congruent trapeziums to make a tessellation.

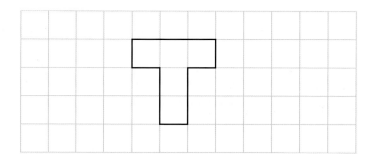

2 **a** Copy the diagram.
   b Draw another 10 congruent 'T' shapes to make a tessellation.

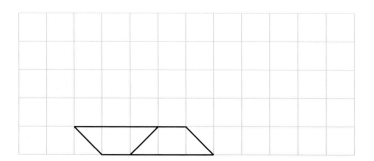

3 Draw a tessellation using congruent triangles.

4 Draw a tessellation using congruent hexagons.

● **5** **a** Find the size of the interior angle of a regular octagon.
   b Explain why a regular octagon will not tessellate.

Drawing regular polygons

You can draw a regular polygon by marking equally spaced points around a circle.

To draw a pentagon, start by drawing a circle. If you have an angle measurer you can do this by drawing around it.

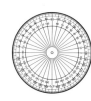

Next, divide the 360° by the number of sides. 360° ÷ 5 = 72°.

Mark points around the circumference of the circle at 72° intervals.

Now join the points with a ruler.

The pentagon is now inscribed in the circle.

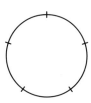

If you are drawing a regular hexagon, you can do this without an angle measurer.

Draw a circle with a pair of compasses.
Without changing the compasses, mark points around the circumference of the circle.

You should be able to mark exactly 6 points.

Join these points to form the hexagon.

6 Draw the following regular polygons.
   a Pentagon   **c** Octagon
   b Hexagon   **d** Decagon

3 Similar triangles

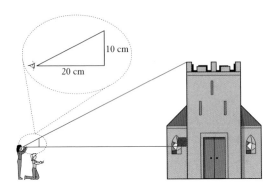

Lin and Karina are finding the height of the church tower.
They haven't got a clinometer to measure the angle.
They are using a triangle made from card.
This section will show you how to find a height like this.

Exercise 32:8

1 a You need a piece of 1 cm squared paper.
You will need to draw these triangles accurately.
Start near the bottom left hand corner of your paper.
Draw triangle AB_1C_1 with a right angle at B_1.
$AB_1 = 3$ cm, $B_1C_1 = 2$ cm.

b Now draw AB_2 6 cm long.
Draw another right angle at B_2
and draw in B_2C_2.

c Carry on drawing triangles like this to get this diagram.

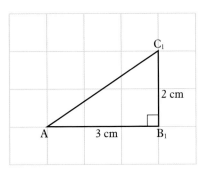

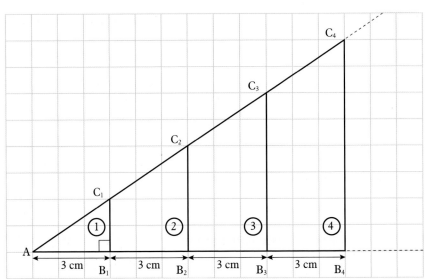

d Copy this table. Measure the sides of the triangles. Fill in the table.
The first row has been filled in for you.

Triangle number	Length	Length	Length (2 sf)	Angle (2 sf)	Angle (2 sf)	Ratio	Ratio	Ratio
1	AB_1 = 3 cm	B_1C_1 = 2 cm	AC_1 = 3.6 cm	$C_1\hat{A}B_1$ = 34°	$B_1\hat{C}_1A$ = 56°	$\dfrac{AB_1}{AB_1} = 1$	$\dfrac{B_1C_1}{B_1C_1} = 1$	$\dfrac{AC_1}{AC_1} = 1$
2	AB_2 = ...	B_2C_2 = ...	AC_2 = ...	$C_2\hat{A}B_2$ = ...	$B_2\hat{C}_2A$ = ...	$\dfrac{AB_2}{AB_1} = ...$	$\dfrac{B_2C_2}{B_1C_1} = ...$	$\dfrac{AC_2}{AC_1} = ...$

e Continue your table for at least 5 triangles.

2 **a** What do you notice about the angles $C_1\hat{A}B_1$, $C_2\hat{A}B_2$, ...?
  b What do you notice about the angles $B_1\hat{C}_1A$, $B_2\hat{C}_2A$, ...?
  c What do you know about the angles at B_1, B_2, B_3, ...?
  d What do your results to parts **a**, **b** and **c** tell you about the angles in these triangles?

3 **a** Write down the lengths AB_1, AB_2, AB_3, ... as a sequence.
  b Copy this. Fill it in.
    The lengths are all .... of 3.
  c Write down the lengths B_1C_1, B_2C_2, B_3C_3, ... as a sequence.
  d Describe this sequence.
  e Write down the lengths AC_1, AC_2, AC_3, ... as a sequence.
  • f Describe this sequence.
  • g What do your results to parts **b**, **d** and **f** tell you about the sides in these triangles?

4 **a** What do you notice about the ratios $\dfrac{AB_2}{AB_1}$, $\dfrac{B_2C_2}{B_1C_1}$, $\dfrac{AC_2}{AC_1}$, ...?

  b What do you notice about the ratios $\dfrac{AB_3}{AB_1}$, $\dfrac{B_3C_3}{B_1C_1}$, $\dfrac{AC_3}{AC_1}$, ...?

  c What do your results suggest about the ratios of corresponding sides in these triangles?

Similar

If two objects are **similar**, one is an enlargement of the other.
They have the same shape but different sizes.

| Similar triangles | **Similar triangles** have all 3 pairs of angles equal. Their three pairs of sides are in the same ratio. |

Triangles ABC and DEF are similar. $\widehat{ABC} = \widehat{DEF}$ and $\widehat{CAB} = \widehat{FDE}$.
Find the missing length.

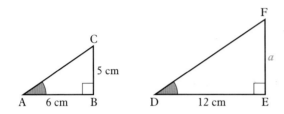

Use common sense. Triangle DEF is bigger than ABC.
So the scale factor going from left to right is **more than 1**

So from triangle ABC to triangle DEF, scale factor $= \dfrac{DE}{AB} = \dfrac{12}{6} = 2$

So $a = 2 \times 5 = 10$ cm

Exercise 32:9

Each pair of triangles in questions **1** to **4** are similar.
Find the missing lengths marked with letters.

1

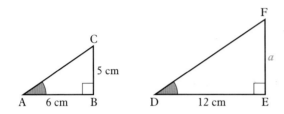

3

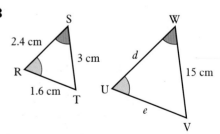

2

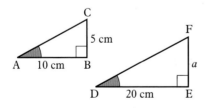

4

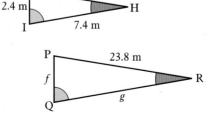

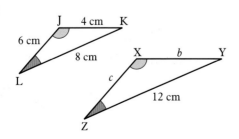

Triangles ABC and FGH are similar. $B\hat{C}A = G\hat{H}F$ and $C\hat{A}B = H\hat{F}G$.
Find the missing lengths.

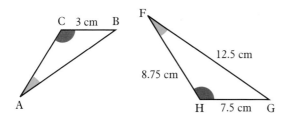

The colours show the pairs of matching angles.
You can trace the triangle on the left.
Rotate it and reflect it so the angles match the positions in the triangle on the right. Your triangles should now look like this.

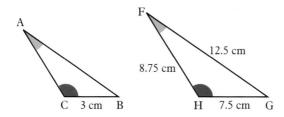

Now use common sense. Triangle BCA is smaller than triangle FGH
so the scale factor going from right to left is **less than 1**

So from triangle GHF to triangle BCA, scale factor $= \dfrac{BC}{GH} = \dfrac{3}{7.5} = 0.4$

So $AC = 0.4 \times 8.75 = 3.5$ cm   and $AB = 0.4 \times 12.5 = 5$ cm

For each pair of triangles in questions **5–12**:
a sketch the diagrams
b write down which pairs of angles are equal
c use tracing paper to show the triangles in matching positions.
d find the lengths marked with letters.

5

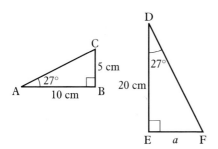

6

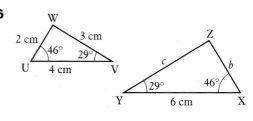

7

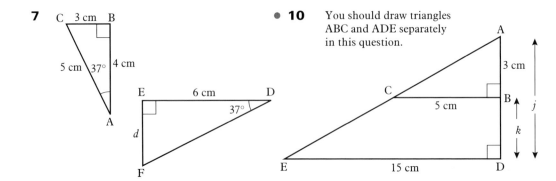

10 You should draw triangles ABC and ADE separately in this question.

8

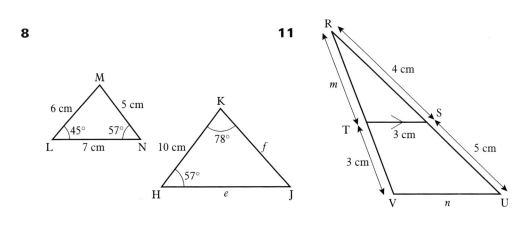

11

9

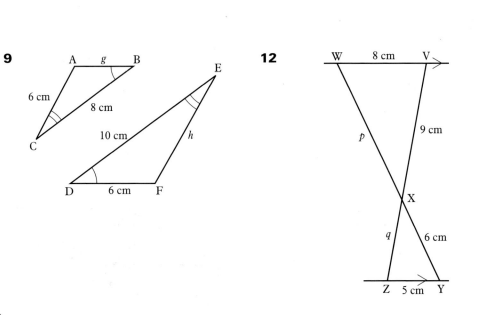

12

1   **a**   Copy the diagram.
       b   Complete figures B and C so that A, B and C are congruent.

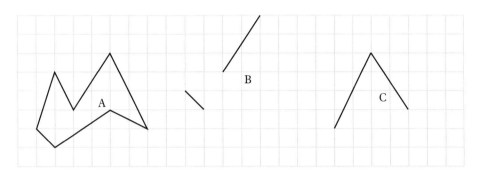

2   These two triangles are similar. Work out the lengths marked with letters.

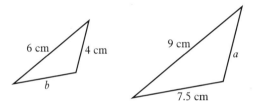

3   **a**   Copy these shapes onto squared paper.
       b   Use the red lines of symmetry to complete each shape.

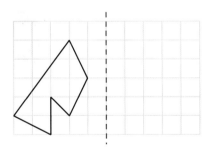
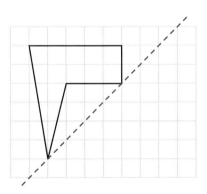

4   **a**   Copy the diagram.
       b   Show the two planes of
          symmetry on your drawing.

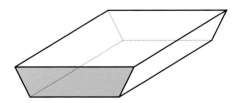

5 **a** Copy the diagrams.
b Complete each figure so that it has rotational symmetry of order 4 with centre at O.

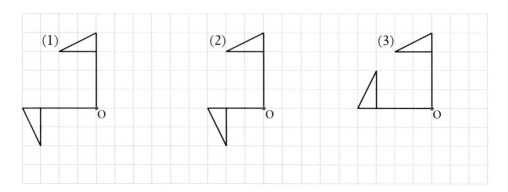

6 Write down the order of rotational symmetry of a:
a parallelogram
b rhombus
c regular decagon.

7 A dodecagon has 12 sides.
a Write down the order of rotational symmetry of a regular dodecagon.
b Find the size of the exterior angle of a regular dodecagon.
c Find the sum of the interior angles of a dodecagon.

8 The diagram shows two of the sides of a regular polygon. How many sides does the polygon have?

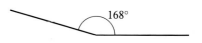

168°

9 Work out the size of the missing angle x in this irregular polygon.

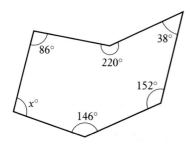

86°
220°
38°
152°
$x°$
146°

1 **a** Copy the diagram.
   b Draw its plane of symmetry.

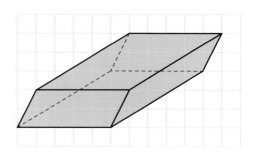

2 The interior angles of a pentagon are $2x°$, $3x°$, $3x°$, $4x°$ and $6x°$.
   a Find the value of x.
   b Write down the size of each of the interior angles.

3 Only 3 regular polygons will tessellate.
   How many sides do they have?

4 These triangles are similar.
   Find the value of x.

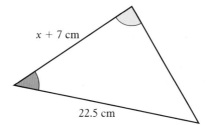

5 **a** Use Pythagoras' theorem to work out the length of CD.

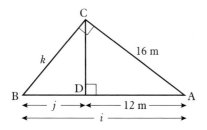

   b Write down which pairs of angles are equal in triangles ADC and ABC.
   c Find the lengths marked with letters.
   d How many similar triangles are there in the diagram?

1 Two of these triangles are congruent. Write down their letters.

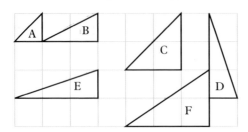

2 Two of the triangles in question **1** are similar but not congruent. Write down their letters.

3 How many planes of symmetry does each of these shapes have?

a 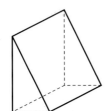 **b**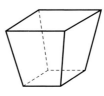

4 Write down the order of rotational symmetry of each of these shapes.

a  **b**

5 The interior angle of a regular polygon is 162°.
  a Write down the size of the exterior angle.
  b How many sides does the polygon have?

6 These two triangles are similar.
Find the value of *x*.

33 Constructions and loci

1 Constructions
Bisecting an angle
Bisecting a line
Constructing angles

2 Loci
Drawing a locus
Drawing a locus to scale
Looking at boundaries
Solving problems with more than one locus
Investigating goats!

CORE

QUESTIONS

EXTENSION

TEST YOURSELF

1   Constructions

Geometrical constructions are used at sea to plan routes.
Ships need to avoid rocks and sandbanks. They aim to travel in the deepest water. This chapter looks at how to do these constructions.

Bisecting an angle	**Bisecting an angle** means splitting it exactly in half. You do not need an angle measurer to do this. It is more accurate to do it with compasses.

Exercise 33:1

1 **a** Draw a 70° angle.

  b Open your compasses a small distance.
      You **must** keep your compasses fixed from now on.

  c With the compass point on the vertex of the angle, draw a small arc which crosses both arms of the angle. Label these points A and B.

  d Place your compasses on point A and draw another arc in the middle of the angle.

  e Now place your compasses on point B. Draw another arc in the middle of the angle. It should cross the first one.

  f Finally, draw a line from the vertex of the angle through the point where your two arcs cross. This line bisects the angle.

  g Measure the two parts of the angle to check that it is correct.

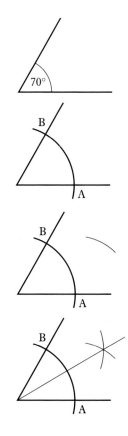

2 **a** Draw a 50° angle.
   b Draw an arc crossing both arms of the angle.
      Label the points A and B.
   c Draw arcs from points A and B.
   d Draw the line which bisects the angle.
   e Measure the two parts of the angle to check that it is correct.

3 **a** Draw a right angle.
   b Bisect the angle.
      Use the instructions in question **2** to help you.

4 **a** Draw an angle of 120°.
   b Bisect the angle.

**Equidistant
from two lines**

All the points on the line which bisects an angle are **equidistant** from the two arms of the angle.
This means that they are always the same distance from the two lines. Both the red lines marked are the same length. So are both the blue ones.

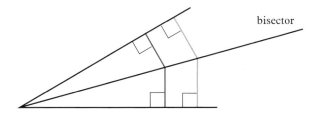

---

5 **a** Draw two lines AB and AC which are at 66° to each other.
   b Draw a line which is equidistant from AB and AC.

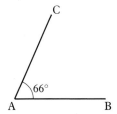

6 **a** Draw two lines PQ and PR which are at 140° to each other.
   b Draw a line that is equidistant from PQ and PR.

Exercise 33:2

1 Construct this triangle using a ruler and compasses. Start by drawing the line AB.

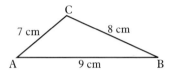

2 **a** Bisect the angle at vertex A of the triangle you have constructed for question **1**.
  b Bisect the angle at vertex B of the triangle.
  c Bisect the angle at vertex C of the triangle.
  The three bisectors should cross at one point.

3 **a** Construct an equilateral triangle with sides 9 cm.
  Label your triangle PQR.
  b Bisect all three angles of the triangle.
  c Mark the point X in the middle of PR.
  d Place the point of your compasses on the point where the bisectors cross. Move your pencil point until it touches point X.
  e Draw a circle with your compasses. This circle should just touch all three edges of the triangle. This is called the **inscribed circle**.

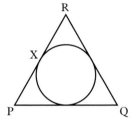

4 The sketch shows the path near to the edges of a cliff.
  For safety, the path goes down the centre of the cliff edges.
  This means that the path is equidistant from the cliff edges.
  Draw a scale drawing of the cliff edges and the path.
  Use a scale of 1 cm = 100 m.

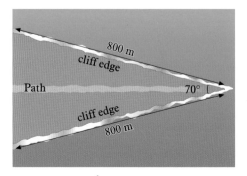

Bisecting a line	**Bisecting a line** means cutting it exactly in half.
Perpendicular	Two lines that are at right angles to each other are called **perpendicular**.
Perpendicular bisector	On this diagram, CD is perpendicular to AB and CD bisects AB. CD is called the **perpendicular bisector** of AB.

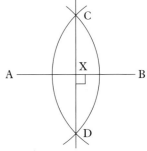

Exercise 33:3

1 a Draw a line 10 cm long.
Label the ends A and B.
Put your compass point on A.

b Move your pencil until you can tell it is more than half way along the line.

c Draw an arc from above the line to below it.

d **Without changing your compasses,** move the compass point to B.

e Draw another arc from B.

f Your arcs should cross above and below the line.
Label these points C and D.

g Join C to D. Use a ruler.
Line CD bisects line AB at right angles.
Mark the point of intersection X.
Measure AX and BX with a ruler to check that they are equal.

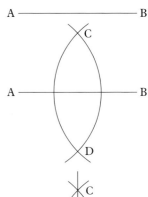

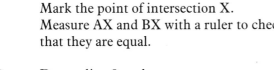

2 a Draw a line 8 cm long.
Label your line AB.

b Draw arcs from A and B.

c Label the crossing points of the arcs C and D.

d Join C to D to bisect the line.

e Check that CD bisects AB by measuring.

3 a Draw a line AB 7.4 cm long.

b Bisect the line using ruler and compasses.

| **Equidistant from two points** | All the points on the perpendicular bisector of a line are **equidistant from the two points** at the ends of the original line. |

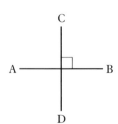

Every point on CD is equidistant from A and B.

In particular, CD passes through the midpoint of AB.

---

4 **a** Draw points A and B which are 7 cm apart.
  b Join the points with a straight line.
  c Construct a line that is made up of points that are equidistant from A and B.

5 The diagram shows the position of two buoys near a coastline.
Ships must stay exactly in the middle of the buoys to be in the deepest water.
  a Make a copy of the diagram.
    It does not have to be exact.
  b Draw the path that the ship should take between the buoys.

6 The diagram shows a plan of a factory floor. The red points show the positions of emergency power shutoff buttons A, B and C.
  a Make a scale drawing of the factory. Use a scale of 1 cm = 10 m.
  b By constructing a line on your diagram, shade the area of the factory where the workers are closer to button A than button B.
  c By constructing another two lines on your diagram, shade the area of the factory where workers are closer to button C than either of the other buttons.

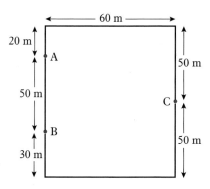

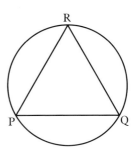

7 **a** Construct an equilateral triangle with
sides 10 cm.
Label your triangle PQR.

b Bisect all three sides of the triangle.

c Place the point of your compasses on the
point where the bisectors cross.
Move your pencil point until it touches
point P.

d Draw a circle with your compasses.
This circle should go through all three
points P, Q and R.
This is called **circumscribing the
triangle**.

It is possible to construct some angles just using a ruler and compasses.
If you do it carefully, it is more accurate than using an angle measurer.

To construct a 60° angle:

Start with a horizontal line.
Label it AB.

A _____ B

Set your compasses a small distance
apart and put the point on A.

Draw an arc from the line upwards until
you can see that you have turned through
more than 60°

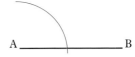

Put the point of your compass on the point
where the arc crosses your line.
Draw another arc which crosses the first one.

Join A to the point where the two arcs cross.

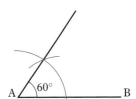

The angle is 60°
You can measure it to check.

Exercise 33:4

1 Construct a 60° angle using ruler and compasses.

2 **a** Construct a 60° angle using ruler and compasses.
   b Bisect your angle.
   This is how to draw a 30° angle.

3 **a** Construct a 30° angle using the steps in question **2**.
   b Bisect your angle.
   This is how to draw a 15° angle.

4 **a** Construct a 60° angle using ruler and compasses.
   b Bisect your angle.
   c Bisect the upper of the two 30° angles you now have.
   d Clearly mark a 45° angle.

5 **a** Construct a 60° angle using ruler and compasses.
   b Construct another 60° angle using the upper line of the first angle as your base line.
   c Clearly mark a 120° angle.

Constructing a 90° angle at a point is the same as drawing the perpendicular from a point on a line.

To draw the perpendicular from X on the line AB:
Set your compasses a small distance
apart and put the point on X.

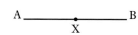

Draw a 180° arc so that it crosses
AB either side of X.
Label the points C and D.

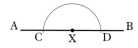

Put the point of your compass on C and draw an
arc above X. Put your compass on D and draw
another arc. It should cross the first one.
Join X to the point where the two arcs cross.
You now have a 90° angle.

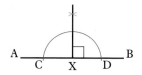

6 Construct a 90° angle using ruler and compasses.

7 **a** Construct a 90° angle using ruler and compasses.
   b Bisect your angle.
      This is another way to draw a 45° angle.

8 **a** Construct a 90° angle using ruler and compasses.
   b Bisect your angle.
   c Add a 60° angle to your diagram to construct an angle of 105°.

9 Use the angle constructions you have seen in the previous questions to construct the following angles.
   a 150°   **d** 165°
   b 75°   **e** 210°
   c $22\frac{1}{2}°$ **f** 330°

10 This is a sketch of a regular hexagon.
    Make an accurate drawing of this sketch.

5 cm

11 By bisecting at least two angles of each shape, find the exact centre of each polygon.

12 Lawrence has found an old Egyptian treasure map.
    Of course, the Ancient Egyptians were excellent mathematicians.
    So all the instructions on the treasure map involve maths.
    Get your copy of the map and the instructions. Happy hunting!

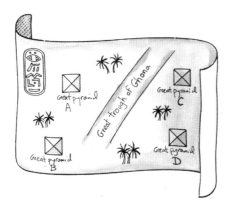

You need to know how to construct a perpendicular
from a point down to a line.

To construct the perpendicular from P onto AB

Put your compass point on P and make sure your
compasses are open wide enough to be able to draw
an arc that crosses AB at two points.
Label the points C and D.

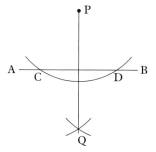

Now put your compass on C and then D and draw
two arcs that cross below the line.
Call this point Q.

Now join P to Q.

This line will be perpendicular to AB.

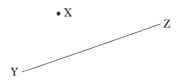

13 Draw the perpendicular from X onto YZ.

14 Lucy is orienteering.
She sees a road and wants to
get there as quickly as possible.
Draw a diagram to show this.
Mark a point for Lucy. Label it L.
Draw a line for the road.
Construct the route
that Lucy should take.

2   Loci

In Norway it is not unusual for people to keep animals on the roof!
It is important to keep Sven tied up so that he doesn't fall off.
Sven is attached to a post.
He can eat the grass in a circle.
The radius of the circle is the length of the rope.
The centre of the circle is the post.
Sven can be anywhere inside the circle.

When something can only be on a line or a curve then this line or curve is called a locus.
Loci is the plural of locus.

Locus

The **locus** of an object is the set of all the points which fit a certain condition.
You can describe a locus in words or with a diagram.

The tip of the hour hand on this clock moves in a circle.

The hour hand is 3 cm long.

The locus of the tip of the hour hand is a circle of radius 3 cm.
The centre of the circle is the centre of the clock.

You can also draw the locus.
The locus of the tip of the hour hand is the blue circle.

Exercise 33:5

In questions **1–4**:   **a**   describe the locus in words
                        b   draw a diagram to show the locus.

1   The locus of the tip of the minute hand on a clock. The hand is 5 cm long.

2   The locus of the midpoint of the minute hand in question **1**.

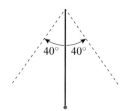

3 The locus of the bob of this pendulum as it swings through a total angle of 80°.
The pendulum is 30 cm long.
Use a scale of 1 cm to 10 cm.

● **4** The locus of a point that is always 4 cm away from a point O.

Example Draw the locus of a point that moves so that it is always 1 cm away from the line AB.

The point can be above or below the line.

A ————————————————— B

The two red lines are part of the locus of the point.
They are both 1 cm from the line.
The red lines are parallel to the original line and are the same length as AB.

Now look at the points at the ends of the line.

If you stay 1 cm away from each point you get a semicircle at each end of the line.
You should use compasses to draw the semicircles.
The blue line is the locus of a point that is always 1 cm away from the line AB.

Exercise 33:6

1 a Draw a 7 cm line.
Label it AB.

A —————————————————————— B

b Draw the locus of a point that is
always 3 cm away from this line.

2 This fence is 10 metres long.

a Draw a line to represent the fence.
Use a scale of 1 cm to 1 m.

b Draw the locus of a point that is
always 2 m away from the fence.

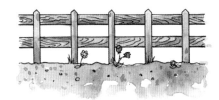

3 A wall is 40 metres long.

a Draw a line to represent the wall.
Use a scale of 1 cm to 10 m.

b Draw the locus of a point that is
always 10 m away from the wall.

4 a Copy this shape.

b Draw the locus of a point that
lies outside the shape and 1 cm
from the edge of the shape.

c Draw the locus of a point that
lies inside the shape and 1 cm
from the edge of the shape.

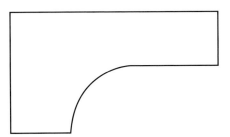

5 The rectangle represents a box.

a Copy the rectangle.

b Draw the locus of a point that is
3 cm from the edge of the box.
Remember the locus can be both
inside and outside the box.

c Copy the rectangle again.

d This coin is rolled around the
inside of the box so that is
always touching the sides.
Draw the locus of the centre
of the coin.

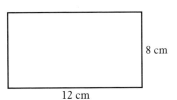

8 cm

12 cm

6 **a** Sketch the locus of the centre of this wheel as it rolls along the ground.

b Sketch the locus of the black point on the rim of the wheel.

7 **a** Copy this diagram.

b Draw the locus of a point that moves so that it is always the same distance from the points A and B.

c What is the mathematical name of this locus?

A •   • B

8 **a** Copy this diagram.

b Draw the locus of a point that moves so that it is the same distance from the lines AB and AC in this diagram.

c What is the mathematical name of this locus?

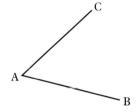

9 **a** Copy this diagram.

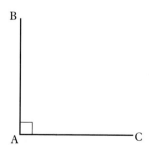

b Construct the locus of a point that moves so that it is the same distance from the lines AB and AC.

You can also use regions to describe where something can be.

Example   Sven the goat is tethered to a post in the centre of a roof.

The roof is 8 m long and 7 m wide.
The rope is 3 m long.
Make a scale drawing to show the area where Sven can graze.
Use a scale drawing of 1 cm to 2 m.

You need to draw a rectangle
4 cm by 3.5 cm.
The post, P, is at the centre
of the rectangle.
Now draw a circle, centre P,
with radius 1.5 cm.

Sven can eat grass anywhere
inside the red circle.

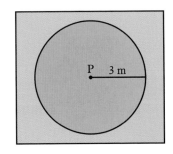

Exercise 33:7

1 a Mark a point D in the middle of your paper.
Leave a space of about 8 cm above and below your point.

D is an ambulance depot.
Ambulances answer calls anywhere in a 12 mile radius from the depot.

b Make a scale drawing to show the area covered by the ambulances
from this depot.
Use a scale of 1 cm to 2 miles.

2 A horse is tied to a wall at W.
The length of the rope is 3 m.
Make a scale drawing to show
where the horse can graze.
Use a scale of 1 cm to 1 m.

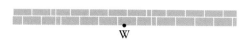

W

3 A guard dog is on a chain of length 4 m.
The other end of the chain is fixed to a ring.
The ring can move along the rail.
The rail is 5 m long.
Use shading to show the area where the
dog can reach.
Use a scale of 1 cm = 1 m.

4 Draw points R and S which are 5 cm apart.

a Construct the locus of the points which are equidistant from R and S.

b Shade on your drawing the region which is closer to R than to S.

5 A bull is chained to a ring in the
ground with a 4 m chain.
The ring is in the centre of a yard
10 m by 15 m.
Draw a diagram to show the area
of the yard that the bull cannot
reach.
Use a scale of 1 cm = 1 m.

You use dotted lines for some boundaries.
This is when the boundary is not included in the region.

Example   Show the region where the
points are **less than** 2 cm
from the point A.

The region is shaded.
The blue circle is dotted because
it is not included in the region.

You use a solid line when the
line is included in the region.

Example   Show the region where the points are **at least** 1 cm from the line AB.

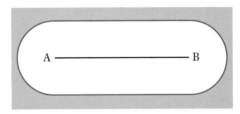

The region is shaded.
The red boundary is a solid line because it is included in the region.

Exercise 33:8

1   Draw a diagram to show the region where the points are less than 5 cm
from a fixed point A.

2   Draw a diagram to show the region where the points are 4 cm or less
from a fixed point B.

3   Draw a diagram to show the region where the points are at least 3 cm
from a fixed point C.

4   T is a radio transmitter.
Transmissions can be received in a region up to 8 km from the transmitter.
Make a scale drawing and shade in the region covered by the transmitter.

5   Simon wants to live more than 5 miles from a pig farm.
Draw a point P to represent the pig farm.
Make a scale drawing and shade in the region where Simon wants to live.

Sometimes there is more than one condition to satisfy.

Example   This is a diagram of Kate's garden.
She is going to plant a tree.
The tree must be more than 4 m from the wall of the house.
Kate also wants the tree to be 6 m or less from the gate G.
Where can Kate plant the tree?

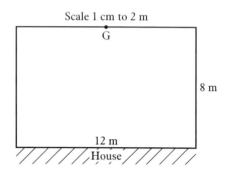

Scale 1 cm to 2 m

G

8 m

12 m

House

The tree must be more than 4 m from the wall of the house.
The red line is 4 m from the house wall.
The tree can be planted on the opposite side of this line to the wall. The red line is dotted because the tree cannot be planted on the line.

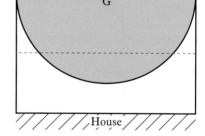

G

House

The tree must be 6 m or less from G.
The tree can be planted on the part of the circle centre G and radius 6 m or inside the circle.
This is shown in blue.

Kate can plant the tree where these two regions overlap.
This is shown in green.

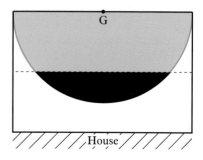

G

House

Exercise 33:9

1 A and B show the positions of
two radio transmitters.
Each transmitter can cover a
distance of up to 40 km.

A ———————————————————— B
60 km
Scale: 1 cm to 10 km

   a Copy the diagram.
   b Draw the boundary of the region
covered by transmitter A.
   c Draw the boundary of the region
covered by transmitter B.
   d Use shading and a key to show the
region covered by both transmitters.

2 The diagram shows the floor area
of a room. The points A and B
show the positions of alarm
sensors. Each sensor can cover a
distance of up to 4 m.
   a Copy the diagram.
   b Draw the boundary of the
region covered by sensor A.
   c Draw the boundary of the
region covered by sensor B.
   d Use shading and a key to show the
region covered by both sensors.

A

Scale: 1 cm to 1 m   B

3 A company wants to build a
storage depot. The depot must
be equal distances from
Shrewsbury and Birmingham.
It must also be less than 30
miles from Hereford.
   a Copy the diagram.
   b Show on your diagram
where the depot can be.

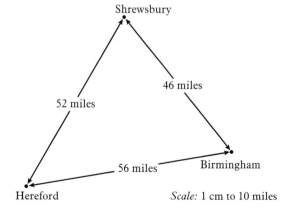

Shrewsbury

46 miles

52 miles

56 miles   Birmingham

Hereford   *Scale:* 1 cm to 10 miles

4 A television transmitter at Glasgow has a range of 110 miles.
A transmitter at Inverness has a range of 60 miles.
Glasgow and Inverness are 150 miles apart.
Make a scale drawing to show the region covered by both transmitters.

5　**a**　Make a rough copy of this treasure map.
It does not have to be exact.

b　The treasure is buried at a point which is equidistant from A and B. It is also equidistant from C and D. Find the treasure!

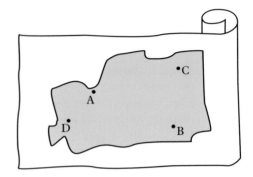

6　Laura plugs her electric mower into the socket on the side of the house.
The mower lead is 5 m long.

a　Copy the diagram.

b　Shade the part of the lawn that Laura can reach with the mower.

c　What is the minimum length of lead that Laura would need to cover all the lawn?

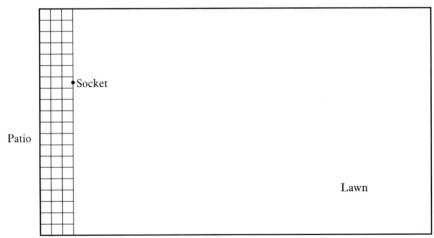

Scale: 1 cm to 1 m

7　The diagram shows the position of two dogs, Shep and Recall, sent out to locate an injured walker.
The walker is less than 4 km from Shep and more than 2 km from Recall. The walker is also closer to Recall than to Shep.
Draw an accurate diagram to show the region where the walker can be.
Use a scale of 1 cm : 1 km

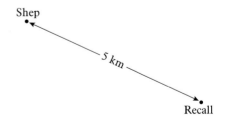

A goat on a lead and where it leads

Billski is a rare type of Russian goat.

He is tied to a post in the centre of his field.
The post is square and with sides of 50 cm.
Billski's rope is 3 m long and is attached to
one corner of the post.

Billski is not very bright!
He has a habit of always moving around his
field in the same direction.
As it happens this is usually anti-clockwise.

As a result he gets gently wound up
(in more ways than one).
He always ends up in the middle of his field,
wrapped around his post.

Farmer Gileski always has to go and rescue Billski from his post.

To add some variety into his otherwise dull life, Farmer Gileski often changes the
shape of Billski's post. Although he still walks around it in an anti-clockwise
direction, at least he takes a slightly different route!

1 Start with Billski's square post.
Assume the rope is fully extended at the beginning of the day.
Draw the area that Billski can reach as he walks around his post.
Think very carefully what happens to the rope as Billski reaches each corner of
the post.

2 Change the shape of Billski's post to a rectangle 1 m by 50 cm.
Draw a diagram of the area that Billski can now reach.

3 Invent some post shapes of your own.

You could try: different types of triangle
different types of quadrilateral
regular polygons
irregular shapes.

You could try to calculate the area of grass that Billski can reach.

1 a Draw a 65° angle.
   b Draw an arc crossing both arms of the angle.
      Label the points A and B.
   c Draw arcs from points A and B. They should cross each other.
   d Draw the line which bisects the angle.
   e Measure the two parts of the angle to check that it is correct.

2 a Draw two lines AB and AC which are at
      52° to each other.
   b Draw the locus of the points which are
      equidistant from AB and AC.

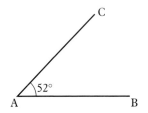

3 a Construct this triangle using a ruler and
      compasses.
      Start by drawing the line AB.
   b Bisect the angle at vertex A of the triangle.
   c Bisect the angle at vertex B of the triangle.
   d Bisect the angle at vertex C of the triangle.
      The three bisectors should cross at one point.

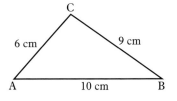

4 a Draw two points A and B that are 5 cm apart.
   b Join the points with a straight line.
   c Construct the locus of the points, which are equidistant from A and B.

5 Construct each of the following angles using ruler and compasses.
   a 60°   b 90°   c 30°   d 45°   e 75°

6 This diagram shows the positions of three
   emergency telephones. Sharon has broken down.
   She needs to walk to an emergency phone.
   a Make a copy of the diagram.
      It does not have to be exact.
   b By constructing three lines on your diagram,
      show which areas on the map are closer to
      each phone.

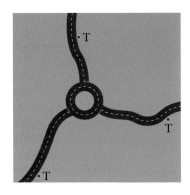

7 a Copy this shape. It doesn't have to be exact.

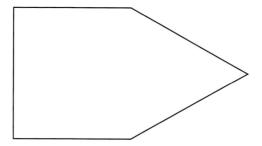

b Draw the locus of a point that is always 3 cm from the edge of the shape and on the outside of the shape.

8 Draw a diagram to show the locus of:

a The midpoint of this ladder as the ladder slides down the wall.

b The lock on this up-and-over garage door as it opens.

c The path of a ball that Richard throws to Thomas.
The ball leaves Richard's hand at 45° above the horizontal.

9 A bull is tethered to a ring, R.
The rope is 9 m long.
Make a scale drawing to show where the bull can move.
Use a scale of 1 cm to 2 m.

10 The diagram shows a plan of a rectangular park.
A and B are two drinking fountains.
a Using a scale of 1 cm to 50 m, draw a plan of the park.
b Draw a line on your diagram to help you show the areas of the park which are nearer to fountain A than to fountain B.

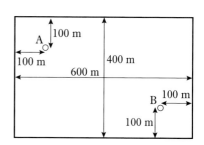

1 This diagram shows three towns in Derbyshire.

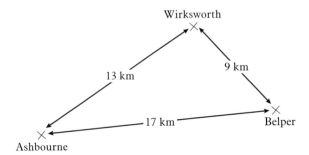

a Make an accurate scale drawing of this diagram.
Use a scale of 1 cm = 2 km.
b A mobile telephone mast is to be placed so that it is equidistant from all three towns. Draw the position of the mast on your diagram.

2 The diagram shows a large room and the position of 3 TV monitors.

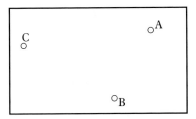

a Make a rough copy of the diagram.
b Lightly shade the area which is nearer to monitor A than monitor B.
c Lightly shade the area which is nearer to monitor A than monitor C.
d Show the area which is closer to monitor A than either of the other 2 monitors.

3 **a** Copy this hexagon.
b Shade the region that is:
closer to AB than DE
and closer to CD than AF
and closer to B than C.

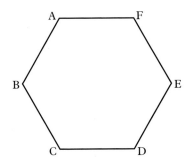

4 Captain Fortiz is patrolling a hazardous piece of coastline.

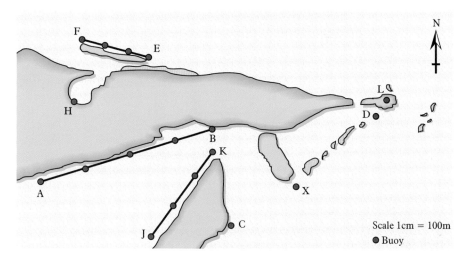

Scale 1cm = 100m
● Buoy

He starts from a point 150 m south of A.
From here he pilots his boat so it is equidistant from the lines of buoys AB and JK.
He continues on this course until he reaches the line BK.
He then steers his boat so that it is always equidistant from buoys C and X.
He continues on this course until he is due east of buoy C.
At this point Captain Fortiz pilots the boat so that it is parallel with the line XD, until he is due south of lighthouse L.
He then travels so that the boat is always 50 m from the lighthouse, until he is due north of it.
Then he sets a course so that he finishes 50 m due north of buoy E.
Now he stays the same distance from the line of buoys EF. He continues on this course until he comes around to the entrance to the harbour north east of H. He then sails directly to a mooring buoy at H.

a Trace the diagram.   **b** Draw Captain Fortiz's course.

5 Billy the buffalo is tethered by a rope 28 m long to two posts F and G.
The distance FG is 20 m.
The rope can move freely through a ring on Billy's collar. Billy can then be in a region on either side of the line FG.

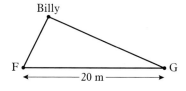

a Draw the locus of the perimeter of the region that Billy can be in.

Billy is then moved.
He is tethered by a rope 28 m long to the point A.
b A is on the outside of a barn that is 20 m long and 10 m wide.
Show the region that Billy can be in.

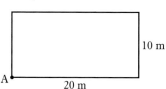

1   Draw two points A and B that are 6 cm apart.
Construct the locus of points that are closer to A than to B.

2   **a**   Construct this triangle using ruler and compasses.

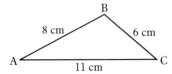

     b   Measure angle ∠ABC. Give your answer to the nearest degree.

3   Copy the diagram. It doesn't have to be exact.

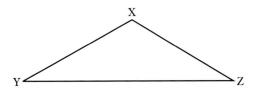

     Show the region, inside the triangle, that shows points that are closer to XY than to YZ.

4   **a**   Construct this triangle using a ruler and compasses.
Don't remove any construction lines.

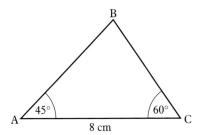

     b   Measure AB to the nearest mm.

34 Solving equations

1 Using graphs
Solving quadratic equations using graphs
Changing equations to match your graph
Solving equations using two graphs
Solving equations using more complex graphs

CORE

2 Trial and improvement
Revising trial and improvement for whole
  number answers
Revising solving equations to 1 dp and 2 dp
  accuracy
Solving numerical problems
Linking this to solving equations using graphs

QUESTIONS

EXTENSION

TEST YOURSELF

1 Using graphs

This rocket needs to dock with the space station.

The trajectory of the rocket must meet the orbit of the space station at exactly the right point.

Timing is all important!

In maths, problems can be solved by looking at the points where two graphs intersect.

Exercise 34:1

In this exercise write all the co-ordinates to 1 dp.
You need to keep all your graphs for the next exercise.

1   **a**   Copy and complete this table for $y = x^2 - 3$

x	−5	−4	−3	−2	−1	0	1	2	3	4	5
x^2	25	16			1	0	1	4			
−3	−3	−3			−3	−3	−3	−3			
y	22	13			−2	−3	−2	1			

  b   Plot the graph of $y = x^2 - 3$ from your table.
Draw your x axis from −5 to 5 and your y axis from −5 to 25.

  c   Look at the points where the graph crosses the x axis.
Write down the x co-ordinates of the points.

Your graph for question **1** should look like this:

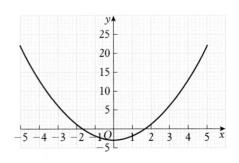

On the x axis, $y = 0$

This means that the points where $y = x^2 - 3$ crosses the x axis are the solutions to $x^2 - 3 = 0$

The points are $x = -1.7$ and $x = 1.7$ (1 dp)

You can use graphs to solve lots of different types of equations.
You need to draw your graphs as accurately as possible.
You also need to read off values as carefully as you can.

---

2 a Copy and complete this table for $y = x^2 - 10$

x	-5	-4	-3	-2	-1	0	1	2	3	4	5
x^2		16			1	0	1				
-10		-10			-10	-10	-10				
y		6			-9	-10	-9				

b Plot the graph of $y = x^2 - 10$ from your table.
Draw your x axis from -5 to 5 and your y axis from -10 to 15.

c Look at the points where the graph crosses the x axis.
Write down the solutions to the equation $x^2 - 10 = 0$

---

3 a Copy and complete this table for $y = x^2 + 3x - 5$

x	-5	-4	-3	-2	-1	0	1	2	3
x^2	25	16				0			
$+3x$	-15	-12				0			
-5	-5	-5				-5			
y	5	-1				-5			

b Draw an x axis from -5 to 3 and a y axis from -10 to 15.
c Plot the graph of $y = x^2 + 3x - 5$ from your table.
d Write down the solutions to $x^2 + 3x - 5 = 0$

---

4 a Draw a table for $y = 2x^2 + x - 8$
Use x values from -4 to 4.
b Draw an x axis from -4 to 4 and a y axis from -10 to 20.
c Plot the graph of $y = 2x^2 + x - 8$ from your table.
d Write down the solutions to $2x^2 + x - 8 = 0$

You can use graphs to solve equations that are not equal to 0.
To do this you have to draw another line on your graph.

Example   **a** Draw a graph of $y = x^2 - 3x - 1$
Use x values from -3 to 5.
b Use your graph to solve the equation $x^2 - 3x - 1 = 5$

a Draw a table and plot the values to draw the graph.

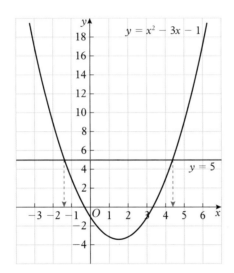

b To solve the equation $x^2 - 3x - 1 = 5$ draw the line $y = 5$ onto the
graph. This is the line shown in red.

Next, write down the x co-ordinates of the points where the curve
crosses this line. Use the blue dotted lines to help you.
The points are $x = -1.4$ and $x = 4.4$
These x values are the solutions to $x^2 - 3x - 1 = 5$

Exercise 34:2

In this exercise give all the co-ordinates to 1 dp.

1 Find your graph of $y = x^2 - 3$ from Exercise 34:1 question **1**.
  a On your graph, draw the line $y = 5$
  b Write down the points of intersection between the curve and this line.
    These are the solutions to $x^2 - 3 = 5$

2 a On your graph of $y = x^2 - 3$, draw the line $y = 10$

  b Write down the points of intersection between the curve and this line.
    These are the solutions to $x^2 - 3 = 10$

3 a On your graph draw the line $y = 17$

  b Write down the solutions to $x^2 - 3 = 17$

4 Find your graph of $y = x^2 - 10$ from Exercise 34:1 question **2**.

  a On your graph, draw the line $y = 5$

  b Write down the solutions to $x^2 - 10 = 5$

5 a On your graph of $y = x^2 - 10$, draw the line $y = -7$

  b Write down the solutions to $x^2 - 10 = -7$

6 Find your graph of $y = x^2 + 3x - 5$ from Exercise 34:1 question **3**.

  a Use your graph to find the solutions to $x^2 + 3x - 5 = 2$

  b Use your graph to find the solutions to $x^2 + 3x - 5 = -6$

7 This diagram shows the graphs of $y = 3x^2 - 4x - 2$
                                            $y = 8$ and $y = 16$

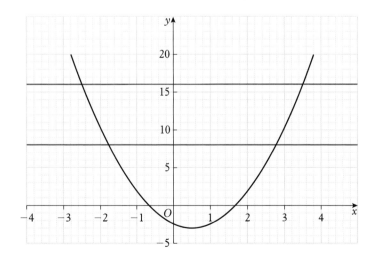

  a Use the graph to find the solutions to $3x^2 - 4x - 2 = 8$

  b Use the graph to find the solutions to $3x^2 - 4x - 2 = 16$

Sometimes you have to re-arrange an equation to fit the graph you have drawn.

Example   Use the graph of $y = x^2 - 3$ to solve $x^2 - 22 = 0$

To solve this problem follow these stages:

1 Write down the equation you want to solve: $x^2 - 22 = 0$

2 Write down the equation of the graph: $x^2 - 3$

3 Add an extra term to make this
match the first equation: $(-3 - 19 = -22)$ $x^2 - 3 - 19 = 0$

4 Get the extra term onto the RHS of the equation: $x^2 - 3 = 19$

5 Draw the line $y = 19$ on your graph
of $y = x^2 - 3$

6 Write down the points of intersection
of the curve and the line.
The solutions to the equation
are $x = -4.7$ and $x = 4.7$ (1 dp).

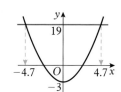

Exercise 34:3

1 **a** Copy and complete this table for $y = x^2 + 4$

x	-5	-4	-3	-2	-1	0	1	2	3	4	5
x^2											
$+4$											
y											

b Plot the graph of $y = x^2 + 4$ from your table.
Draw axes with x from -5 to 5 and y from 0 to 30.

2 Use your graph to solve the equation $x^2 + 4 = 10$
Write your answers to 1 dp.

3 Follow these steps to solve the equation $x^2 - 1 = 0$
a Write down the equation you want to solve: $x^2 - 1 = 0$
b Write down the equation of the graph: $x^2 + 4$

c Add an extra term to make this
match the first equation: $x^2 + 4 - \ldots = 0$

d Get the extra term onto the RHS of the equation: $x^2 + 4 = \ldots$

e Draw the line $y = \ldots$ on your graph of $y = x^2 + 4$

f Write down the points of intersection of the curve and the line.

4 Use the method in question **3** to solve the equation $x^2 - 6 = 0$
Write your answers to 1 dp.

5 a Copy and complete this table for $y = x^2 - x + 2$

x	-5	-4	-3	-2	-1	0	1	2	3	4	5
x^2											
$-x$											
$+2$											
y											

b Plot the graph of $y = x^2 - x + 2$ from your table.
Draw axes with x from -5 to 5 and y from 0 to 35.

6 Use your graph to solve the equation $x^2 - x + 2 = 5$
Write your answers to 1 dp.

7 Follow these steps to solve the equation $x^2 - x - 8 = 0$

a Write down the equation you want to solve: $x^2 - x - 8 = 0$

b Write down the equation of the graph: $x^2 - x + 2$

c Add an extra term to make this
match the first equation: $x^2 - x + 2 - \ldots = 0$

d Get the extra term onto the RHS of the equation: $x^2 - x + 2 \quad = \ldots$

e Draw the line $y = \ldots$ on your graph of $y = x^2 - x + 2$

f Write down the points of intersection of the curve and the line.
Write your answers to 1 dp.

8 Use the method in question **7** to solve the equation $x^2 - x - 13 = 0$
Write your answers to 1 dp.

You can solve more complicated equations by plotting graphs.
To solve an equation using graphs:
(1) Draw graphs of both sides of the equation.
(2) Write down the x co-ordinates of the points of intersection.

Example   Solve the equation $x^2 - 3x + 4 = 3x + 2$ graphically.

(1) Draw the graph of $y = x^2 - 3x + 4$
(2) Draw the graph of $y = 3x + 2$

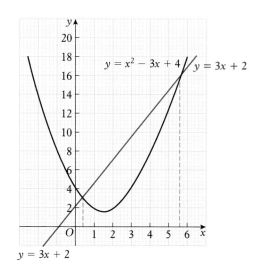

The graphs intersect at $x = 0.4$ and $x = 5.6$
These values are the solutions to $x^2 - 3x + 4 = 3x + 2$

Exercise 34:4

1 **a** Copy and complete this table for $y = x^2 - 2x - 2$

x	−5	−4	−3	−2	−1	0	1	2	3	4	5
x^2			9				1				
$-2x$			6				−2				
-2			−2				−2				
y			13				−3				

b Plot the graph of $y = x^2 - 2x - 2$ from your table.
Draw axes with x from −5 to 5 and y from −10 to 35.

2 **a** Copy and complete this table for $y = 2x + 2$

x	-5	-4	-3	-2	-1	0	1	2	3	4	5
$2x$			-6			0					
$+2$			2			2					
y			-4			2					

b Draw the graph of $y = 2x + 2$ over the top of your graph from question **1**.

c Write down the x co-ordinates of the points of intersection of the curve and the line to 1 dp.

These are the solutions to the equation $x^2 - 2x - 2 = 2x + 2$
More exact values are $x = -0.83$ and $x = 4.83$

3 **a** Draw a table for the equation $y = x^2 - 4x + 3$
Use x values from -2 to 7.

b Draw a graph of $y = x^2 - 4x + 3$
Draw your x axis from -2 to 7 and your y axis from -5 to 25.

c Use your graph to solve the equation $x^2 - 4x + 3 = 0$

4 **a** Draw a table for the equation $y = x + 2$
Use x values from -2 to 7.

b Draw the line $y = x + 2$ on to your graph from question **3**.

c Use your graphs to solve the equation $x^2 - 4x + 3 = x + 2$

5 **a** Draw a table for the equation $y = 3x^2 - 5x - 2$
Use x values from -3 to 4.

b Draw a graph of $y = 3x^2 - 5x - 2$
Draw your x axis from -3 to 4 and your y axis from -5 to 40.

c Draw another line on your graph to solve the equation $3x^2 - 5x - 2 = 3x - 2$

Solving equations using more complex graphs

You can use the same method you have used with quadratic graphs to solve other types of equations.

The next exercise involves cubic graphs and graphs of $\dfrac{1}{x}$
You plotted these graphs in Chapter 19.

Exercise 34:5

1 **a** Copy and complete this table for $y = x^3$

x	-4	-3	-2	-1	0	1	2	3	4
y		-27			0		8		

b Draw a graph of $y = x^3$
Draw your x axis from -4 to $+4$ and your y axis from -70 to 70.

c Copy and complete this table for $y = 10x + 10$

x	-5	-4	-3	-2	-1	0	1	2	3	4	5
$10x$			-30				10				
$+10$			10				10				
y			-20				20				

d Draw the graph of $y = 10x + 10$ over the top of your graph from part **b**.

e Use your graphs to solve the equation $x^3 = 10x + 10$

2 **a** Copy and complete this table for $y = \dfrac{1}{x}$

x	-5	-4	-3	-2	-1	0	1	2	3	4	5
y	-0.2	-0.25									

b Draw the graph of $y = \dfrac{1}{x}$. Draw both axes from -5 to 5.

c Copy and complete this table for $y = 0.5x$

x	-5	-4	-3	-2	-1	0	1	2	3	4	5
y		-2				0			1.5		

d Add a line to your graph to solve the equation $\dfrac{1}{x} = 0.5x$

3 **a** Copy and complete this table for $y = x^3 - 5x + 2$

x	-4	-3	-2	-1	0	1	2	3	4
x^3			-8					27	
$-5x$			10					-15	
$+2$			2					2	
y			4					14	

b Plot the graph of $y = x^3 - 5x + 2$ from your table.
Draw axes with x from -5 to $+5$ and y from -50 to 50.

c By drawing a suitable straight line on your graph, solve the equation $x^3 - 5x + 2 = 3$. Make sure that you write down all the solutions.

d By drawing a suitable straight line on your graph, solve the equation $x^3 - 5x + 8 = 0$

4 This graph shows $y = x + \dfrac{1}{x}$ and $y = x^2 - 5$

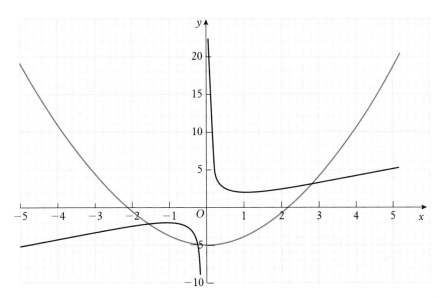

a Which of the two equations is shown by the black graph?
b Use the graph to solve $x^2 - 5 = 0$
c Explain why there are no solutions to $x + \dfrac{1}{x} = 0$
d Write down the solutions to $x + \dfrac{1}{x} = x^2 - 5$
e Show that this equation can also be written as $x^2 - x - 5 - \dfrac{1}{x} = 0$

2 Trial and improvement

Evariste Galois (1811–1832) was a French mathematician who was killed in a duel at the age of only 20. The night before his duel he stayed up and wrote down all of his ideas. It took mathematicians more than 100 years to deal with what he wrote down in one night!

Galois proved that it is impossible to solve equations with x^5 terms and higher powers using an algebraic formula.

You can use trial and improvement to solve these equations.
You can also use trial and improvement for easier equations if you are told to.

Example

Solve $x^2 = 1444$ using trial and improvement.

Value of x	Value of x^2	
30	900	smaller than 1444
40	1600	bigger than 1444
38	1444	correct

Answer $x = 38$
This is only part of the answer.
There may be another answer.
You may need to think about negative values.

Value of x	Value of x^2	
−30	900	smaller than 1444
−40	1600	bigger than 1444
−38	1444	correct

So $x = -38$ as well.

You can get two answers when you have to solve an equation with an x^2 term. When this happens, you can get two positive answers, two negative answers or one of each.

Exercise 34:6

1 Solve these equations by trial and improvement.
For each part:
(1) copy the table
(2) fill it in
(3) add more rows until you find *two* answers.

a $x^2 + 45 = 670$

Value of x	Value of $x^2 + 45$	
20	...	...
30	...	...
25	...	...

b $x^2 - 41 = 155$

Value of x	Value of $x^2 - 41$	
10	...	...
20	...	...
14	...	...

c $x^2 - 54 = 622$

Value of x	Value of $x^2 - 54$	
20	...	...
30	...	...
...	...	...

d $x^2 + x = 870$

Value of x	Value of $x^2 + x$	
...	...	...

2 Solve these equations using trial and improvement.
Draw a table to help you set out your working.
There are two answers for each part.

a $2x^2 + 3x = 5$ **b** $2x^2 + 3x = -1$

3 Solve these equations by trial and improvement.
You only need to find one answer for each part.

a $x^3 = 512$

Value of x	Value of x^3	
...	...	...

b $m^3 + 3m = 1764$

Value of m	Value of $m^3 + 3m$	
...	...	...

4 This Origami crane is made from
a square piece of Origami paper.
The area of the square is 324 cm².

a Call the length of a side x.
Copy this. Fill it in.
The area of the square is $x \times x = x^2$.
So $x^2 = ...$

b Solve the equation in part a by trial
and improvement to find the length
of the side of the paper.

5 The length of this rug is 18 inches
more than its width.
The area of the rug is 1215 in².
Call the width x.

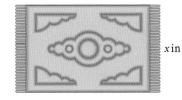

x in

a Copy this. Fill it in.
The length of the rug is ... + ... inches.
The area of the rug is $x \times (... + ...)$
So $x \times (... + ...) = ...$

b Solve the equation in part a by trial and improvement to find the
length and width of the rug.

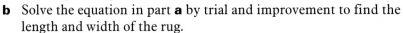

Sometimes answers do not work out exactly.
When this happens, you may have to give your answer correct to 1 dp.
Start by trapping the answer between two consecutive whole numbers.
Then look at values to 1 dp.
When your answer is trapped between two 1 dp values you check the value half-way
between them.

If this number gives you an answer that is too big then the smaller value is correct to 1 dp.
If this number gives you an answer that is too small then the bigger value is correct to 1 dp.

Example   Solve $x^3 = 135$

Value of x	Value of x^3	Bigger or smaller than 135?
5	125	smaller
6	216	bigger
5.5	166.375	bigger
5.1	132.651	smaller
5.2	140.608	bigger
5.15	136.590 875	bigger

x is between 5 and 6
x is between 5 and 5.5
x is between 5.1 and 5.5
x is between 5.1 and 5.2
x is between 5.1 and 5.15

This value is half-way between 5.1 and 5.2

x must be somewhere in the green part of the number line.
Any number in the green part rounds down to 5.1 to 1 dp.

Answer: $x = 5.1$ to 1 dp.

Exercise 34:7

1   Solve these equations by trial and improvement.
Draw a table to help you find each answer.
When the equation has an x^2 term you need to find two answers.
The other equations only have one answer.
Give all of your answers to 1 dp.

a $x^2 = 150$ **d** $x^2 + x = 800$
b $x^2 - 50 = 41$ **e** $x^3 + x = 67$
c $x^3 = 350$ **f** $x^3 + 4x = 50$

You can use trial and improvement to solve number questions too.
You can use it to find square roots and other roots.

2   Find the value of $\sqrt{175}$ using trial and improvement.
Copy this table. Fill it in. Give your answers to 1 dp.

Guess	Value of (guess)^2	Bigger or smaller than 175?
...	...	...

3 Find the value of $\sqrt[3]{146}$ to 1 dp. You need to solve $x^3 = 146$.

4 Find the value of each of these to 1 dp.
You need to decide what equation you need to solve.

a $\sqrt[3]{178}$ **c** $\sqrt[4]{67}$ **e** $\sqrt[4]{563}$

b $\sqrt[3]{456}$ **d** $\sqrt[4]{157}$ **f** $\sqrt[5]{168}$

You can give greater accuracy than 1 dp in your answers.
$x^2 = 135$ gives $x = 11.6$ to 1 dp but you can carry on to get the answer to 2 dp.

Value of x	Value of x^2	Bigger or smaller than 135?
11.6	134.56	smaller
11.7	136.89	bigger
11.65	135.7225	bigger
11.61	134.7921	smaller
11.62	135.0244	bigger
11.615	134.908 225	smaller

x is between 11.6 and 11.7
x is between 11.6 and 11.65
x is between 11.61 and 11.65
x is between 11.61 and 11.62
x is between 11.615 and 11.62

this value is half-way between 11.61 and 11.62

11.61   11.615   11.62

x must be somewhere in the green part of the number line.
Any number in the green part rounds up to 11.62 to 2 dp.

Answer: $x = 11.62$ to 2 dp.

---

5 Solve the equations in question **1** giving your answers to 2 dp.

6 Find the value of each of the roots in question **4** to 2 dp.

You can use the graph of an equation to help you to find a starting value for trial and improvement.

If you have drawn a graph you will be able to see where it crosses the x axis.

This is part of the graph of $y = 5 - x^2$
It crosses the x axis between 2 and 3.

If you are trying to solve $5 - x^2 = 0$ by trial and improvement you can definitely start with $x = 2$ and $x = 3$ before using trial and improvement to get closer to the answer.

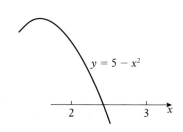

$y = 5 - x^2$

Exercise 34:8

1 This is a sketch of the graph of $y = x^2 - 3x - 5$

The graph crosses the x axis at two points.

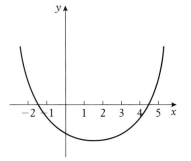

a Write down the whole numbers on each side of both points.

b Copy this table. Fill in the spaces.

Value of x	Value of $x^2 - 3x - 5$	Bigger or smaller than 0?
-2	...	...
-1	...	...

c Add extra rows to your table to find both the answers to $x^2 - 3x - 5 = 0$ using trial and improvement. Give your answers to 1 dp.

2 a Copy and complete this table for $y = x^3 - 3x + 5$

x	-3	-2	-1	0	1	2	3
x^3		-8					27
$-3x$		6					-9
$+5$		5					5
y		3					23

b Plot the graph of $y = x^3 - 3x + 5$ from your table.
Draw axes with x from -3 to 3 and y from -20 to 30.

Your graph should cross the x axis once.
c Solve $x^3 - 3x + 5 = 0$ using trial and improvement.
Use your graph to help you find the x values to start from.
Give your answer to 1 dp.

3 a Draw a graph of $y = x^4 - 2x^2$ using values of x from -2 to 2.
b Solve the equation $x^4 - 2x^2 = 0$ using your graph and trial and improvement.
There are three answers. One of them is exact. Give the other two to 1 dp.

1 **a** Copy and complete this table for $y = x^2 + 2x - 7$

x	-5	-4	-3	-2	-1	0	1	2	3
x^2	25	16				0			
$+2x$	-10	-8				0			
-7	-7	-7				-7			
y	8	1				-7			

b Draw an x axis from -5 to 3 and a y axis from -10 to 15.

c Plot the graph of $y = x^2 + 2x - 7$ from your table.

d Write down the solutions to $x^2 + 2x - 7 = 0$

2 **a** Draw axes with x from -5 to 5 and y from 0 to 30.

b Copy and complete this table for $y = x^2 + x - 5$

x	-5	-4	-3	-2	-1	0	1	2	3	4	5
x^2											
$+x$											
-5											
y											

c Plot the graph of $y = x^2 + x - 5$ from your table.

d Use your graph to solve the equation $x^2 + x - 5 = 5$
Write your answers to 1 dp.

e Follow these steps to solve the equation $x^2 + x - 15 = 0$

(1) Write down the equation you want to solve: $\qquad$ $x^2 + x - 15 = 0$

(2) Write down the equation of the graph: $\qquad$ $x^2 + x - 5$

(3) Add an extra term to make this
match the first equation: $\qquad$ $x^2 + x - 5 - \ldots = 0$

(4) Get the extra term onto the RHS of the equation: $x^2 + x - 5 \qquad = \ldots$

(5) Draw the line $y = \ldots$ on your graph of $y = x^2 + x - 5$

(6) Write down the points of intersection of the curve and the line.
Write your answers to 1 dp.

3 **a** Copy and complete this table for $y = \dfrac{6}{x}$

x	-5	-4	-3	-2	-1	0	1	2	3	4	5
y	-1.2	-1.5					6				

b Draw the graph of $y = \dfrac{6}{x}$. Draw both axes from -5 to 5.

c On your graph draw the line $y = x$

d Write down the solutions to $\dfrac{6}{x} = x$

4 **a** Copy this table. Allow space to add more rows.

x	x^3	$3x$	$x^3 + 3x$	Bigger or smaller than 6?
0	0	0	0	smaller
1	1	3	4	smaller
2				

b Fill in the missing values in your table.
c Continue your table to solve the equation $x^3 + 3x = 6$ correct to 1 dp.

5 Rod wants to make a circular pond in his garden.
He wants the surface area of the pond to be
exactly 4 m².
Use trial and improvement to find the radius
of the pond correct to 1 dp.
You need to solve the equation $\pi r^2 = 4$

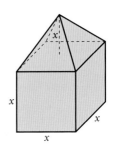

6 Aiden wants to solve the equation $x^4 = 56$
  a The positive answer lies between two
    consecutive whole numbers.
    Find these two consecutive numbers.
  b Use trial and improvement to find the
    positive solution to 1 dp.

7 The volume of this shape is found

  using the formula $V = \dfrac{4x^3}{3}$

x is the length of the side of the cube and
also the height of the pyramid in centimetres.
Find the value of x to 1 dp which will give
the shape a volume of 1000 cm³.

1 **a** Copy and complete this table for $y = x^2 + 2x - 1$

x	-4	-3	-2	-1	0	1	2	3	4
x^2	16				0				
$+2x$	-8				0				
-1	-1				-1				
y	7				-1				

b Draw the graph of $y = x^2 + 2x - 1$ using x values from -4 to 4.
c Use your graph to write down the solutions to $x^2 + 2x - 1 = 4$
d Use your graph to write down the solutions to $x^2 + 2x - 7 = 0$
e On your graph for part **b** draw the line $y = x + 3$
f Use your graphs to solve the equation $x^2 + x - 4 = 0$

2 **a** Draw the graph of $y = 3x^2 - 3x - 3$ using x values from -4 to 4.
b On your graph draw the line $y = 2x - 1$
c Use your graph to write down the solutions to $3x^2 - 5x - 2 = 0$

3 **a** Copy and complete this table for $y = \dfrac{1}{x^2}$

x	-5	-4	-3	-2	-1	0	1	2	3	4	5
y	0.04	0.06	0.1								

b Draw the graph of $y = \dfrac{1}{x^2}$ Draw both axes from -5 to 5.

c Copy and complete this table for $y = \dfrac{1}{x}$

x	-5	-4	-3	-2	-1	0	1	2	3	4	5
y	-0.2	-0.3	-0.3								

d Draw the graph of $y = \dfrac{1}{x}$ on the same graph as part **b**.

e Write down the solution to the equation $\dfrac{1}{x^2} = \dfrac{1}{x}$

4 Solve these equations using trial and improvement.
Give all your answers to 1 dp.
a $x^4 + x^3 + x^2 + x = 100$

b $\dfrac{12}{x^2 - 5} = 6$

1   The diagram shows the graphs of $y = 2x^2 - 3x - 2$ and $y = 10$

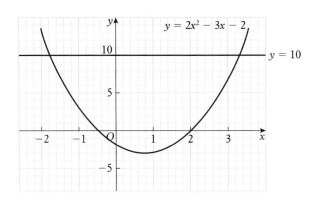

a   Use the diagram to write down the solutions of $2x^2 - 3x - 2 = 0$
b   Use the diagram to write down the solutions of $2x^2 - 3x - 2 = 10$

2   **a**   Copy and complete this table for $y = x^2 - x - 3$.

x	-3	-2	-1	0	1	2	3	4
x^2		4						
$-x$		2						
-3		-3						
y		3						

b   Draw the graph of $y = x^2 - x - 3$ from your table.
c   Use the graph to write down the solutions of $x^2 - x - 3 = 0$.
d   Draw the line $y = 5$ on the same axes.
e   Write down the solutions of $x^2 - x - 3 = 5$.

3   **a**   Copy and complete this table for $y = x^2 - 3x + 1$.

x	-2	-1	0	1	2	3	4	5
x^2								
$-3x$								
$+1$								
y								

b Draw the graph of $y = x^2 - 3x + 1$ from your table.

c Copy and complete this table for $y = 2x + 3$.

x	-2	-1	0	1	2	3	4	5
$2x$								
$+3$								
y								

d Draw the graph of $y = 2x + 3$ on the same axes.

e Use your graphs to find the solutions of the equation $x^2 - 3x + 1 = 2x + 3$.

4 a Copy and complete this table for $y = \dfrac{1}{x} + 3$.

x	-4	-3	-2	-1	0	1	2	3	4
$\dfrac{1}{x}$									
$+5$									
y									

b Use your table to draw the graph of $y = \dfrac{1}{x} + 3$.

c Draw the graph of $y = x + 2$ on the same axes.

d Use your graphs to solve the equation $\dfrac{1}{x} + 3 = x + 2$.

5 Lisa has drawn a graph of the equation $y = x^3 - x^2 + 5$.
She wants to solve the equation $x^3 = 2x^2 - 4$.
Find the equation of the extra graph she should draw on the same axes.

35 Using trigonometry

CORE

1 Angles and lengths
Revising trigonometry
– finding angles
– finding sides
– working in isosceles triangles

2 Bearing up
Using trigonometry in bearings problems
Looking at angles of elevation and depression

3 Finding the hypotenuse
Using trigonometry to find the hypotenuse

QUESTIONS

EXTENSION

TEST YOURSELF

1 Angles and lengths

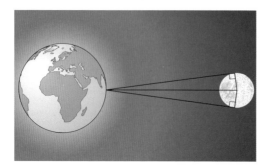

What angle does the moon take up in the sky?

You can use SOH CAH TOA to remember trigonometric formulas.

$$\text{Sin } a = \frac{\text{Opposite}}{\text{Hypotenuse}} \qquad \text{Cos } a = \frac{\text{Adjacent}}{\text{Hypotenuse}} \qquad \text{Tan } a = \frac{\text{Opposite}}{\text{Adjacent}}$$

To find the angle marked a in this triangle.

Write out   **S** O **H**   **C** A **H**   **T** O **A**

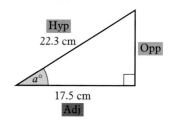

Cross out the sides that you know.

   S O H   C A H   T O A

The formula you need is the one with two sides crossed out.

$$\cos a = \frac{\text{adjacent}}{\text{hypotenuse}}$$

Substitute into the formula:

$$\cos a = \frac{17.5}{22.3}$$

Make sure that your calculator is working in degrees.

Key in:

   2nd F   **cos**   **(**   **1**   **7**   **.**   **5**   **÷**   **2**   **2**   **.**   **3**   **)**   **=**

   SHIFT   **cos**   **(**   **1**   **7**   **.**   **5**   **÷**   **2**   **2**   **.**   **3**   **)**   **=**

to get $a = 38.3°$ (1 dp)
You can use the other two formulas in the same way.

Exercise 35:1

In questions **1–10**:
a Copy the triangle. Label the sides hyp, opp, adj.
b Find the angle marked with a letter. Round your answer to 1 dp.
Check that your answer seems reasonable.

1
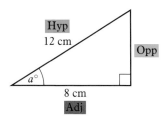

6
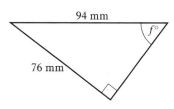

2
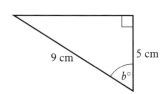

7
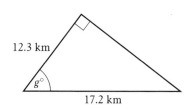

3
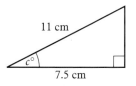

8
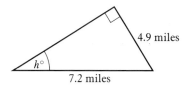

4

9
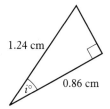

5
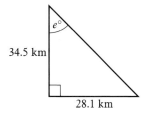

10
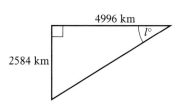

11 John wants to find the angle of
slope in one of his fields.
He wants to know if it is safe
to drive his tractor.
What is the angle of slope?

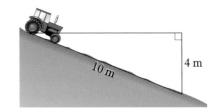

12 Steep roads in Britain have gradients
like 1 in 10, 1 in 8, etc.
  a Use this diagram to work out the
    angle of slope of a 1 in 10 road.
Work out the angle of slope for a road
with a gradient of:
  b 1 in 7   **c** 1 in 5.

In some questions you have to find more
than one angle.
You draw a separate triangle for each
angle that you need to find.
In this diagram you need to find angles
$x°$ and $y°$.

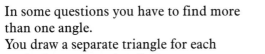

To find x draw triangle ADC separately.
Then you work out $x°$ in the usual way.

Cross out the sides that you know.

The formula you need is the one
with two sides crossed out.

$$\tan x = \frac{56}{38}$$

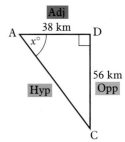

Make sure that your calculator is working in degrees.

Key in:

to get $x = 55.8°$ (1 dp)
You then work out y by drawing triangle BCD separately. This gives $y = 48.3°$ (1 dp)

13 Find the angles marked with letters.

a

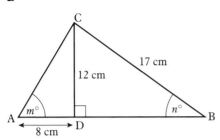

b

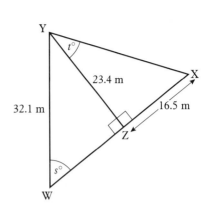

To find the side marked a in this triangle:

Write out SOH CAH TOA.

Cross out the side that you know.
Cross out the side that you need to find.

$$\boxed{S \cancel{O} \cancel{H}} \quad \boxed{C A \cancel{H}} \quad \boxed{T \cancel{O} A}$$

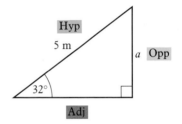

The formula you need is the one with two sides crossed out.

$$\sin 32° = \frac{\text{opposite}}{\text{hypotenuse}}$$

Substitute into the formula:

$$\sin 32° = \frac{a}{5} \qquad \text{So} \qquad 5 \times \sin 32° = a$$

Make sure that your calculator is working in degrees.

Now press:

to get $a = 2.65$ m (3 sf)

You can use the other two formulas in the same way.

Exercise 35:2

In each of questions **1–8**:
a Copy the triangle. Label the sides hyp, opp, adj.
b Find the length of the side marked with a letter.
   Round your answer to 3 sf.

Check that your answer seems reasonable.

1

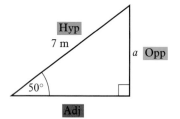

5

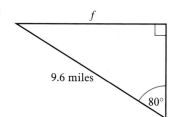

2

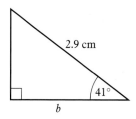

6

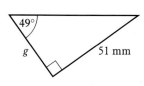

3

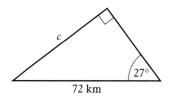

● **7**

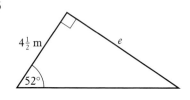

4

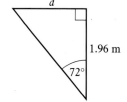

8

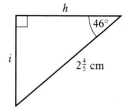

In questions **9** to **14** draw a separate triangle for each length that you need to find.

9

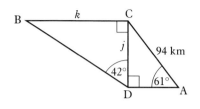

10

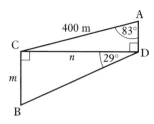

Working in isosceles triangles

You can split an isosceles triangle into 2 right angled triangles.

To find the base in this triangle split the triangle down the middle.

Now you have 2 right angled triangles that are exactly the same.
They are congruent.
Call the base of each triangle a

The angle in each half is $36 \div 2 = 18°$

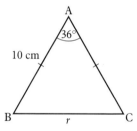

Look at triangle ABD: $\quad\quad \sin 18° = \dfrac{a}{10}$

Multiply by 10 $\quad\quad 10 \times \sin 18° = a$

$r = 2a$ so multiply
both sides by 2 to get $\quad\quad 20 \times \sin 18° = r$

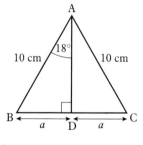

This gives $r = 6.18$ cm (3 sf)

11

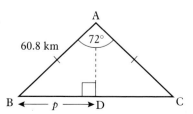

12

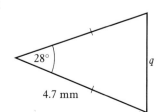

13

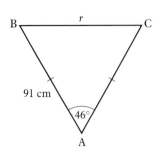

● 14

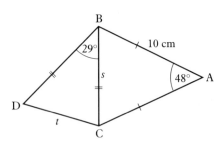

Exercise 35:3

In this exercise you will need to find angles and sides.
Round your answers to 3 sf.

1 Steve is painting the boards on the side of his house.
   a Find the length of the vertical board AB.
   b Find the length of the horizontal board CD.
   He leans his ladder against the side of the
   house.
   The ladder is 5 m long.
   It makes an angle of 68° with the ground.
   c Find the height of the wall EC.
   d Find the distance of the base of
      the ladder from the wall.
   e Find the total height of the house
      if the chimney is 2.1 m tall.
   f Find the angle $C\hat{E}D$.
   g Find the length of the beam DE.
      Use Pythagoras' theorem.

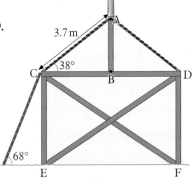

2 The diagram shows a boat.
Find the angles and sides marked with letters.
Use Pythagoras' theorem to find length d.

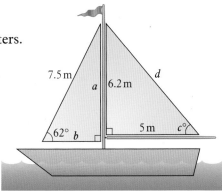

2 Bearing up

Sailing is a sport where you need to know where you are going.

Sailors use bearings to find their way around.

You have seen bearings in Chapter 26. You often need to use trigonometry in questions involving bearings.

Example The diagram shows the positions of two lighthouses, A and B.

The bearing of B from A is 075°.
B is 35 km east of A.
How far north of A is B?

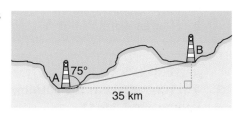

You need to find the length x.
Draw a right angled triangle to help you.

C is the point that is
directly east of A and directly south of B
So $A\hat{C}B$ is 90°

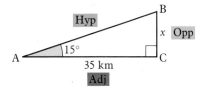

In triangle ABC
$C\hat{A}B = 90 - 75 = 15°$

Using trigonometry gives:

$$\tan 15° = \frac{x}{35}$$

$$x = 35 \times \tan 15$$

S**∅**H   C**∕**H   T**∅**∕

Make sure that your calculator is working in degrees.

$x = 9.4$ km to 1 dp.
So B is 9.4 km north of A.

Exercise 35:4

1 The diagram shows the position of two ships A and B.
The bearing of B from A is 075°.
B is 25 km east of A.
a Copy the diagram.
Show the information on your diagram.
b How far north of A is B?

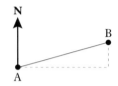

2 The diagram shows the position of two ships A and B.
The bearing of A from B is 244°.
A is 80 km west of B.
a Copy the diagram.
Show the information on your diagram.
b How far south of B is A?

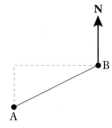

3 The diagram shows the position of two
lighthouses P and Q.
The bearing of P from Q is 305°.
P is 63 km west of Q.
a Copy the diagram.
Show the information on your diagram.
b How far north of Q is P?

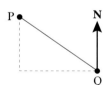

4 The diagram shows the position of two jets Y and Z.
The bearing of Z from Y is 115°.
Z is 377 km east of Y.
a Copy the diagram and
fill in the given information.
b How far south of Y is Z?

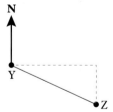

5 The diagram shows the position of two boats A and B.
The bearing of B from A is 122°.
The distance of B from A is 36 miles.
a Copy the diagram and
fill in the given information.
b How far south of A is B?

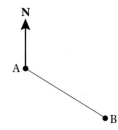

6 A helicopter flies 254 km from Aberdeen
on a bearing of 047°.
   a Draw a diagram to show this information.
   b How far east of Aberdeen is the helicopter?
   c How far north of Aberdeen is the helicopter?

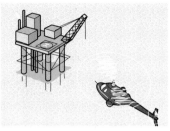

7 A ship sails 40 km from Plymouth on a bearing of 216°.
   a Draw a diagram to show this information.
   b How far west of Plymouth is the ship?
   c How far south of Plymouth is the ship?

8 A jet flies 430 km from its base on a bearing of 315°.
   a Draw a diagram to show this information.
   b How far west of its base is the jet?
   c How far north of its base is the jet?

You often need to do bearings questions in stages.

Example   A plane flies 20 km from Ampton to Boxford on a bearing of 044°.
It then flies 15 km on a bearing of 102° to Canborough.
   a Find the distance from Ampton to Canborough.
   b Find the bearing of Canborough from Ampton.

You need to start by drawing a diagram.
Show all of the information that you are given.
Use A, B and C for the towns. Use extra letters to label all the important points.

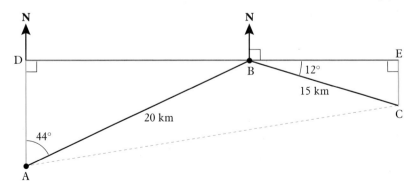

You want to find out about   **a** the length from A to C
                       and   **b** the bearing of C from A

First, you need to think about the distances east/west and north/south.

The distance east from A to C is **DB + BE**

In triangle ABD:

$$\sin 44° = \frac{DB}{20}$$

$$DB = 20 \sin 44°$$

In triangle BCE:

$$\cos 12° = \frac{BE}{15}$$

$$BE = 15 \cos 12°$$

So the distance east from A to C is
$$20 \sin 44° + 15 \cos 12°$$
$$= 28.56 \text{ km} \qquad \text{(4 sf)}$$

Give 4 sf in your working if you want to give your final answer to 3 sf.

The distance north from A to C is **AD − EC**

In triangle ABD:

$$\cos 44° = \frac{AD}{20}$$

$$AD = 20 \cos 44°$$

In triangle BCE:

$$\sin 12° = \frac{EC}{15}$$

$$EC = 15 \sin 12°$$

So the distance north from A to C is
$$20 \cos 44° - 15 \sin 12°$$
$$= 11.27 \text{ km} \qquad \text{(4 sf)}$$

Now draw a separate triangle that shows the relevant information.
Label any missing points.

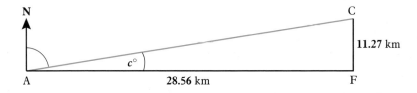

Now you can answer the question!

a In triangle ACF:
$$AC^2 = 28.56^2 + 11.27^2 \quad \text{(by Pythagoras' theorem)}$$
$$AC^2 = 942.6865$$
$$AC = 30.7 \text{ km (3 sf)}$$

b $\tan c = \dfrac{11.27}{28.56} = 0.3946 \ldots$

$$c = 21.53°$$

The angle needed for the bearing is $90° - 21.53° = 68.47°$ (2 dp)
So the bearing of C from A is $068°$ (to the nearest degree).

Exercise 35:5

In this exercise, give all distances to 3 sf and bearings to the nearest degree.

1 A plane flies 13 km from Abingdon to Bampton on a bearing of 285°.
It then flies 28 km on a bearing of 260° to Cirencester.
   a Draw a diagram to show this information.
   b Find the distance from Abingdon to Cirencester.
   c Find the bearing of Cirencester from Abingdon.

2 A plane flies 15 km from Harlow to Chelmsford on a bearing of 100°.
It then flies 25 km on a bearing of 135° to Southend-on-Sea.
   a Draw a diagram to show this information.
   b Find the distance from Harlow to Southend-on-Sea.
   c Find the bearing of Southend-on-Sea from Harlow.

3 A jet flies 300 km from Manchester on a bearing of 170°.
Then it flies 100 km on a bearing of 047° and arrives at Guildford.
   a Draw a diagram to show this information.
   b Find the shortest distance from Manchester to Guildford.
   c Find the bearing of Guildford from Manchester.

4 A jet flies 8100 km from Dover in England on a bearing of 159°.
Then it flies 5400 km on a bearing of 123° and arrives at Perth on the coast of Australia.
   a Draw a diagram to show this information.
   b Find the shortest distance from Dover to Perth.
   c Find the bearing of Perth from Dover.

5 Frank is repairing lighthouses around the Irish Sea.
He flies by helicopter.
He sets off from Holyhead in Anglesey and flies for 50 km to Llandudno on a bearing of 089°.
Then he flies for 105 km to Douglas in the Isle of Man on a bearing of 330°.
His final call is to Fleetwood in Lancashire.
He flies 100 km from Douglas on a bearing of 105° to get there.

   a Draw a diagram to show this information.
   b Find the shortest distance from Holyhead to Fleetwood.
   c Find the bearing of Fleetwood from Holyhead.

Angles of elevation and depression

Start by looking horizontally.
When you look *up* at something, the angle is called an angle of *elevation*.
When you look *down* at something, the angle is called an angle of *depression*.

Angle of elevation If you are at A and you look up to a point B, the **angle of elevation of B from A** is the angle between the horizontal and the line AB. It is the angle *above* the horizontal.

a is the angle of elevation of B from A.

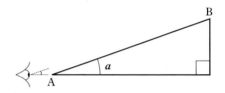

Angle of depression If you are at P and you look down to a point Q, the **angle of depression of Q from P** is the angle between the horizontal and the line PQ. It is the angle *below* the horizontal.

b is the angle of depression of Q from P.

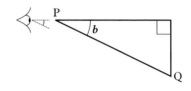

Exercise 35:6

In this exercise round your answers to 3 sf.

1 Sid is standing at point A, 26 metres from the base of a tree.
The angle of elevation of the top of the tree from A is 42°.
Find the height of the tree.

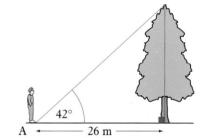

2 Graham is standing at point B, 52 m from a church tower.
The tower is 32 m high.
Work out the angle of elevation of the top of the church tower from B.

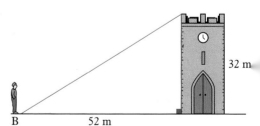

3 Fiona is looking over the edge of a cliff.
She sees a boat on the water below.
The cliff is 105 m high. The angle of depression of the boat from Fiona is 7°.
a Draw a diagram to show this information.
b Work out the distance of the boat from the foot of the cliff.

3   Finding the hypotenuse

Sometimes it helps to know the distance along the hypotenuse.

Look at this triangle. Suppose you need to find the hypotenuse h
You cannot use Pythagoras' theorem, because you only have one side.

To find the side marked h in this triangle:

Write out SOH CAH TOA.

Cross out the side that you know.
Cross out the hypotenuse because
you want to find it.

$\boxed{\text{S}\cancel{\text{O}}\cancel{\text{H}}}$ $\boxed{\text{CA}\cancel{\text{H}}}$ $\boxed{\text{T}\cancel{\text{O}}\text{A}}$

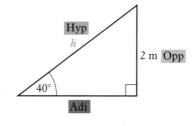

The formula you need is the one with two sides crossed out.

$$\sin 40° = \frac{\text{opposite}}{\text{hypotenuse}}$$

Substitute into the formula: $\sin 40° = \dfrac{2}{h}$

You need to make h the subject of the formula.
Here it is a denominator, so multiply by h on both sides.

So $h \times \sin 40° = 2$

Now divide both sides by $\sin 40°$ $h = \dfrac{2}{\sin 40°}$

Make sure that your calculator is working in degrees.

Now press:

$$2 \;\div\; \sin \; 4 \; 0 \; =$$

to get $h = 3.11$ m (3 sf)

You can use the formula for cos in the same way.
The formula for tan will also give the unknown in the denominator if you are finding the adjacent.

Exercise 35:7

1 **a** Write out SOH CAH TOA.
        Cross out the hypotenuse.
        Cross out the side you know.

    b Copy this. Fill it in.

$$\sin 32° = \frac{\cdots}{h}$$

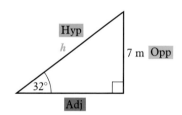

    c Multiply both sides by h.
        Copy this. Fill it in. $h \times \sin 32° = \ldots$

    d Divide both sides by sin 32°.
        Copy this. Fill it in. $h = \dfrac{\cdots}{\cdots}$

    e Now use your calculator to work out h to 3 dp.

2 **a** Write out SOH CAH TOA.

    b Cross out the side you want and the side you know.

    c Copy this. Fill it in. $\ldots 18° = \dfrac{\cdots}{j}$

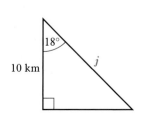

    d Rearrange this equation to make j the subject.

    e Now use your calculator to work out j to 3 dp.

In questions **3–8** find the lengths of the sides marked with letters.
Give your answers to 3 sf.

3

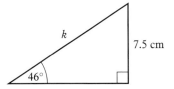

k
7.5 cm
46°

6

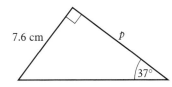

7.6 cm
p
37°

4

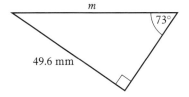

m
73°
49.6 mm

7

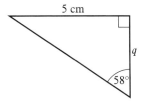

5 cm
q
58°

5

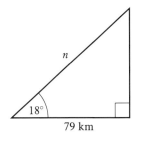

n
18°
79 km

8

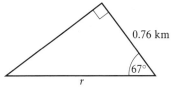

0.76 km
67°
r

9 Every day Sue and her dog Jumble walk across the diagonal AB of this field. How far does she walk?

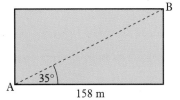

B
A
35°
158 m

10 The Pan Trophy hill climb course goes up the red route shown in the diagram.
 a Find the distances AB, BC and CD.
 b Work out the total distance of the course.

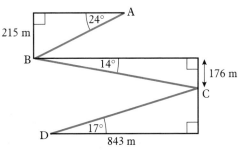

215 m
24°
A
B
14°
176 m
C
17°
D
843 m

411

1 Find the labelled angle in each of these triangles.
Give your answers to the nearest degree.

a

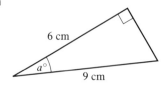

6 cm

9 cm

$a°$

b

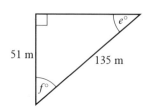

51 m

135 m

$e°$

$f°$

2 Find the labelled side in each of these triangles.
Give your answers to 3 sf.

a

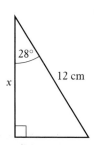

28°

12 cm

x

b

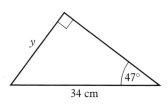

y

47°

34 cm

3 This diagram shows a chord in a sector of a circle.
The radius of the circle is 6 cm.
The length of the chord is 10 cm.
Find the angle, x, in the sector to 1 dp.

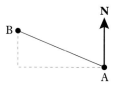

x

In questions **4–9**, give your answers to 3 sf.

4 The diagram shows two aircraft A and B.
The bearing of B from A is 293°.
B is 615 km west of A.
a Copy the diagram.
b How far north of A is B?

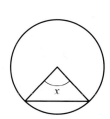

N

B

A

5 A helicopter flies 2500 km from Manchester on a bearing of 130°.
a Draw a diagram to show this information.
b How far east of Manchester is the helicopter?
c How far south of Manchester is the helicopter?
d What is the bearing of Manchester from the helicopter?

6 A ferry leaves a port P and travels 4.7 km on a bearing of 156° to a port Q.
It then travels 8.2 km on a bearing of 054° to a port R.
  a Draw a diagram to show this information.
  b Show that PQ̂R is 78°.
  c Find the shortest distance from P to R.
  d Find the bearing of P from R.

7 The diagram shows two buildings.
The distance between the buildings is 80 m.
The smaller building is 34 m high.
The angle of elevation of the top
of the taller building from the top
of the smaller building is 27°.
Find the height of the taller
building.

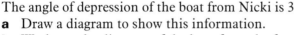

34 m

27°

80 m

8 Canary Wharf tower in London's docklands
is the tallest building in Britain.
Nicki is at the top of the Canary Wharf tower.
She sees a boat on the river below.
The tower is 243.8 m high.
The angle of depression of the boat from Nicki is 37°.
  a Draw a diagram to show this information.
  b Work out the distance of the boat from the foot
of the tower.

9 Find the length of the hypotenuse in each of these triangles.
Give your answers to 3 sf.

a

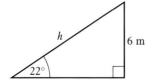

h

23 cm

35 cm

c

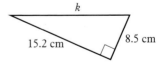

k

15.2 cm

8.5 cm

b

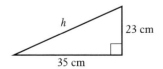

h

6 m

22°

d

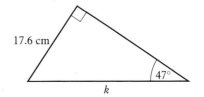

17.6 cm

47°

k

1   Work out the angles marked in this diagram.

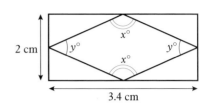

2 cm

3.4 cm

2   **a**   Write down the values of sin A, cos A and tan A.
in this right-angled triangle.
You only need the letters *a* and *b*.
You need to use Pythagoras' theorem.

    b   Use your answers to part **a** to show that

      (1) $(\sin A)^2 + (\cos A)^2 = 1$

      (2) $\tan A = \dfrac{\sin A}{\cos A}$

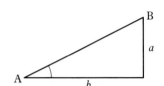

3   Tai is in Paris.
She is looking at the Eiffel tower.
The angle of elevation of the top
of the tower from where she is
standing is 30°.
She walks 200 m towards the tower.
The angle of elevation of the top
of the tower is now 43.2°
Work out:

    a   the height of the tower

    b   the horizontal distance of Tai
from the tower when she started.

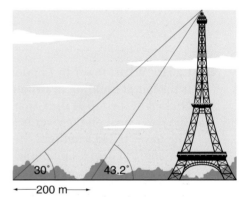

4   Pat is a pylon painter.
One of the sections she has to paint looks like this.

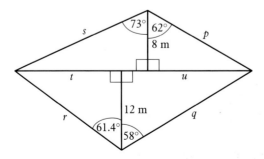

Find the total length of the girders that she paints.

1 Find the size of the angle marked by a letter in each of these triangles.

a

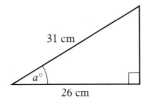

31 cm

$a°$

26 cm

b

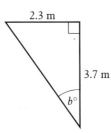

2.3 m

3.7 m

$b°$

2 Find the length of the sides marked by a letter in each of these triangles.

a

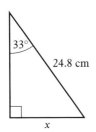

33°

24.8 cm

x

b

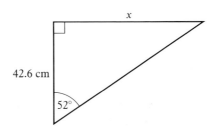

x

42.6 cm

52°

3 A ship leaves a harbour H and travels 9.6 km on a bearing of 072°
to reach a port P.
  a How far north of H is P?
  b How far east of H is P?
  c What is the bearing of H from P?

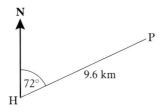

N

P

72°   9.6 km

H

4 Jen is walking in open countryside.
She wants to travel to a village 5 km west and 3 km south
of her present position.

  a Draw a diagram to show this information.
  b Find the bearing that she should take.

5 A helicopter flies 37 km from A on a bearing of 126° to B.
It then flies a further 84 km on a bearing of 238° to reach C.
  a Copy the diagram and show this information.
  b How far south has the helicopter travelled altogether?
  c How far is C to the west of A?
  d What is the bearing of A from C?

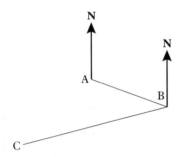

6 Find the length of the hypotenuse in this triangle.

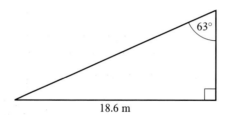

7 The angle of depression of a small boat from the top of a cliff is 18°.
The cliff is 120 m above the sea.
  a Draw a diagram to show this information.
  b How far is the boat from the foot of the cliff?

8 A ladder leans against a wall at an angle of 60° to the horizontal.
The top of the ladder is 2.6 m above the ground.
Find the length of the ladder to 2 significant figures.

9 Chris measures the angle of elevation of the top of a building as 25°.
He then moves 30 m towards the building.
The angle of elevation is now 40°.
How tall is the building?

36 \<Inequalities\>

1 Solving inequalities using algebra
Showing simple inequalities on the number line
Solving linear inequalities
Multiplying and dividing by a negative number
Solving inequalities with several parts
Solving quadratic inequalities

CORE

2 Solving inequalities using graphs
Showing inequalities with lines parallel to
  the axes
Showing two inequalities on the same graph
Graphing inequalities involving both x and y
Showing multiple inequalities on the same graph
Using inequalities to solve problems
Solving more complex inequalities using graphs

QUESTIONS

EXTENSION

TEST YOURSELF

1 Solving inequalities using algebra

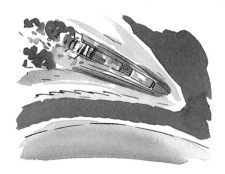

The angle at which a rocket re-enters the earth's atmosphere is critical.

If the angle is too steep then the rocket will travel too quickly.

If it is too shallow, the friction will be too great and the rocket will burn up.

There is only a small range of angles that are suitable.

You use inequalities to describe a range of numbers.

$x > 3$

$x > 3$ means that x can take any value **greater than 3**.
It cannot be 3. On a number line, this is shown like this:

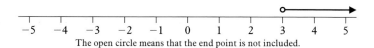

The open circle means that the end point is not included.

$x \leqslant 1$

$x \leqslant 1$ means that x can take any value **less than or equal to 1**.
This includes 1. On a number line, this is shown like this:

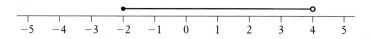

The solid circle means that the end point is included.

$-2 \leqslant x < 4$

$-2 \leqslant x < 4$ means that **x is greater than or equal to -2.**
$-2 \leqslant x < 4$ means that **x is less than 4.**
So $-2 \leqslant x < 4$ means that **x is between -2 and 4.**
-2 is included, 4 is not.

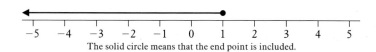

Exercise 36:1

1 Write down inequalities to describe each of these number lines.

a

b
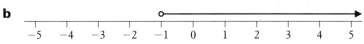

c
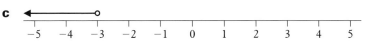

d
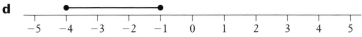

e
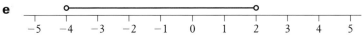

f
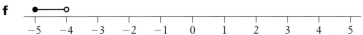

g

2 Draw each of these inequalities on a number line.

a $x > 2$	**c** $x \leqslant -3$	**e** $1 < x < 2$	**g** $-3 \leqslant x \leqslant -1$
b $x < 1$	**d** $x \geqslant -2$	**f** $-1 < x < 4$	**h** $-5 < x \leqslant 4.5$

Integer	An **integer** is a whole number.
	Integers are ... $-4, -3, -2, -1, 0, 1, 2, 3, 4$ ...

---

3 List the integers that are included in each of these inequalities.

a $1 < x < 4$	**c** $-3 < x < 2$	**e** $-2 \leqslant x \leqslant 6$	**g** $-3 \leqslant x \leqslant -2$
b $1 \leqslant x \leqslant 4$	**d** $-4 < x < 4$	**f** $0 < x < 7$	**h** $-3 < x < -2$

Most inequalities you will see are written in algebra. They are used to solve problems.

Inequalities are solved in a very similar way to equations. This means you can:
- add the same number to both sides of an inequality
- subtract the same number from both sides of an inequality
- multiply or divide both sides of an inequality by any **positive** number.

If you multiply or divide by a **negative** number, there is a new rule that you will see later.

Examples **1** Solve $3x - 5 > 8$

$$3x - 5 > 8$$

Add 5 to both sides: $3x > 13$

Divide both sides by 3: $x > \dfrac{13}{3}$

2 Solve $5 - x < 2x - 1$

$$5 - x < 2x - 1$$

Add x to both sides: $5 < 3x - 1$

Add 1 to both sides: $6 < 3x$

Divide both sides by 3: $2 < x$

It is better to write this
the other way round: $x > 2$

Exercise 36:2

Solve each of these inequalities.

1 $x + 4 < 7$

2 $3x - 3 > 9$

3 $5x - 6 \leqslant 9$

4 $y + 2.4 > 8$

5 $\dfrac{y}{5} - 6 > 20$

6 $\dfrac{f}{2} - 7 \geqslant 11$

7 $4(3t + 10) < 20$

8 $\dfrac{x - 9}{4} \leqslant 6$

9 $6x - 4 > 2x + 6$

10 $3.5g - 2 < 7 - g$

11 $2x - 6 \leqslant x + 7$

● **12** $\dfrac{5n + 2}{2} \geqslant 2n$

Look at this simple statement: $14 > 4$ Clearly this is true.
Now add 2 to both sides: $16 > 6$ It is still true.

Multiply both sides by 3: $48 > 18$ Still true!

But, dividing both sides by -2 gives $-24 > -9$ This is **not** true.
-24 is *less* than -9 not greater than it.

This is because of the way negative numbers work.
If numbers go **up** in twos, you can write: $2 < 4 < 6 < 8 < 10$

But if they go **down** in twos,
the inequalities are the other way around: $-2 > -4 > -6 > -8 > -10$

You need a new rule to deal with this.

- If you multiply or divide an inequality by a **negative** number then you must **change the direction** of the inequality sign.

This means that taking an inequality like $14 > 4$
and multiplying both sides by -1 gives $-14 < -4$

Example   Solve the inequality $6 - 2x < 12$

$$6 - 2x < 12$$

Subtract 6 from both sides: $-2x < 6$

Divide both sides by -2 **and**
change the direction of the inequality $\boldsymbol{x > -3}$

Exercise 36:3

Solve each of these inequalities.
Be careful if you multiply or divide by a negative number.

1 $4 - x < 7$

2 $-3 > 9 + 6x$

3 $5x - 6 \leqslant 20 + 7x$

4 $6 - 3y > 8 - 5y$

5 $-4(t + 10) < 48$

6 $\dfrac{7 - 2x}{4} \leqslant 6$

7 $3 - 5x > -2x + 6$

8 $6 - 4g < 7 - g$

Some inequalities have three parts to them.

Example   Solve $15 < 4x + 7 < 19$

This is the same as the two separate inequalities $15 < 4x + 7$ and $4x + 7 < 19$.
You can solve this by working on both at once.
The aim is to leave a single x in the middle of the inequality.

First remove the $+7$. $15 < \quad 4x + 7 \quad < 19$

To do this, subtract 7 from all three parts: $15 - 7 < \quad 4x + 7 - 7 \quad < 19 - 7$

This gives $8 < \quad 4x \quad < 12$

Now divide through by 4: $\dfrac{8}{4} < \quad \dfrac{4x}{4} \quad < \dfrac{12}{4}$

This gives the answer $2 < \quad x \quad < 3$

Exercise 36:4

Solve each of these inequalities.

1 $4 < 2x < 8$

2 $12 \leqslant 3t \leqslant 27$

3 $55 \leqslant x + 12 < 74$

4 $24 \leqslant y + 15 \leqslant 38$

5 $3 < \dfrac{t}{4} < 20$

6 $13 < 2x + 5 < 21$

7 $-7 < 3z + 2 < 20$

8 $3 \leqslant \dfrac{3x}{4} \leqslant 6$

9 $20 > 6x - 4 > 2$

10 $0 < 10x < 15$

11 $16 > -2x > 24$

● **12** $19 > 6 - 2x > 37$

Solving problems using inequalities

Inequalities can be used to solve problems.
You need to give each item a letter before you write down the inequality.

Example　Ben has 30 m of fencing to build a sheep pen.
He wants it to be twice as long as it is wide.
Work out the maximum length of the pen.

Call the width of the sheep pen x.

This is a sketch of the pen.

The length of the pen is $2x$.

The total perimeter of the pen is $x + 2x + x + 2x = 6x$
Ben only has 30 m of fencing, so the perimeter
must be **less than or equal to 30**.

In algebra this is written:　　$6x \leqslant 30$
So　　　　　　　　　　　　　$x \leqslant 5$
The maximum length of the pen is $2x = 2 \times 5 = 10$ m

Exercise 36:5

Write down an inequality to describe each problem.
Solve the inequality to answer the problem.

1　I think of a number, double it and add 5.
The answer must be less than 70.
What range of numbers can I choose?

2　Howard is given £10 to spend.
He is told that he can buy as many CD singles as he likes
but he must keep 75p for his bus fare.
The CDs cost £2.05 each.
What is the maximum number of CDs he can buy?

3　The perimeter of this triangle must not
be more than 50 cm.
What is the maximum value x can be?

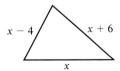

Quadratic inequalities

If you come across an inequality with x^2 in it, you need to be very careful!

Solving the equation $\qquad\qquad x^2 = 16$
gives two answers $\qquad\qquad x = -4$ and $x = 4$
This is because $4^2 = 16$ and $(-4)^2 = 16$.

If you start with $\qquad\qquad x^2 \geqslant 16$
you might be tempted to say $x \geqslant -4$ and $x \geqslant 4$

If you show $x \geqslant -4$ and $x \geqslant 4$ on a number line, it looks like this:

This is the same as just saying $x \geqslant -4$.

But this can't be the right answer to the problem.
Think about $x = -2$.
-2 is greater than -4 so it fits the answer.
But $(-2)^2 = 4$ and 4 is not greater than 16.
So -2 does not fit the inequality.

The $x \geqslant 4$ part of the solution does work.
The other part of the solution should be $x \leqslant -4$.

If you look at these on the number line, it looks like this:

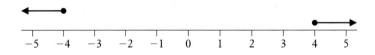

Example Solve the inequality $x^2 + 5 > 30$

$$x^2 + 5 > 30$$
gives $\qquad\qquad x^2 > 25$

This means that $x > 5$ or $x < -5$

Exercise 36:6

Solve each of these inequalities.

1 $x^2 + 5 > 21$

2 $2x^2 > 32$

3 $x^2 - 6 \geqslant 10$

4 $x^2 + 5 \geqslant 69$

5 $2x^2 - 10 > 190$

6 $x^2 + 5 > 6$

7 $x^2 - 7 > 9$

8 $3x^2 - 9 > 66$

9 $\frac{1}{2}x^2 + 5 > 37$

● **10** $x^2 > 0$

Example

Solve the inequality $3x^2 + 10 \leqslant 37$.
Show your answer on a number line.

$$3x^2 + 10 \leqslant 37$$

Take away 10: $\qquad 3x^2 \qquad \leqslant 27$
Divide by 3: $\qquad\quad x^2 \qquad\quad \leqslant 9$

This means that you are looking for numbers that are **less** than 9 when they are squared.

The solution is $x \geqslant -3$ and $x \leqslant 3$.
This can be written $-3 \leqslant x \leqslant 3$.

On the number line it looks like this:

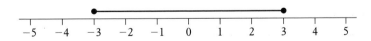

---

11 $x^2 + 10 < 46$

12 $3x^2 + 2 < 5$

13 $x^2 - 6 < 94$

14 $2(x^2 + 5) < 60$

● **15** $3x^2 - 5 < 25$

● **16** $x^2 - 9 < 81$

2 Solving inequalities using graphs

Ali and Graham are visiting a theme park.

They have a maximum of £25 to spend.

They can split their money between rides and food.

There are lots of ways they can do this.

You can use graphs to solve inequalities.
This gives you a 'picture' of the problem which often makes it easier to solve.

The easiest inequalities to show on a graph are those that have a boundary line that is parallel to one of the axes.

Example   Show each of these inequalities on a graph.
a $x \geqslant 3$ **b** $y < -2$

a $x \geqslant 3$
The line is $x = 3$.
All the points in the shaded region have an x co-ordinate greater than 3
The solid line shows that the boundary **is** included.

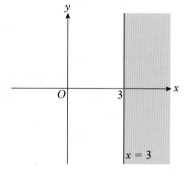

b $y < -2$
The line is $y = -2$.
All the points in the shaded region have a y co-ordinate less than -2
The dashed line shows that the boundary is **not** included.

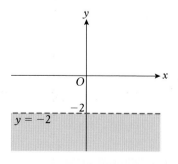

Exercise 36:7

Draw graphs to illustrate each of these inequalities.
Shade the region where each inequality is true.

1 $y \geqslant 3$ **4** $y > 5$ **7** $y < -1$

2 $x \geqslant 3$ **5** $x > 5.5$ **8** $x > -3.5$

3 $y < 4$ **6** $x \leqslant -3$ **9** $y < \frac{1}{2}$

For each of the following graphs, write down the inequality that
describes the shaded region.

10

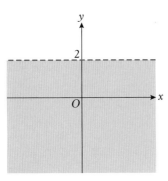

13

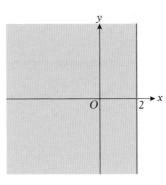

11

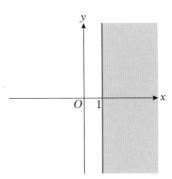

14

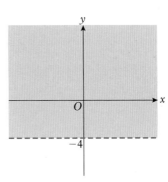

12

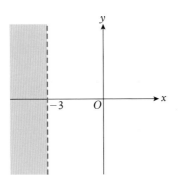

15

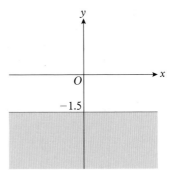

Sometimes a region is sandwiched between two lines.

Example   Show each of these inequalities on a graph.
   a $-2 < x \leqslant 3$ **b** $-4 \leqslant y < -2$

a $-2 < x \leqslant 3$
The lines are $x = -2$ and $x = 3$
All the points in the shaded
region have an x co-ordinate
greater than -2 but less than
or equal to 3

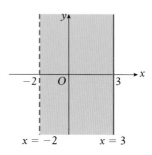

b $-4 \leqslant y < -2$
The lines are $y = -4$
and $y = -2$
All the points in the shaded
region have a y co-ordinate
greater than or equal to -4
but less than -2

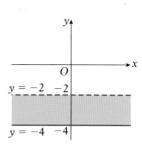

Exercise 36:8

1 Draw graphs to illustrate each of these inequalities.
Shade the region where each inequality is true.
   a $2 < x \leqslant 4$ **c** $3 \leqslant y < 5$ **e** $-2 < x \leqslant 0$
   b $-1 < x \leqslant 4$ **d** $0 \leqslant y < 2$ **f** $-\frac{1}{2} \leqslant x < \frac{1}{2}$

2 For each of the following graphs, write down the inequality that
describes the shaded region.

a
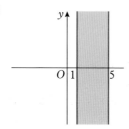

b
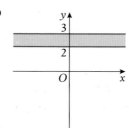

c 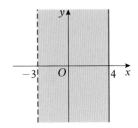   **d**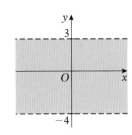

Sometimes you need to use more than one inequality to define a region.

Example   Draw a graph to show the region defined by the inequalities
$x \geqslant 1$ and $y < 5$

This graph shows $x \geqslant 1$ This graph shows $y < 5$

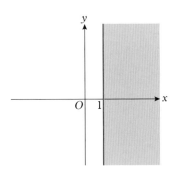 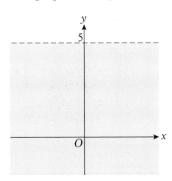

This graph shows both inequalities together.
The purple area shows where both inequalities are true.

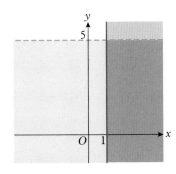

It is important that you label your graphs carefully.
You must say which area represents your answer.
You can use shading in different directions instead of colours.

Exercise 36:9

Draw graphs to show the regions defined by these inequalities.
Label each graph carefully.

1 $y \geqslant 3$ and $x > 3$

2 $x \geqslant 2$ and $y < 4$

3 $y < -2$ and $x > 0$

4 $x \leqslant -2$ and $y > 2$

5 $x > -2$ and $0 \leqslant y \leqslant 3$

6 $x \geqslant -2$ and $2 < y < 3$

● **7** $-2 \leqslant x \leqslant 4$ and $-3 \leqslant y \leqslant 4$

● **8** $-2 < x \leqslant -1$ and $3 \leqslant y \leqslant 4$

For each of the following graphs, write down the inequalities that
describe the shaded region.

9

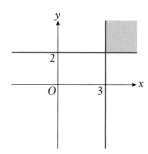

12

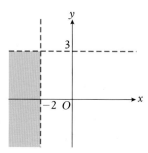

10

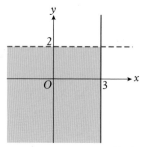

● **13**

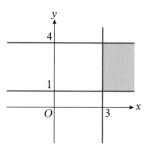

11

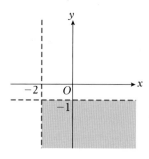

● **14**

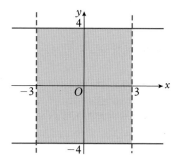

Inequalities with two variables

Sometimes, the lines that form the borders of the regions are not parallel to one of the axes. When this happens, the inequalities will have both x and y in them.

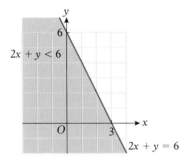

In this type of question, it can be more difficult to decide which side of the line you want. You often have to test a couple of points to help you to decide where to shade.

Example   Draw a graph to show the inequality $3x + 2y < 12$

First draw the boundary line on the graph.
This is the line $3x + 2y = 12$

There is a quick way to draw lines when they are written in this way.
There is no need to write out a table of values.
To draw the line, just find the points where it crosses the axes.

The line crosses the y axis when $x = 0$
Putting $x = 0$ gives $2y = 12$ so $y = 6$
So the line crosses at $(0, 6)$

The line crosses the x axis when $y = 0$
Putting $y = 0$ gives $3x = 12$ so $x = 4$
So the line crosses at $(4, 0)$

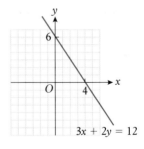

The graph of $3x + 2y = 12$ looks like this:

You now need to check which
side of the line you want.
It may seem obvious in this case,
but it isn't always!

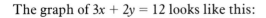

Pick one point below the line and one point above it. Substitute the co-ordinates into the inequality:

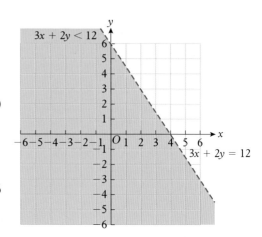

$$3x + 2y < 12$$

Below the line: $(0, 0)$ $3x + 2y$
$$= 3 \times 0 + 2 \times 0$$
$$= 0$$

This is **less** than 12

Above the line: $(6, 6)$ $3x + 2y$
$$= 3 \times 6 + 2 \times 6$$
$$= 30$$

This is **greater** than 12

You want $3x + 2y$ to be less than 12 so the required region is **below** the line. The boundary should be drawn with a dashed line as it is not included.

Exercise 36:10

1 Follow these steps to show the region given by $3x + 5y < 15$

  a Draw x and y axes from -6 to 6.

  b Copy this. Fill it in.
    The boundary line is $3x + 5y = 15$
    The line crosses the y axis when $x = 0$.
    Putting $x = 0$ gives $5y = \ldots$ so $y = \ldots$
    So the line crosses at $(\ldots, \ldots)$.

    The line crosses the x axis when $y = 0$.
    Putting $y = 0$ gives $3x = \ldots$ so $x = \ldots$
    So the line crosses at $(\ldots, \ldots)$.

  c Draw the line $3x + 5y = 15$ onto your graph.

  d Copy this. Fill it in.
    Point below the line: $(\ldots, \ldots)$ $3x + 5y$
                                    $= \ldots$
                                    $= \ldots$

    This is ... than 15

    Point above the line: $(\ldots, \ldots)$ $3x + 5y$
                                    $= \ldots$
                                    $= \ldots$

  e Shade the required region.

2 Follow these steps to show the region given by $3x + 7y \geq 21$
   a Draw x and y axes from -8 to 8.
   b Write down the equation of the boundary line.
   c Find the point where the boundary line crosses the y axis.
   d Find the point where the boundary line crosses the x axis.
   e Draw the boundary line on your graph.
   f Test two points to see which region represents $3x + 7y \geq 21$
   g Shade and label the required region.

3 Draw graphs to show the regions defined by these inequalities.
Label each region carefully.
   a $2x + y > 8$ **e** $2x + 3y - 12 \leq 0$
   b $3x + 2y \leq 6$ **f** $2x + 3y > 18$
   c $x + 2y < 10$ **g** $2y > 3x - 9$
   d $3x - 5y \geq 15$ **h** $y > x$

4 **a** Draw a graph of the line $y = 2x + 1$
      Use x values from -3 to 4
   b Shade the region where $y > 2x + 1$

5 Draw a graph to show the region $y < 3x - 4$
Use x values from -4 to 4

Again, you need to be able to draw graphs that show more than one inequality.
There can sometimes be three or even four separate inequalities to show on one
diagram. It can become rather difficult to find the required region once the diagram
is complete.
For this reason, it is sensible to shade the region you do **not** want.
This is called **shading out**.
It means that the region you want is the region left with no shading at all.

Example   Show on a graph the region defined by the following set of
             inequalities: $x \geq 0$, $y \geq 0$, $x + y < 6$, $x + 3y > 6$

             Separately, these inequalities are the unshaded regions shown:

$x \geq 0$

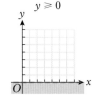
$y \geq 0$

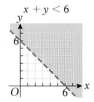
$x + y < 6$

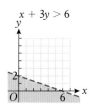
$x + 3y > 6$

When you draw these on the same diagram, the area left white is the required region.

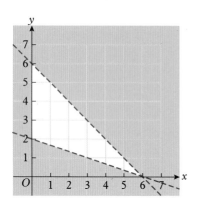

Exercise 36:11

Draw graphs to show the regions defined by these sets of inequalities.
Draw the x and y axes from -10 to 10.
Leave the required region unshaded.
Label each graph.

1 $x \geqslant 0$ $y \geqslant 0$ $x + 2y \leqslant 8$

2 $x \geqslant 0$ $y \leqslant 0$ $x - 2y \leqslant 8$

3 $y \geqslant 0$ $x < 6$ $y < x$

4 $x \geqslant 0$ $y \geqslant 0$ $x + 2y \leqslant 10$

5 $x + 2y < 6$ $y > x$ $x > -2$

6 $y > 2x$ $y < 3x$ $x + y > 4$ $x + y < 9$

● **7** $y > \dfrac{x}{3}$ $y < 6 - 2x$ $y < 2.5x$

Solving problems using inequalities

Many real life problems involve the use of limited quantities of materials or resources. These can range from allocating staff to jobs or buying stock from a limited budget. Inequalities can often be used to solve these problems.

In the next exercise, you will see how inequalities can be used to solve problems. You will need the skills you have learnt in the first part of the chapter.

Example   A property developer has a plot of land with area 5400 m².
He builds two types of house.
The 3 bedroomed Family requires an area of 450 m².
The 4 bedroomed Executive requires an area of 600 m²
He wants to build at least 3 Family houses and at least 4 Executive houses.

a Write down inequalities which describe the restrictions on the builder.
b Draw a graph to show the possible combinations of the two types of house which he can build.
c On your graph, circle all the possible combinations.

a First give letters to each type of house.
Say that the developer builds f Family houses and e Executive houses.
Now write down the inequalities.

He wants to build at least 3 Family houses so $f \geqslant 3$
He wants to build at least 4 Executive houses so $e \geqslant 4$

The total area taken up by the Family houses is $450f$
The total area taken up by the Executive houses is $600e$
The total area taken up by both types of house is $450f + 600e$
The builder only has 5400 m² so $450f + 600e \leqslant 5400$
This can be simplified by dividing by 150 to give $3f + 4e \leqslant 36$

b The graph of these inequalities looks like this:

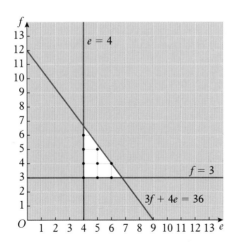

c Each point that is circled shows possible values of e and f as co-ordinates.
The point $(5, 4)$ is circled so the builder could build 5 Executive houses and 4 Family houses.
The maximum number of houses he can build is 10.
He can build 4 Executive and 6 Family houses or 6 Executive and 4 Family houses.

Exercise 36:12

1 Alan wants to buy a combination of chart singles on CD and tape.
CDs cost £4 and tapes cost £3.
He has £24 to spend altogether.
He wants to buy at least one of each type of single.

a Copy each of these. Complete each one with an inequality.
Call the number of tapes t and the number of CDs c.

Alan buys at least one CD so ....
Alan buys at least one tape so ....

The total cost of the CDs is ....
The total cost of the tapes is ....
The total cost of the tapes and CDs
must not be more than £24 so ....

b Draw x and y axes from 0 to 8.
Draw a graph showing all of the inequalities you have written down
in part **a**.
Put t on the vertical axis and c on the horizontal axis.

c Alan decides to buy 4 tapes.
Write down the possible numbers of CDs he can buy.

2 Fred the farmer needs to re-stock.
He wants to buy at least 30 sheep
and at least 12 cows.
Sheep cost £40 and cows cost £70.
He has £5600 to spend altogether.

a Copy and complete these three inequalities that describe the
constraints on Fred.
He wants to buy at least 30 sheep so ....
He wants to buy at least 12 cows so ....
He must not spend more than £5600 so ....

b Draw a graph showing all of the inequalities you have written down
in part **a**.

c Fred decides he wants to buy as near equal numbers of cows and
sheep as possible. He also wants to spend as much of his money as
possible. How many of each animal can he buy?

- **3** A radio DJ has to play a mixture of Chart Hits and Golden Oldies. He can only fit 35 records into his show. He wants to play at least 10 of each. Royalties on Chart Hits are £50 per record but on Golden Oldies are only £30 per record. The budget for the show is £1400.

    a Write down four inequalities to describe these constraints.

    b Draw a graph showing all of the inequalities you have written down in part **a**.

    c What is the largest number of Chart Hits that the DJ can play?

More complex inequalities

It is possible to use graphs to solve inequalities that would be quite difficult to solve using algebra.

These can involve quite complicated functions. You will need to sketch or plot a graph of the function like you did in Chapters 19 and 27.

Example **a** Sketch a graph of $y = x^2 + 5x - 6$
b Use your graph to solve the inequality $x^2 + 5x - 6 > 0$

a First solve $x^2 + 5x - 6 = 0$

$x^2 + 5x - 6 = 0$
$(x - 1)(x + 6) = 0$
$x = 1$ or $x = -6$
This means that the graph cuts
the x axis at $x = 1$ and $x = -6$

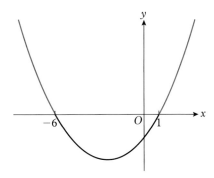

b You want to know when $x^2 + 5x - 6 > 0$
This is when $x^2 + 5x - 6$ is positive.
$x^2 + 5x - 6$ is positive when the **curve is above the x axis**.
So $x^2 + 5x - 6 > 0$ when $x > 1$ or when $x < -6$

Exercise 36:13

1 Look at this sketch graph of $y = x^2 - x - 6$
Use the graph to solve the inequality $x^2 - x - 6 > 0$

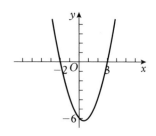

2 Look at this sketch graph of $y = 9 - x^2$
Use the graph to solve the inequality $9 - x^2 > 0$

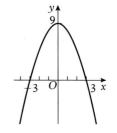

3 Look at this sketch graph of $y = x^2 - 3x$
Use the graph to solve the inequality $x^2 - 3x < 0$

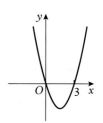

● **4** **a** Copy and complete this table for $y = x^2 - 2x - 2$

x	-5	-4	-3	-2	-1	0	1	2	3	4	5
y											

   b Plot the graph of $y = x^2 - 2x - 2$ from your table.
   Draw axes with x from -5 to 5 and y from -5 to 30.
   c Copy and complete this table for $y = 2x + 2$

x	-5	-4	-3	-2	-1	0	1	2	3	4	5
y											

   d Draw the graph of $y = 2x + 2$ over the top of your graph from part **b**.
   e Write down the x co-ordinates of the points of intersection of the curve and the line to 1 dp.
   f Use your answers to solve the inequality $x^2 - 2x + 2 > 2x + 2$

1 Write down inequalities to describe each of these number lines.

a

b

2 Solve each of these inequalities.

a $2x < 18$

e $5(4t - 10) < 20$

b $z - 7 > 14$

f $\dfrac{8x - 2}{5} \leqslant 6$

c $2x - 10 \leqslant 8$

g $4x - 7 > 2x + 19$

d $2r + 2.8 > 6$

h $3k - 8 < 7 - 2k$

3 Solve each of these inequalities.

a $4 < x - 4 < 10$

e $-15 < 3z + 3 < -6$

b $18 \leqslant 3p \leqslant 27$

f $-2 \leqslant 2(2x + 5) \leqslant 6$

c $63 \geqslant x - 3 > 72$

g $18 \leqslant \dfrac{2x - 6}{3} \leqslant 20$

d $96 \leqslant 8y + 12 \leqslant 108$

4 Draw a graph to illustrate each of these inequalities.
Shade the region where each inequality is true.

a $y \geqslant 4$ **b** $y > -3$ **c** $-6 \leqslant x \leqslant 1$

5 For each of the following graphs, write down the inequality that describes the shaded region.

a
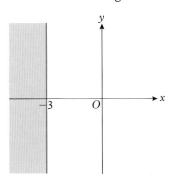

b
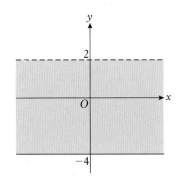

6 Draw graphs to show the regions defined by these inequalities.

    a $2x + y > 10$ **c** $2x - 3y - 6 \leqslant 0$

    b $3x + 4y \leqslant 12$ **d** $y > 2x + 4$

7 Draw graphs to show the regions defined by these sets of inequalities.
Leave the required region unshaded.
Label each graph.

    a $x \geqslant 0$ $y \geqslant 0$ $x + 3y \leqslant 9$

    b $x \geqslant 1$ $y \geqslant 2$ $x + 2y \leqslant 10$

    c $x \geqslant 2$ $y \leqslant 10$ $x - 2y \leqslant 6$

8 Look at this sketch graph of $y = x^2 + 2x - 15$
Use your graph to solve the inequality $x^2 + 2x - 15 < 0$

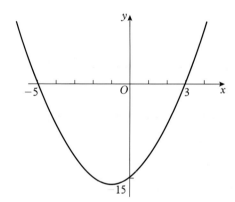

9 Mr Grout is tiling his bathroom.
He is using two types of tiles.
Blank tiles cost £2 each and patterned tiles cost £3 each.
He has a maximum of £600 to spend on tiles.
He has decided to use at least 100 blank tiles and at least 50 patterned tiles.

    a Copy and complete these three inequalities that describe the constraints on
       Mr Grout. Use b for blank tiles and p for patterned tiles.

        He wants to buy at least 100 blank tiles so ....
        He wants to buy at least 50 patterned tiles so ....
        He must not spend more than £600 so ....

    b Draw a graph showing all of the inequalities you have written down in **a**.

    c What is the maximum number of patterned tiles that Mr Grout can buy?

1 A computer company makes two types of laser printer.
The details are given in this table.

	Model DB30	Model DB50
Cost to produce	£120	£90
Worker hours	2	2.5
Machine hours	3	4
Profit	£15	£20

In any one day, the factory has 80 worker hours and 150 machine hours available. They have £3600 to spend on production each day.

a Write down inequalities to describe the constraints described above.

b Draw a graph to show these inequalities.

c What combination of printers should the company make in order to make the most profit?

2 a Draw a graph to solve the equation $x^2 + 5x + 6 = 0$
Draw your x axis from -4 to $+2$ and your y axis from -5 to 15.

b Use your graph to solve $x^2 + 5x + 6 > 2$

c By drawing the line $y = -x$ on your graph, solve the inequality
$x^2 + 5x + 6 > -x$

3 A lorry is loaded with two different sizes of box.
Small boxes have a volume of 2 m³ whilst large boxes have a volume of 3.5 m³. The lorry has a maximum capacity of 70 m³.
The small boxes weigh 30 kg and the large boxes weigh 40 kg. The total weight of the load must not exceed 1225 kg.

a Write down four inequalities to describe these constraints.

b Draw a graph showing all of the inequalities you have written down in part **a**.

c What is the maximum number of large boxes that the lorry can carry?

1 Write down inequalities to describe each of these number lines.

a

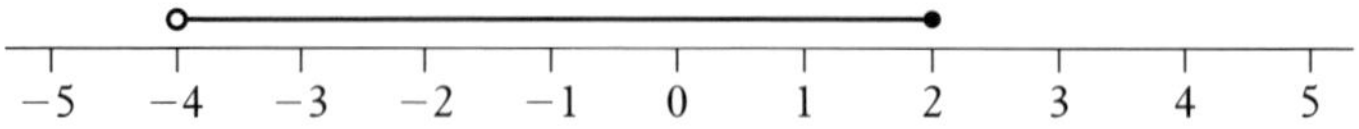

b

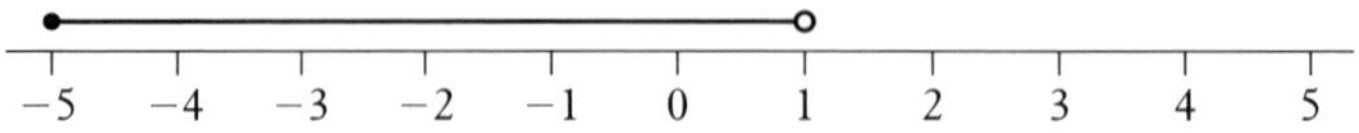

c

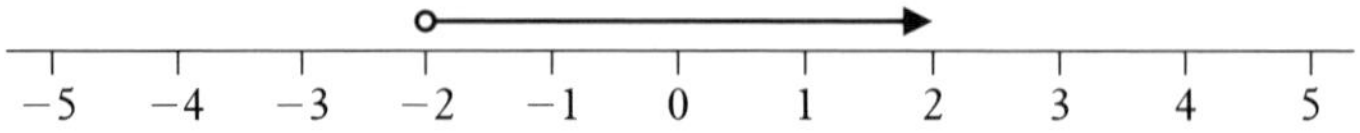

2 List the integers that are included in each of these inequalities.
  a $2 < x \leqslant 5$
  b $-3 \leqslant x < 1$
  c $-5 \leqslant x \leqslant -1$
  d $-3 < x < 3$

3 Solve each of these inequalities.
  a $x - 3 < 8$
  b $2x + 5 \geqslant 17$
  c $4x - 7 \leqslant 12$
  d $\dfrac{x}{4} - 9 > 2.3$
  e $\dfrac{3x + 1}{5} < -4$
  f $5x + 11 \geqslant 3x + 7$

4 Solve each of these inequalities.
  a $11 - x > 3$
  b $\dfrac{5 - 2x}{7} < -3$
  c $3x + 7 \leqslant 8x - 9$
  d $10 - 3x \geqslant -2x + 6$

5 Solve each of these inequalities.
  a $6 \leqslant 3x < 12$
  b $11 < x + 7 \leqslant 19$
  c $5 \leqslant 2x - 1 \leqslant 11$
  d $-10 < -5x < 0$

6 Write down the inequality that describes the shaded region on each of these graphs.

a

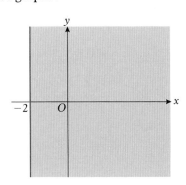

b

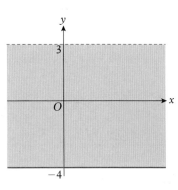

7 Write down inequalities to describe the shaded region on each of these graphs.

a

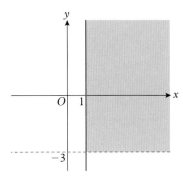

b

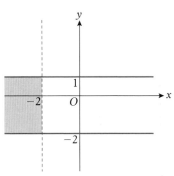

8 Look at this sketch graph of $y = x^2 - 3x + 2$
Use the graph to solve the inequality $x^2 - 3x + 2 > 0$

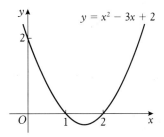

$y = x^2 - 3x + 2$

9 A bakery makes both sliced and unsliced loaves of bread. The maximum number of loaves it can make in a day is 800. The number of sliced loaves made is always at least double the number of unsliced loaves. At least 200 unsliced loaves must be made.
   a Explain the inequality $s + u \leqslant 800$.
   b Write down four other inequalities to describe the situation.
   c Draw a graph to show all of the inequalities.
   d What is the maximum number of unsliced loaves that can be made?

CHAPTER 19

1 **a** $y = 2x - 3$

x	−1	0	1	2
2x	−2	0	2	4
−3	−3	−3	−3	−3
y	−5	−3	−1	1

b, c, e

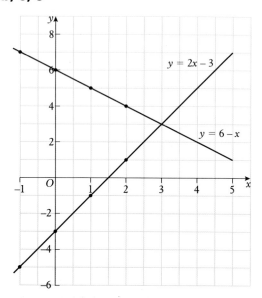

d $y = 6 - x$

x	−1	0	1	2
6	6	6	6	6
−x	1	0	−1	−2
y	7	6	5	4

f $(3, 3)$

2 A quadratic B linear C cubic

3 **a**

x	−2	−1	0	1	2	3	4	5	6
x^2	4	1	0	1	4	9	16	25	36
−4x	8	4	0	−4	−8	−12	−16	−20	−24
+3	+3	+3	+3	+3	+3	+3	+3	+3	+3
y	15	8	3	0	−1	0	3	8	15

b, c, d

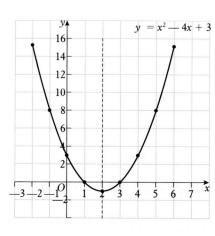

e $x = 2$
f $y = -0.8$
   (approximately)
g $x = -1.3$ and 5.3
   (approximately)
h $x = 2$

4　**a**　$y = x^3 - x^2 - 6x$

x	-3	-2	-1	0	1	2	3	4
x^3	-27	-8	-1	0	1	8	27	64
$-x^2$	-9	-4	-1	0	-1	-4	-9	-16
$-6x$	$+18$	12	6	0	-6	-12	-18	-24
y	-18	0	4	0	-6	-8	0	24

b, c, f

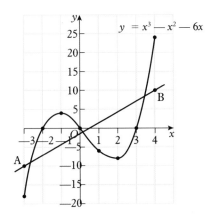

d　$y = 3$ (approximately)

e　$x = -1.9, -0.1, 3.1$ (approximately)

g

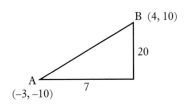

B (4, 10)

20

A
(−3, −10)

7

$$\text{gradient} = \frac{20}{7} = 2.9 \text{ (1 dp)}$$

h　$(-2.7, -9)$　$(0.1, -1)$　$(3.5, 8.5)$ (approximately)

5　**A** (3),　**B** (4),　**C** (2),　**D** (1),　**E** (6),　**F** (5)

CHAPTER 20

1 **a, b, c, d, e**

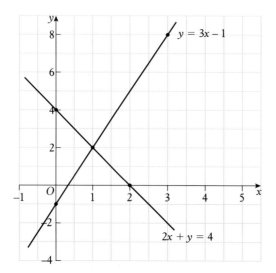

f $x = 1$, $y = 2$

g $y = 3x - 1$; when $x = 1$, $y = 3x - 1 = 3 \times 1 - 1 = 3 - 1 = 2$ ✓
$2x + y = 4$; when $x = 1$ and $y = 2$, $2x + y = 2 \times 1 + 2 = 2 + 2 = 4$ ✓

2 **a**   (1) $3x - 2y = 7$
       (2) $\underline{x + 2y = 5}$

   Adding $4x = 12$
               $x = 3$

   Put $x = 3$ in (2)
           $3 + 2y = 5$
              $2y = 2$
               $y = 1$

   Check in (1)
      $3x - 2y = 3 \times 3 - 2 \times 1$
              $= 9 - 2$
              $= 7$ ✓

b   (1) $5x - 2y = 10$
       (2) $3x - 2y = 2$

   Subtracting $2x = 8$
                 $x = 4$

   Put $x = 4$ in (1)
           $20 - 2y = 10$
              $20 = 10 + 2y$
        $20 - 10 = 2y$
              $10 = 2y$
               $y = 5$

   Check in (2)
      $3x - 2y = 3 \times 4 - 2 \times 5$
              $= 12 - 10$
              $= 2$ ✓

c (1) $3x - y = 13$
(2) $2x + 3y = 5$
(1) $\times 3$ $9x - 3y = 39$
(2) $2x + 3y = 5$

Adding $11x = 44$
$x = 4$
Put $x = 4$ in (1)
$12 - y = 13$
$12 = 13 + y$
$12 - 13 = y$
$y = -1$
Check in (2)
$2x + 3y = 2 \times 4 + 3 \times (-1)$
$= 8 - 3$
$= 5$ ✓

d (1) $7x + 2y = 28$
(2) $2x + 3y = 25$
(1) $\times 3$ $21x + 6y = 84$
(2) $\times 2$ $4x + 6y = 50$

Subtracting $17x = 34$
$x = 2$
Put $x = 2$ in (1)
$14 + 2y = 28$
$2y = 14$
$y = 7$
Check in (2)
$2x + 3y = 4 + 21$
$= 25$ ✓

3 a $g = 4h - 7$
$4h - 7 = g$
$4h = g + 7$
$h = \dfrac{g + 7}{4}$

c $y = \dfrac{3x}{4} - 6$
$\dfrac{3x}{4} - 6 = y$
$\dfrac{3x}{4} = y + 6$
$3x = 4(y + 6)$
$x = \dfrac{4(y + 6)}{3}$

b $w = \dfrac{t}{5} + 2$
$\dfrac{t}{5} + 2 = w$
$\dfrac{t}{5} = w - 2$
$t = 5(w - 2)$

d $s = 10 + 3t^2$
$10 + 3t^2 = s$
$3t^2 = s - 10$
$t^2 = \dfrac{s - 10}{3}$
$t = \sqrt{\dfrac{s - 10}{3}}$

4 a $A = \dfrac{\sqrt{w^2 + 3xy}}{10}$
$= \dfrac{\sqrt{(-1)^2 + 3 \times 8 \times 2}}{10}$
$= \dfrac{\sqrt{1 + 48}}{10}$
$= \dfrac{\sqrt{49}}{10}$
$= \dfrac{7}{10}$
$= 0.7$

b $\dfrac{\sqrt{w^2 + 3xy}}{10} = A$

$\sqrt{w^2 + 3xy} = 10A$

$w^2 + 3xy = (10A)^2$

$w^2 = (10A)^2 - 3xy$

$w = \sqrt{(10A)^2 - 3xy}$

c $w = \sqrt{(10 \times 1)^2 - 3 \times 4 \times 7}$

$= \sqrt{10^2 - 84}$

$= \sqrt{100 - 84}$

$= \sqrt{16}$

$= 4$

5 a (1) $y = 5 - 2x$
(2) $3y + x = 10$

Substitute for y in (2)

$3(5 - 2x) + x = 10$

$15 - 6x + x = 10$

$15 - 5x = 10$

$15 = 10 + 5x$

$5 = 5x$

$x = 1$

Put $x = 1$ in (1)

$y = 5 - 2 \times 1$

$= 5 - 2$

$= 3$

Check in (2)

$3y + x = 3 \times 3 + 1$

$= 9 + 1$

$= 10$ ✓

b (1) $x = 4y - 6$
(2) $14 = 8y - 3x$

Substitute for x in (2)

$14 = 8y - 3(4y - 6)$

$14 = 8y - 12y + 18$

$14 = -4y + 18$

$14 + 4y = 18$

$4y = 4$

$y = 1$

Put $y = 1$ in (1)

$x = 4 \times 1 - 6$

$= 4 - 6$

$= -2$

Check in (2)

$8y - 3x = 8 \times 1 - 3 \times (-2)$

$= 8 + 6$

$= 14$ ✓

CHAPTER 21

1 a

	red	blue	green	yellow	brown	purple
1	1, R	1, B	1, G	1, Y	1, Br	1, P
2	2, R	2, B	2, G	2, Y	2, Br	2, P
3	3, R	3, B	3, G	3, Y	3, Br	3, P
4	4, R	4, B	4, G	4, Y	4, Br	4, P
5	5, R	5, B	5, G	5, Y	5, Br	5, P
6	6, R	6, B	6, G	6, Y	6, Br	6, P

b (1) $\frac{1}{36}$ (2) $\frac{3}{36} = \frac{1}{12}$ (3) $\frac{18}{36} = \frac{1}{2}$

(4) The prime numbers are 2, 3 and 5; $\frac{3}{36} = \frac{1}{12}$

2 a $\frac{3}{50}$ **b** P(faulty tyres) $= \frac{7}{50}$; $200 \times \frac{7}{50} = 28$

3 P(even number) $= \frac{2}{5}$

so P(3 even numbers) = P(even no. on 1st spin)

$\qquad\qquad\qquad\qquad\qquad \times$ P(even no. on 2nd spin) $\times$ P(even no. on 3rd spin)

$\qquad\qquad\qquad\qquad = \frac{2}{5} \times \frac{2}{5} \times \frac{2}{5}$

$\qquad\qquad\qquad\qquad = \frac{8}{125}$

4 a $0.7 \times 0.9 = 0.63$ **b** $0.3 \times 0.1 = 0.03$

5 a P(Q and R) = P(Q) $\times$ P(R) $= \frac{1}{4} \times \frac{3}{8} = \frac{3}{32}$

b P(S or T) = P(S) + P(T) $= \frac{1}{2} + \frac{1}{6} = \frac{3}{6} + \frac{1}{6} = \frac{4}{6} = \frac{2}{3}$

c If events A and B are independent then P(A and B) = P(A) $\times$ P(B)
P(A) $\times$ P(B) $= 0.4 \times 0.2 = 0.08 \neq 0.075$ so
A and B are not independent.

d If events C and D are mutually exclusive then P(C or D) = P(C) + P(D)
P(C) + P(D) $= 0.85 + 0.3 = 1.15$ but probability must be less than 1 so
1.15 is impossible.
So C and D are not mutually exclusive.

6 a $0.15 + 0.25 + 0.05 + 0.3 + 0.05 = 0.8$
$1 - 0.8 = 0.2$
Probability of scoring a 2 is 0.2

b (1) 5   (2) $0.15 + 0.25 + 0.3 = 0.7$

c He needs 2 sixes to get a total score of 12
so probability $= 0.05 \times 0.05 = 0.0025$

7 $35\,600 \times 0.0045 = 160.2$
$\qquad\qquad\qquad \approx 160$ faulty resistors

CHAPTER 22

1 a 4.5×10^5 **c** 8.2×10^{-3} **e** 3×10^6

b 3.683×10^8 **d** 3.751×10^{-1} **f** 6×10^{-8}

2 a $69\,000$ **c** $0.000\,000\,04$

b 0.0024 **d** $361\,800\,000$

3 a B, D, A, E, C, F

b $8.9 \times 10^{12} - 6.5 \times 10^{11} = 8.25 \times 10^{12}$

4 $6.34 \times 10^9 \div 25 = 253\,600\,000$ minutes
$$= 4\,226\,666.667\ldots \text{ hours}$$
$$\approx 4\,230\,000 \text{ hours (3 sf)}$$

5 **a** $35 \times 10^{5+8} = 35 \times 10^{13} = 3.5 \times 10 \times 10^{13} = 3.5 \times 10^{14}$

   b $(1.5 \div 6) \times 10^{4--5} = 0.25 \times 10^9 = 0.25 \times 10 \times 10^8 = 2.5 \times 10^8$

   c $40\,000 + 6000 = 46\,000 = 4.6 \times 10^4$

   d $300\,000 - 20\,000 = 280\,000 = 2.8 \times 10^5$

6 **a** $1.084\,88 \times 10^{17} \approx 1.08 \times 10^{17}$ (3 sf)

   b $9.694\,533\ldots \times 10^{11} \approx 9.69 \times 10^{11}$ (3 sf)

   c $3.154\,956\ldots \times 10^{-23} \approx 3.15 \times 10^{-23}$ (3 sf)

CHAPTER 23

1 **a** 20 cm^2 **b** Allow 27 cm^2 or 28 cm^2

2 **a** $(18 \times 14) \div 2 = 252 \div 2 = 126\text{ cm}^2$

   b $\frac{1}{2} \times 13.5 \times 10 = 67.5\text{ m}^2$

   c $\frac{1}{2} \times 7 \times 14 = 49\text{ cm}^2$

   d $\dfrac{(6 + 10)}{2} \times 5 = 8 \times 5 = 40\text{ cm}^2$

   e $20 \times 30 = 600\text{ cm}^2$

   f $15 \times 12 = 180\text{ m}^2$

3 **a**

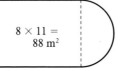

Diameter $= 8$ m, radius $= 8 \div 2 = 4$ m
Area of semicircle $= (\pi \times \text{radius} \times \text{radius}) \div 2$
$$= (\pi \times 4 \times 4) \div 2$$
$$= (50.265\ldots) \div 2$$
$$= 25.1\text{ m}^2 \text{ (3 sf)}$$
Area of shape $= 88 + 25.1 = 113.1\text{ m}^2$

   b Total area $= 372 \times 270$
$$= 642\text{ cm}^2$$

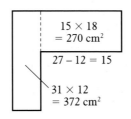

c For triangle, base $= 25 - 9 = 16$ mm;
height $= 18 - 12 = 6$ mm

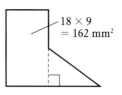

18×9
$= 162$ mm^2

$$\text{Area} = \frac{(16 \times 6)}{2} = \frac{96}{2} = 48 \text{ mm}^2$$

Total area $= 162 + 48 = 210$ mm^2

d Area of A $= 12 \times 12 = 144$ cm^2
Area of B $= (\pi \times \text{radius} \times \text{radius}) \div 4$
$\quad\quad\quad = (\pi \times 12 \times 12) \div 4$
$\quad\quad\quad = 113$ cm^2 (3 sf)
Area of D is the same as B
Area C $= (\pi \times 6 \times 6) \div 2 = 56.5$ cm^2 (3 sf)
Total area $= 144 + 113 + 113 + 56.5$
$\quad\quad\quad = 426.5$ cm^2 (3 sf)

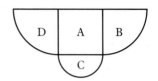

4 **a** (1)

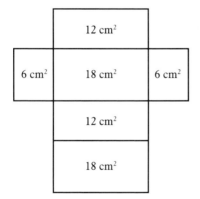

(2) Surface area $= 6 + 12 + 18 + 12 + 18 + 6 = 72$ cm^2

b (1)

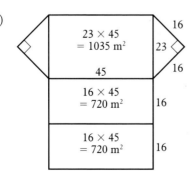

(2) Area of each triangle $= (16 \times 16) \div 2 = 128$ m^2

Surface area $= 128 + 1035 + 720 + 720 + 128$ m^2
$\quad\quad\quad = 2731$ m^2

5 **a** $1 \text{ cm}^2 = 100 \text{ mm}^2$ so $3 \text{ cm}^2 = 300 \text{ mm}^2$

    b $1 \text{ m}^2 = 10\,000 \text{ cm}^2$ so $4 \text{ m}^2 = 40\,000 \text{ cm}^2$

    c $1 \text{ cm}^2 = 100 \text{ mm}^2$ so $750\,000 \text{ mm}^2 = 750\,000 \div 100 = 7500 \text{ cm}^2$

    d $1 \text{ km}^2 = 1\,000\,000 \text{ m}^2 = 1 \times 10^6 \text{ m}^2$

          so $5 \times 10^{12} \text{ m}^2 = (5 \times 10^{12}) \div (1 \times 10^6) = 5 \times 10^{12-6}$

                          $= 5 \times 10^6 \text{ km}^2$

CHAPTER 24

1 **a** 5 horses $= 5 \times 2$ guns $= 10$ guns

    b 2 cannons $= 2 \times 5$ horses $= 10$ horses

                    $= 10 \times 2$ guns $= 20$ guns

                    $= 20 \times 20$ arrows $= 400$ arrows

    c 15 archers $= 15 \div 3$ horses $= 5$ horses

    d 4 horses $= 4 \times 3$ archers $= 12$ archers

                    $= (12 \div 2) \times 5$ foot soldiers

                    $= 6 \times 5 = 30$ foot soldiers

2   1st term $= 10$

    2nd term $= 10 \times 2 - 12 = 20 - 12 = 8$

    3rd term $= 8 \times 2 - 12 = 16 - 12 = 4$

    4th term $= 4 \times 2 - 12 = 8 - 12 = -4$

    5th term $= -4 \times 2 - 12 = -8 - 12 = -20$

3 **a** 1st term $= 7 \times 1 + 3 = 7 + 3 = 10$

    2nd term $= 7 \times 2 + 3 = 14 + 3 = 17$

    3rd term $- 7 \times 3 + 3 = 21 + 3 = 24$

    4th term $= 7 \times 4 + 3 = 28 + 3 = 31$

    b 10th term $= 7 \times 10 + 3 = 70 + 3 = 73$

4 **a** 50th term $= 250 + 27 \times 50 = 250 + 1350 = 1600$

    b

Value of n	Value of $250 + 27n$
20	$250 + 27 \times 20 = 790$ too big
15	$250 + 27 \times 15 = 655$ too small
16	$250 + 27 \times 16 = 682$ too small
18	$250 + 27 \times 18 = 736$ too big
17	$250 + 27 \times 17 = 709$ ✓

Or solve the equation
$250 + 27n = 709$
To get $27n = 459$
$n = 17$

    The 17th term.

5 **a** (1) 3, 6, 9, 12, 15   **b** (1) $7n$

        (2) 4, 8, 12, 16, 20   (2) $11n$

        (3) 5, 10, 15, 20, 25   (3) $15n$

6 **a** $4n + 1$ **b** $4n + 9$ **c** $4n - 3$

7

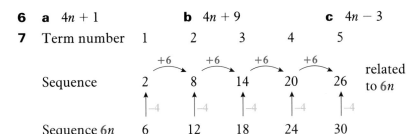

Term number   1   2   3   4   5

Sequence   2   8   14   20   26   related to $6n$

Sequence $6n$ 6   12   18   24   30

You need to take 4 from every term in $6n$ to make the sequence.
So the formula for the nth term of the sequence is $6n - 4$

8 **a** 4   15   32   55   84

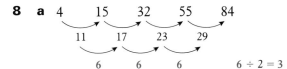

11   17   23   29

6   6   6 $6 \div 2 = 3$

The first part of the formula is $3n^2$

Term number	1	2	3	4	5
Sequence	4	15	32	55	84

$+1$ $+3$ $+5$ $+7$ $+9$

Value of $3n^2$ 3   12   27   48   75

Term number   1   2   3   4   5

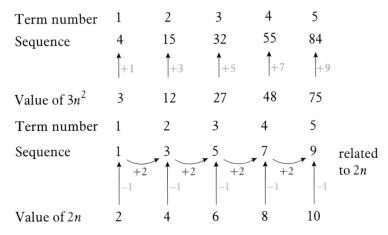

Sequence   1   3   5   7   9   related to $2n$

$+2$ $+2$ $+2$ $+2$

-1 -1 -1 -1 -1

Value of $2n$ 2   4   6   8   10

The second part of the formula is $2n - 1$
b The whole formula is $3n^2 + 2n - 1$

9 **a** 1st term $= 1^2 - 5 \times 1 + 10 = 6$
2nd term $= 2^2 - 5 \times 2 + 10 = 4$
3rd term $= 3^2 - 5 \times 3 + 10 = 4$
4th term $= 4^2 - 5 \times 4 + 10 = 6$
5th term $= 5^2 - 5 \times 5 + 10 = 10$

b 20th term $= 20^2 - 5 \times 20 + 10 = 400 - 100 + 10 = 310$

c Value of n Value of $n^2 - 5n + 10$

40   $40^2 - 5 \times 40 + 10 = 1410$ too small

42   $42^2 - 5 \times 42 + 10 = 1564$ too big

41   $41^2 - 5 \times 41 + 10 = 1486$ ✓

41st term.

10 **a** 1st term $= \dfrac{16 - 2}{1 + 1} = \dfrac{14}{2} = 7$

2nd term $= \dfrac{16 - 4}{2 + 1} = \dfrac{12}{3} = 4$

3rd term $= \dfrac{16 - 6}{3 + 1} = \dfrac{10}{4} = 2.5$

b $\dfrac{16 - 2n}{n + 1} = 1$ means $16 - 2n = n + 1$

(because dividing two expressions to get 1 means they are equal)

$$16 - 2n = n + 1$$
$$16 = 3n + 1$$
$$15 = 3n$$
$$n = 5$$

The 5th term has value 1.

Check $\dfrac{16 - 2n}{n + 1} = \dfrac{16 - 10}{5 + 1} = \dfrac{6}{6} = 1$ ✓

CHAPTER 25

1 **a** Mean $= (245 + 239 + 220 + 218 + 248 + 233 + 219 + 226) \div 8$
$= 1848 \div 8$
$= 231$

Range $= 248 - 218 = 30$

b Mean $= (232 + 235 + 225 + 231 + 230 + 236 + 228 + 229) \div 8$
$= 1846 \div 8$
$= 230.75$

Range $= 236 - 225 = 11$

c On average they both jump the same length but Sam's jumps are more consistent than Mike's.

2

14	15	16	16	18	19	21	23	26	31	33
		↑			↑			↑		
		lower quartile			median			upper quartile		

a median $= 19$
b lower quartile $= 16$
c upper quartile $= 26$
d interquartile range $= 26 - 16 = 10$

3 **a** (1)

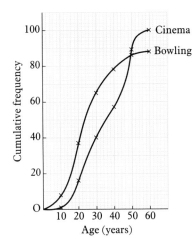

Age (years)

(2) Cinema median = 36 years   Bowling median = 22 years
(3) Cinema interquartile range = 46 − 25 = 21 years
      Bowling interquartile range = 30 − 15 = 15 years

b On average the people who go bowling are younger than those who
go to the cinema and there is less variation in their ages.

4

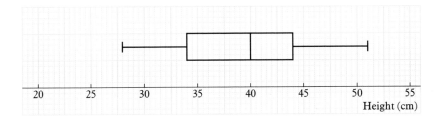

Height (cm)

5 **a** 17, 17, 19, 19, 20, 20, 21, 23, 24, 26, 27, 27, 31, 33, 34, 36, 37, 38, 39, 41
b Median time (26 + 27) ÷ 2 = 26.5
c Lower quartile (20 + 20) ÷ 2 = 20
d Upper quartile (34 + 36) ÷ 2 = 35
e

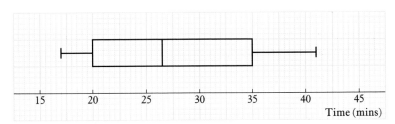

Time (mins)

f (1) 27 minutes   (3) 20
      (2) 31.5 − 23 = 8.5 minutes   (4) 36

g They both take about the same time on average to drive to work.
However Rudi's times are more consistent than those of Cara.

CHAPTER 26

1 **a** $a = 180 - 47 - 52$ (angles in a traingle)
$a = 81°$

$b = 180 - 81$ (angles on a straight line)
$b = 99°$

b $c = 36°$ (alternate angles)

c $d = \dfrac{180 - 40}{2}$ (base angles of isosceles triangle)

$d = 70°$

$e = 180 - 2 \times 70$ (missing angle is $70°$ base angle of isosceles triangle)
$e = 40°$

d $f = 360 - 123 - 119 - 70$ (angles in a quadrilateral)
$f = 48°$

e $g = \dfrac{180}{3}$ (angles in an equilateral triangle)

$g = 60°$

$h = 180 - 60$ (angles on a straight line)

$h = 120°$

f $i + 3i = 180°$ (angles on a straight line)
$4i = 180$
$i = 45°$ $3i = 3 \times 45° = 135°$

2 **a** $a = 43°$ (alternate angles)

b $b = 110°$ (corresponding angles)

c $c = 128°$ (alternate angles)
$d = 34°$ (alternate angles)
$e = 180° - 128° - 34°$ (angles in a triangle)
$h = 18°$

d $f = 119°$ (corresponding angles)
$g = 119°$ (corresponding angles with f)
Angle above $g = 61°$ (angles on a straight line)
Angle on the right of $125° = 55°$ (angles on a straight line)
$h = 180° - 61° - 55°$ (angles in a triangle)
$h = 64°$

3 **a** $a = 70°$ (angle at the centre $= 2 \times$ angle at the circumference)

b $b = 90°$ (angle in a semi circle)
$c = 48°$ (angles in the same segment)

c $e = 18°$ (angles in the same segment)
   $f = 36°$ (angle at the centre $= 2 \times$ angle at the circumference)
   $g = 18°$ (base angles isosceles triangle)
   $h = 18°$ (angle in the same segment as g)

d Angle on left of centre of circle

   $= 2 \times (180° - 90° - 34°)$ (twice the angle in the triangle from tangent, radius and across the middle of the diagram)

   $= 112°$

   $m = 56°$ (angle at the centre $= 2 \times$ angle at the circumference)
   $n = 180° - 56°$ (opposite angles in a cyclic quadrilateral)
   $= 124°$

4 **a** (1) 065°
      (2) $180 + 65 = 245°$

   b (1) 110°
      (2) $180 + 110 = 290°$

   c (1) $180 + 155 = 335°$
      (2) 155°

5 **a**

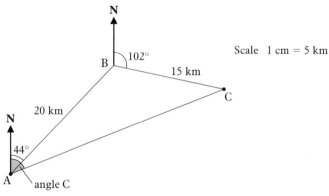

Scale 1 cm = 5 km

   b AC = 6.1 cm
      ∴ Distance from A to C is 30.5 km (allow ±0.5 km)
   c Angle C = 70°
      ∴ Bearing of C from A is 070° (allow ±2°).

CHAPTER 27

1 **a** $3x + 12$ **c** $-15x + 15$
   b $x^2 - 7x$ **d** $6x^3 + 2x^2$

2 **a** $x^2 + 7x + 12$ **c** $6x^2 - 21x + 15$
   b $x^2 - 5x - 14$ **d** $42x^2 - 10x - 8$

3 **a** $3(x + 2y)$
   b $x(x + 3)$
   c $3t(x - 3y)$
   d $3xz(5y - 2)$

4 **a** $(x + 2)(x + 3)$
   b $(x + 3)(x + 7)$
   c $(x - 7)(x + 4)$
   d $(x + 10)(x - 3)$

5 **a** $x^2 + 8x + 15 = 0$
       $(x + 3)(x + 5) = 0$
       $x = -3, x = -5$
   b $x^2 - 8x + 12 = 0$
       $(x - 2)(x - 6) = 0$
       $x = 2, x = 6$
   c $x^2 + 2x - 3 = 0$
       $(x + 3)(x - 1) = 0$
       $x = -3, x = 1$
   d $x^2 - 4x - 12 = 0$
       $(x - 6)(x + 2) = 0$
       $x = 6, x = -2$

6 **a** $y = x^2 - 2x - 15$
       $= (x - 5)(x + 3)$
   b $y = x^2 + 5x - 14$
       $= (x - 2)(x + 7)$

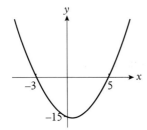

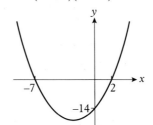

7 **a** $6r = 3rt + 4$
              $6r - 3rt = 4$
              $r(6 - 3t) = 4$
              $r = \dfrac{4}{6 - 3t}$

   b $7x + 3y = 3xt$
           $7x - 3xt = -3y$
           $x(7 - 3t) = -3y$
           $x = \dfrac{-3y}{7 - 3t}$

   c $t = \dfrac{r + 4}{r}$
              $rt = r + 4$
              $rt - r = 4$
              $r(t - 1) = 4$
              $r = \dfrac{4}{t - 1}$

   d $3z = \dfrac{4y - 3}{y}$
              $3yz = 4y - 3$
              $3yz - 4y = -3$
              $y(3z - 4) = -3$
              $y = \dfrac{-3}{3z - 4}$

CHAPTER 28

1 **a** 275 kg
   b 345 kg
   c 380 kg
   d 0.091 Newtons
   e 0.099 Newtons
   f 0.104 Newtons

2 **a** 3.60
   b 0.0507
   c 350 000
   d 600 100
   e 0.0901
   f 0.900

3 **a** answer $\quad$ 8.01 $\;$ (3 sf)

$\qquad$ estimate $\quad \dfrac{5 \times 4^2}{30 - 20} = \dfrac{5 \times 16}{10} = \dfrac{80}{10} = 8$

$\quad$ **b** answer $= 37.8$ $\;$ (3 sf)

$\qquad$ estimate $\quad \dfrac{63 \times 48}{7 \times 12} = \dfrac{63}{7} \times \dfrac{48}{12} = 9 \times 4 = 36$

4 **a** 37 500 $\qquad\qquad\qquad$ **b** $\;$ 38 499

5 **a** $(20 \times 30) \div 2 = 300 \text{ cm}^2$

$\quad$ **b** $(24.8 \times 27.2) \div 2 = 337.28 \text{ cm}^2$

$\quad$ **c** Percentage error $= \dfrac{\text{error}}{\text{exact value}} \times 100\%$

$\qquad\qquad\qquad\quad = \dfrac{37.28}{337.28} \times 100\%$

$\qquad\qquad\qquad\quad = 11\% \; (2 \text{ sf})$

6 $\quad u:$ $\quad$ 23 $\qquad$ lower bound $= 22.5$ $\qquad$ upper bound $= 23.5$
$\qquad t:$ $\qquad$ 4.9 $\quad$ lower bound $= \;$ 4.85 $\qquad$ upper bound $= \;$ 4.95

$\qquad v = u - 4t$

$\quad$ lower bound of $v = 22.5 - 4 \times 4.95 = 2.7$
$\quad$ upper bound of $v = 23.5 - 4 \times 4.85 = 4.1$

7 $\quad$ P: $\quad$ 34 $\qquad$ lower bound $= 33.5$ $\qquad$ upper bound $= 34.5$
$\qquad$ Q: $\quad$ 5.71 $\quad$ lower bound $= \;$ 5.705 $\qquad$ upper bound $= \;$ 5.715
$\qquad$ R: $\quad$ 0.5 $\quad$ lower bound $= \;$ 0.45 $\qquad$ upper bound $= \;$ 0.55

$\quad$ **a** lower bound of $5P = 5 \times 33.5 = 167.5$
$\qquad$ upper bound of $5P = 5 \times 34.5 = 172.5$

$\quad$ **b** lower bound of $P - Q = 33.5 - 5.715 = 27.785$
$\qquad$ upper bound of $P - Q = 34.5 - 5.705 = 28.795$

$\quad$ **c** lower bound of $Q \div R = 5.705 \div 0.55 = 10.37 \;$ (4 sf)
$\qquad$ upper bound of $Q \div R = 5.715 \div 0.45 = 12.7$

$\quad$ **d** lower bound of $3P - 4Q = 3 \times 33.5 - 4 \times 5.715 = 77.64$
$\qquad$ upper bound of $3P - 4Q = 3 \times 34.5 - 4 \times 5.705 = 80.68$

CHAPTER 29

1 **a** 0.08
$\quad$ **b** (1) £5.36 $\qquad$ (3) £3.96 $\qquad$ (5) 6.912 kg
$\qquad$ (2) 19.2 m $\qquad$ (4) 56 cm $\qquad$ (6) 0.152 m^2

2 **a** $100\% - 28\% = 72\% = 0.72$ $\qquad$ **c** $\;$ 0.94
$\quad$ **b** 0.835 $\qquad\qquad\qquad\qquad\qquad\qquad$ **d** $\;$ 0.007

3 **a** $100\% - 72\% = 28\%$ $\qquad\qquad$ **b** $\;$ £1800 $\times$ 0.28 = £504

4 $\quad 100\% - 4.2\% = 95.8\%$
$\quad$ £6520 $\times$ 0.958 = £6246.16

5 **a** 1.07   **b** 1.12   **c** 1.008   **d** 2.5

6 £96 × 1.175 = £112.80

7 6420 × 1.05 = 6741

Andy drove 6740 miles to the nearest 10 miles.

8 £2400 × 1.075 = £2580

9 £15 800 × 0.7 × 0.75 = £8295

10 54 × 1.1 × 0.9 = 53.46 cm^2

11 £904.75 ÷ 1.175 = £770

12 **a** £7600 × 1.067^4 = £9850.79   **b** £9850.79 − £7600 = £2250.79

13 £83 000 × 1.1^5 = £133 672.33

14 **a** £4300 × 0.1 = £430   **c** £430 + £1584 = £2014

     b 16 800 − £5300 − £4300 = £7200

        £7200 × 0.22 = £1584

CHAPTER 30

1

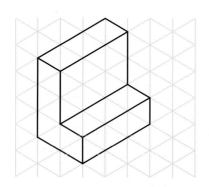

2 **a** 0.037 m   **c** 7.6 tonnes   **e** 0.038 ℓ

     b 800 m   **d** 308 cm   **f** 47.8 cℓ

3 450 ÷ 0.45 = 1000 pounds

4 8^3 = 512 cm^3

5 Area of end = (10 + 6) ÷ 2 × 12 = 8 × 12 = 96 cm^2

     Volume = 96 × 14 = 1344 cm^3

6 Area of end = 86 ÷ 5.4 = 15.925... cm^2 so πr^2 = 15.925 ...

                                         r^2 = 15.925 ...

$$r = \sqrt{\frac{15.925}{\pi}} = 2.3 \text{ cm to the nearest mm.}$$

7 **a** length   **c** area   **e** length

     b area   **d** volume   **f** length

CHAPTER 31

1 **a**

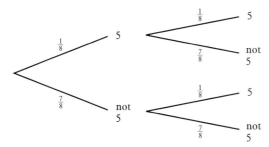

1st spin 2nd spin

$\frac{1}{8}$ 5

$\frac{1}{8}$ 5

$\frac{7}{8}$ not 5

$\frac{7}{8}$ not 5

$\frac{1}{8}$ 5

$\frac{7}{8}$ not 5

b $\frac{1}{8} \times \frac{1}{8} = \frac{1}{64}$ **c** $\frac{1}{8} \times \frac{7}{8} + \frac{7}{8} \times \frac{1}{8} = \frac{14}{64} = \frac{7}{32}$

2 **a**

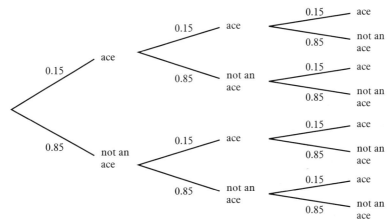

1st serve 2nd serve 3rd serve

0.15 ace

0.15 ace

0.85 not an ace

0.15 ace

0.85 not an ace

0.15 ace

0.85 not an ace

ace

0.15

0.85

not an ace

0.15 ace

0.85 not an ace

0.15 ace

0.85 not an ace

0.15 ace

0.85 not an ace

0.15 ace

0.85 not an ace

b (1) $0.15 \times 0.15 \times 0.15 = 0.003\,375$
(2) $1 - 0.85 \times 0.85 \times 0.85 = 0.385\,875$
(3) $0.15 \times 0.15 \times 0.85 \times 3 = 0.057\,375$
(4) $1 - 0.003\,375 = 0.996\,625$

3 **a**

1st interview 2nd interview

0.7 S

0.6 S

0.3 not S

0.4 not S

b $0.6 \times 0.7 = 0.42$
c $0.6 \times 0.3 = 0.18$

4

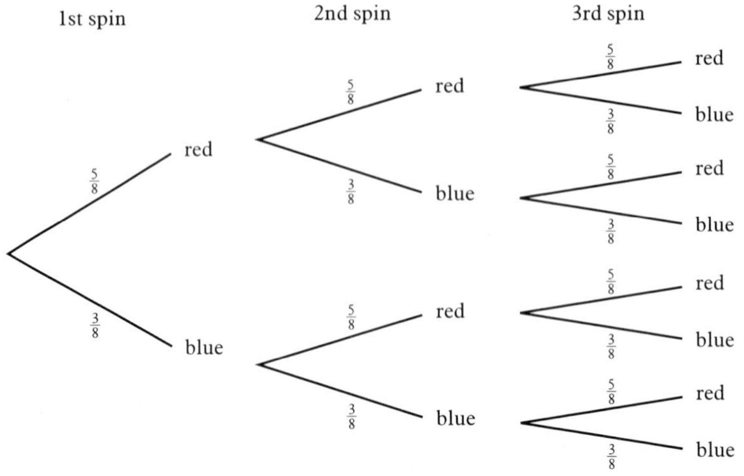

1st spin	2nd spin	3rd spin

a $\frac{5}{8} \times \frac{5}{8} \times \frac{5}{8} = \frac{125}{512}$

b $1 - \frac{125}{512} = \frac{387}{512}$

c $(\frac{5}{8} \times \frac{5}{8} \times \frac{3}{8}) + (\frac{5}{8} \times \frac{3}{8} \times \frac{5}{8}) + (\frac{3}{8} \times \frac{5}{8} \times \frac{5}{8})$

$= \frac{75}{512} \times 3 = \frac{225}{512}$

5 **a** $0.7 \times 0.7 \times 0.7 = 0.343$

   b $1 - 0.343 = 0.657$

   c $1 - 0.3 \times 0.3 \times 0.3 = 0.973$

CHAPTER 32

1 D and E

2 A and C

3 **a** 1

   b 4 only if top and bottom are square. Otherwise 2.

4 **a** 2

   b 4

5 **a** $180° - 162° = 18°$

   b $360 \div 18 = 20$ sides

6 $\dfrac{x}{3} = \dfrac{x + 4}{5}$ $\left(\text{or } \dfrac{5}{3} = \dfrac{x + 4}{x} \right)$

$5x = 3(x + 4)$

$5x = 3x + 12$

$2x = 12$

$x = 6$

CHAPTER 33

1

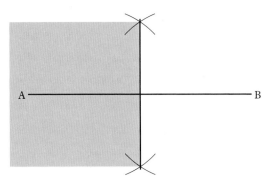

Points on the shaded side of the line are closer to A than to B.

2

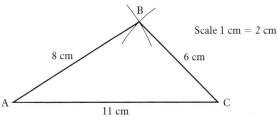

Scale 1 cm = 2 cm

b 102° (allow ±1°)

3

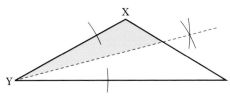

The shaded area shows the points closer to XY than YZ

4 a

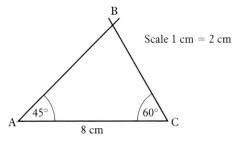

Scale 1 cm = 2 cm

b AB = 7.2 cm to the nearest mm (allow ±1 mm)

CHAPTER 34

1 a −0.5, 2   **b** −1.8, 3.3

2 a

x	−3	−2	−1	0	1	2	3	4
x^2	9	4	1	0	1	4	9	16
$-x$	3	2	1	0	−1	−2	−3	−4
−3	−3	−3	−3	−3	−3	−3	−3	−3
y	9	3	−1	−3	−3	−1	3	9

b, d

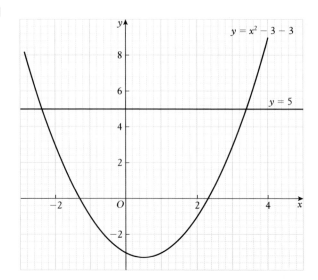

$y = x^2 - 3 - 3$

$y = 5$

c $-1.3, 2.3$ **e** $-2.4, 3.4$

3 **a**

x	-2	-1	0	1	2	3	4	5
x^2	4	1	0	1	4	9	16	25
$-3x$	6	3	0	-3	-6	-9	-12	-15
$+1$	1	1	1	1	1	1	1	1
y	11	5	1	-1	-1	1	5	11

c

x	-2	-1	0	1	2	3	4	5
$2x$	-4	-2	0	2	4	6	8	10
$+3$	3	3	3	3	3	3	3	3
y	-1	1	3	5	7	9	11	13

b, d

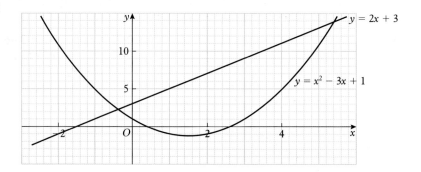

$y = 2x + 3$

$y = x^2 - 3x + 1$

e $-0.4, 5.4$

4 a

x	-4	-3	-2	-1	0	1	2	3	4
$\dfrac{1}{x}$	-0.25	-0.33	-0.5	-1		1	0.5	0.33	0.25
$+3$	3	3	3	3		3	3	3	3
y	2.75	2.67	2.5	2		4	3.5	3.33	3.25

b, c

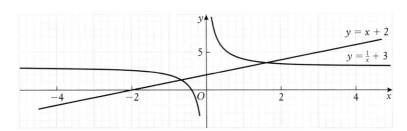

d $-0.6,\ 1.6$

5
$$x^3 = 2x^2 - 4$$
$$x^3 - x^2 = x^2 - 4$$
$$x^3 - x^2 + 5 = x^2 - 4 + 5$$
$$x^3 - x^2 + 5 = x^2 + 1$$

$y = x^2 + 1$ is needed. She would then find the x values where the curves cross.

CHAPTER 35

1 a $\cos a = \dfrac{26}{31} = 0.8387\ldots$

$a = 33.0°$ (1 dp)

b $\tan b = \dfrac{2.3}{3.7} = 0.6216\ldots$

$b = 31.9°$ (1 dp)

2 a $\sin 33° = \dfrac{x}{24.8}$

$x = 24.8 \sin 33°$

$= 13.5$ cm (3 sf)

b $\tan 52° = \dfrac{x}{42.6}$

$x = 42.6 \tan 52°$

$= 54.5$ cm (3 sf)

3 a $9.6 \cos 72°$
$= 2.97$ km (3 sf)

b $9.6 \sin 72°$
$= 9.13$ km (3 sf)

c $180° + 72° = 252°$

4 a

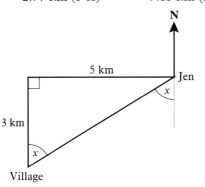

b $\tan x = \frac{5}{3} = 1.666\ldots$

$x = 59.0°$ (1 dp)

Bearing $= 180° + 59°$

$= 239°$

5 a

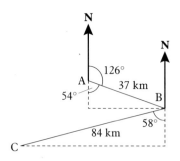

c 84 sin 58° − 37 sin 54°
$$= 71.236 \ldots -29.933 \ldots$$
$$= 41.30 \ldots$$
$$= 41.3 \text{ km (3 sf)}$$

b 37 cos 54° + 84 cos 58°
$$= 21.748 \ldots + 44.513 \ldots$$
$$= 66.261 \ldots$$
$$= 66.3 \text{ km (3 sf)}$$

d

$$\tan x = \frac{41.30}{66.26} = 0.6233$$

$$x = 31.9° \text{ (3 sf)}$$

Bearing of A from C is 032°.

6 $\sin 63° = \dfrac{18.6}{h}$

$$h = \frac{18.6}{\sin 63}$$

$$= 20.9 \text{ m (3 sf)}$$

7 a

cliff   18°   72°   120 m   18° d boat

b $\tan 72° = \dfrac{d}{120}$ or $\tan 18° = \dfrac{120}{d}$

$$d = 120 \tan 72°$$ $$d = \frac{120}{\tan 18°}$$

$$= 369 \text{ m (3 sf)}$$ $$= 369 \text{ m (3 s.f.)}$$

8 $\sin 60° = \dfrac{2.6}{l}$

$$l = \frac{2.6}{\sin 60}$$

$$= 3.0 \text{ m (2 sf)}$$

9

$h = (30 + x) \tan 25°$

$h = x \tan 40°$

$x \tan 40° = 30 \tan 25° + x \tan 25°$

$x (\tan 40° - \tan 25°) = 30 \tan 25°$

$x = \dfrac{30 \tan 25°}{(\tan 40° - \tan 25°)}$

$x = 37.525 \ldots$ m

$h = x \tan 40° = 31.5$ m (3 sf)

CHAPTER 36

1 **a** $-4 < x \leqslant 2$ **b** $-5 \leqslant x < 1$ **c** $x > -2$

2 **a** 3, 4, 5 **c** $-5, -4, -3, -2, -1$
  b $-3, -2, -1, 0$ **d** $-2, -1, 0, 1, 2$

3 **a** $x < 11$

  c $4x \leqslant 12 + 7$ **e** $3x + 1 < -20$
  $4x \leqslant 19$ $3x < -21$
  $x \leqslant 4.75$ $x < -7$

  b $2x \geqslant 17 - 5$ **d** $\dfrac{x}{4} > 11.3$ **f** $2x + 11 \geqslant 7$
  $2x \geqslant 12$ $2x \geqslant -4$
  $x \geqslant 6$ $x > 45.2$ $x \geqslant -2$

4 **a** $-x > -8$ **c** $7 \leqslant 5x - 9$
  $x < 8$ $16 \leqslant 5x$
    $3.2 \leqslant x$
    $x \geqslant 3.2$

  b $5 - 2x < -21$ **d** $10 \geqslant x + 6$
  $-2x < -26$ $4 \geqslant x$
  $2x > 26$ $x \leqslant 4$
  $x > 13$

5 **a** $6 \leqslant 3x < 12$ **c** $5 \leqslant 2x - 1 \leqslant 11$
  $2 \leqslant x < 4$ $6 \leqslant 2x \leqslant 12$
    $3 \leqslant x \leqslant 6$

  b $11 < x + 7 \leqslant 19$ **d** $-10 < -5x < 0$
  $4 < x \leqslant 12$ $-2 < -x < 0$
    $2 > x > 0$
    $0 < x < 2$

6 **a** $x \geqslant -2$ **b** $-4 \leqslant y < 3$

7 **a** $x \geqslant 1, y > -3$ **b** $x < -2, -2 \leqslant y \leqslant 1$

8 $x < 1$ or $x > 2$

9 **a** s represents the number of sliced loaves

        u represents the number of unsliced loaves

        The total number of loaves is less than or equal to 800.

    b $s \geqslant 0, u \geqslant 0, u \geqslant 200, s \geqslant 2u$

    c

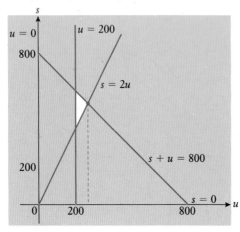

    d The red point on the graph shows the furthest point along the u axis which satisfies all the inequalities. This gives the most unsliced loaves that can be made as 266.